AGGRESSION IN PROXIMITY RELATIONSHIPS
PHILOSOPHIES

The
Neurodynamics
of Abuse and
Violence

AGGRESSION IN PROXIMITY RELATIONSHIPS

PHILOSOPHIES

The Neurodynamics of Abuse and Violence

Yvette P. Kanarick

Chayel Inc.
Orlando, FL

Library in Congress Cataloging-in-Publication Data

Kanarick, Yvette P.
Aggression in Proximity Relationships: Philosophies / Yvette P. Kanarick

    p. 400
    Includes Bibliographical references and index
    ISBN: 978-0-9841939-4-3
    I. Psychology, Aggression   I. Title

                 Library of Congress Control Number: 2019902045

Printed in the United States of America

Chayel Inc.

www.Chayel-fl.net

ISBN 10:   0-9841939-4-4
ISBN 13: 978-0-9841939-4-3

TO: ALBERT BRYAN, ADRIEL BRENT,
ANA ABIGAIL, AND CSARIEL MICHELLE

Copy Editor:	**Ian Parsons**
Graphic Design and Program Engineer:	**Ian** Parsons
Cover Photo Credit:	Eric Ward

(https://commons.wikimedia.org/wiki/File:Family_Portrait.jpg), „Family Portrait",
https://creativecommons.org/licenses/by-sa/2.0/legalcode

CONTENTS

Table of Contents

Table of Contents

Table of Contents

Table of Contents

FIGURES

TABLES

CHARTS

Foreword

Aggression in Proximity Relationships: Philosophies is the first of three volumes addressing all forms of aggression, violence, and abuse in intimate, proximity relationships, including those defined under traditional concepts of DV and IPV. In this volume, there is an evaluation of the foundational theory that informs current service provisions, policies, and program development to address APR.

The theory of evolution by means of natural selection is the primary undergirding theoretical framework for current theories and models used to explain aggression. The theory of evolution is the basis of systems theory and aggression models used to frame policies and programs to address APR. However, a closer evaluation of evolutionary theory shows flaws in its fundamental tenets and its philosophical orientation.

Natural selection, fitness, survivability, and aggression are the fundamental tenets of evolutionary theory; these fundamental tenets inform current studies in genetics and genetically-programmed predispositional vulnerabilities. The genetically-programmed predispositional vulnerabilities present as a diathesis or a tendency toward dysfunctional aggression such as APR. Nevertheless, there are flaws in the philosophical orientation that inform these tenets. Further, the philosophical orientation forms the basis of interpretations and analysis of APR rooted in inequity and discrimination.

In this book, there is a discussion of the fundamental tenets of evolution, their flaws, and the philosophical orientation that guide the theory. There are discussions of the subtle underpinnings of religious, cosmological philosophy that remain intertwined in the theory, and which continue to impinge on current research.

In this book, there is an outline and assessment of the diathesis models of predispositional vulnerability pertaining to APR, the biogenetic and the epigenetic mechanisms involved in the transmission of genetically-programmed predispositional vulnerability and susceptibility to violence and aggression.

Modern-day evolutionary theory has its roots in antiquity and can be traced back to Greek philosophers such as Plato. However, discrimination and inequity that were intertwined in the foundational beliefs of ancient Greek religion from which the theory of evolution developed remained delicately interwoven into the modern-day evolutionary theory.

Foreword

Modern-day evolutionary theory is the platform for social Darwinism and eugenics. Using a series of calculated and ingenious steps, eugenicists wheedled eugenics program into genetic research and employed strategies to use genetic research nefariously to further the eugenic calendar. Forced sterilization and prenatal genetic screenings were wrapped inside the eugenics program. Genetic screening to perform feticides among populations with "defective" genes was the grandparent of sex-selective abortion and gendercide; measures that show up in current gender-biased aggression against girls and women.

In addition to a candid exploration of the dark story behind the evolutionary theory, there are reports from scientific research indicating the weaknesses and flaws of the theory.

Because Charles Darwin is the father of modern-day evolutionary theory, the tenets of the theory of evolution by means of natural selection is referred to as Darwinism. Critics of the theory of evolution are referred to as anti-Darwinists. Hitherto, two antithetical camps polarize around Darwinism and Anti-Darwinism.

Evolutionary theory is a worldview subtly interwoven and covertly transmitted via different media, including religious institutions and academia. This worldview becomes inculcated into the individual's perspective, often without conscious awareness.

Historically, challenges to evolutionary theory are criticized as being due to religious fanaticism. Nevertheless, serious scientific research outside of religious arguments and defense has caused questions to be raised. These concerns should be objectively assessed.

Genetic predisposition is a mainstay of evolutionary theory. Genetic predisposition is currently used to explain aggression and victimization. However, reputable, non-partisan scientists indicated that genome-wide association studies (GWAS) had not yielded conclusive evidence of a link between genes and diathetic predispositional vulnerability, such as those that present as a proclivity to aggression and victimization. In the search for feasible and viable answers concerning the comparatively high species-to-species murder among humans, there is the need to revisit evolutionary theory because it is the central explanation for APR.

Preface

This book is the first in a three-volume title on aggression in proximity relationships (APR). Writing these books has been a journey in fulfillment and increased understanding of self, others, and society.

Abuse and violence have many faces. Hence the renaming of these phenomena to APR.

Being a victim of domestic violence (DV) and interpersonal aggression revealed to me the many faces of abuse and violence. Sadly, there are many professional men and women, more so women, as well as children, who are victims of APR.

Unfortunately, I found from my experience that services and provisions for victims of APR are woefully lacking. APR, a global phenomenon, is a monster that touches the lives of more than a third of the global population, and when relatives and friends who are impacted are added, the numbers become astronomical.

Viewing APR from the standpoint of a professional, who has also been a victim caused the realization that the phenomenon is not well understood. Due to this lack of comprehensive understanding, even the limited service provision and policies to address APR are depressingly inadequate. A more disturbing reality was the absence of understanding of the etiology of APR.

I began this research with the premise that APR is a dysfunctional phenomenon that was in violation of the foundational survival instinct. I reasoned that humans are hard-wired to survive. My second premise was that intimate, child, and family relationships serve the primary functions of survivability and perpetuation of self and species. Consequently, when a man or women in an intimate and or familial relationship turn on their mate, spouse, or children and murders them, this is an aberration of the basic instincts of survivability. My third premise was that innate, instinctive, survivability must be hard-wired in the brain; therefore, neurophysiological malfunctioning might be the root of the dysfunctional behaviors of victims and perpetrators of APR.

As my research deepened, I understood that the theory of evolution by means of natural selection was the primary theoretical framework that addressed survivability and aggression. It soon became evident that this theoretical framework guided almost all, if not all interpretive models, research, and disciplines addressing APR. However, I also discovered that evolutionary theory emerged from ancient religious philosophies and was rooted in bigotry, such as racial supremacy and inequity that could be traced back to as early as the fourth century BCE. My research also uncovered deep flaws and weaknesses in evolutionary theory.

More disturbing was that I had been inadvertently influenced by evolutionary theory without conscious awareness as to when and how this worldview had become embedded in my psyche and perception of life. Up until I began researching the etiology of APR, evolutionary theory was an extant ideology that I understood and debated as an academic pursuit. I had no conscious realization that I had embraced an ideology that I did not quite understand. Further, I had no knowledge as to how this ideology became integrated and embedded in my worldview. To me, this was most disturbing because I believe that one must have full cognizance of one's worldview and also have knowledge of the way that one's worldview is formed and shaped.

I believed that if I had a specific worldview and I did not have full cognizance of how and when it was shaped and formed, then there is the likelihood that a philosophical orientation might have been foisted onto me. I was concerned that I might have been manipulated into a worldview that I did not fully understand.

My research turned into a quest to fully understand the evolutionary theory as a worldview to examine its tenets and philosophical orientation and to determine in what ways this worldview influenced my perception and perspectives on challenges and issues that were personal to me. Being a survivor of APR, I needed to know if my understanding and responses to APR were influenced by this underlying implicit acceptance of the tenets of the theory of evolution and whether the underlying implicit assumptions that I held concerning the evolutionary theory were valid explanations of APR.

As I explored the theory of evolution by means of natural selection, I recognized that evolutionary theory and Charles Darwin were often misrepresented and not fully understood. Charles Darwin was a creationist. In his work, he concluded by saying that life was breathed by the "Creator into a few forms or one."

The research revealed two polarized camps, Darwinists and anti-Darwinists. The contention appeared to center on creation and evolution. However, Darwin concluded that a creator was responsible for the ontogeny of life. Moreover, Darwin's belief in the god Pan as the giver of genes identifies him as being religious. As such, the contention between Darwinists and anti-Darwinists, which assume a religious character might be indicative of a misunderstanding of Darwin and evolutionary theory.

In this title, *Aggression in Proximity Relationships: Philosophies*, I identify evolutionary theory as the theoretical framework used to explain APR. Current theory, research, policies, and service provision for addressing APR are rooted in evolutionary theory. However, flaws and weaknesses in evolutionary theory and its philosophical orientation make it inapplicable as an explanation of the etiology of APR.

The inadequacies and shortfalls of existing models used to address APR warrant a revisiting of the undergirding theoretical framework. I trace the philosophical orientation and development of evolutionary theory. The predispositional genetic diathesis model is a foundational theoretical model emerging from evolutionary theory that is most often used to explain and interpret APR. In this title, there is an evaluation of the primary diathesis models, gene theory, biogenetic, and epigenetic theories of transgenerational and intergenerational transmissions of APR.

I also explore other theories, including panspermia and intelligent design (ID) models that provide alternative ontogenetic explanations. This title ends with an overview of evolutionary theory development and applications, social Darwinism, eugenics, genetics, and their implications for APR.

Yvette P. Kanarick

ABOUT THE AUTHOR

The Author is a clinical neuropsychologist, research analyst, and consultant. The author is a historian, educator, and also holds an MBA.

Recommended Users

This text is designed for use by students and professionals in the various fields and disciplines concerned with aggression. It is ideal for policymakers, consultants, care, and service providers for victims and perpetrators of APR. This text provides details of philosophical orientation and the development of a theoretical framework and is an invaluable research tool for scholars, practitioners, and researchers.

SECTION ONE
PHILOSOPHICAL FRAMEWORK

SECTION SUMMARY

The theory of evolution undergirds modern-day scientific study and research. However, tenets of evolutionary theory have their foundation in mythical beliefs that involve metaphysics.

The theory of evolution emerged from mythical beliefs from antiquity. Mythical beliefs were religious beliefs involving metaphysics. Cosmozoë, a philosophy from antiquity, was foundational to evolutionary theory.

Cosmozoë was an ancient Greek philosophy involving metaphysics. Cosmozoë philosophers held many of the foundational beliefs that are common in Greek legends and mythology. However, cosmozoë philosophers, such as Aristotle, had a slightly different perspective than the religious beliefs held by the masses and the general population.

Cosmozoë philosophers believed that the stars were gods, and the universe was an embodiment of god. Cosmozoë philosophers used gods as an explanation for ontogeny, being, and the nature of being. Because their interpretations involved gods and metaphysics, cosmozoë was religious philosophy. However, cosmozoë philosophers sought to extricate their beliefs from the embellishments of myths and legends that were prevailing religious beliefs of the masses and establish their beliefs as a science.

Cosmozoë philosophers had two goals, to extricate mythical elements from their ontogenetic explanations and to gain acceptance of metaphysics as a discipline of science. Cosmozoë philosophers achieved their goal of disengaging mythological elements from their ontogenetic explanations through the development of philosophical thoughts and disciplines, which they used to develop the scientific method. Evolutionary theory and modern-day scientific study have their roots in ancient cosmozoë religious philosophy.

The foundation of scientific study is evidence. Hypothesis rooted in mythical beliefs and metaphysics cannot be proved. Hypotheses and theories that are not founded in evidence is pseudoscience. In this discussion, the steps that moved the theory of evolution from pseudoscience to credible, acceptable, scientific theory will be discussed.

THE IMPORTANCE OF PHILOSOPHY

All theories are undergirded by philosophy. Philosophy is the undergirding thought and orientation that guides hypothetical assumptions

~1~

and forms the basis of theoretical development. As such, understanding the philosophical elements that are foundational to a theory will increase understanding of the strengths, weaknesses, validity, and reliability of that theory.

Researchers and practitioners are not often cognizant that metaphysics and mythical beliefs are the foundations of evolutionary theory. Without full cognizance of the mythological beliefs and metaphysical, philosophical foundations of evolutionary theory, researchers, practitioners, and scholars accept evolutionary theory without understanding the foundational elements of the undergirding philosophy, and they run the risk of blind acceptance. Blind acceptance of theory reduces the efficacy with which researchers, practitioners, and scholars assess and analyze not just the theory being tested, but also their findings. Discarding philosophical underpinnings also borders on intellectual arrogance, which hinders the search for truth.

In this section, there will be an in-depth analysis of the philosophical tenets that undergird the theory of evolution by natural selection. This critical analysis includes the foundational elements of evolutionary theory derived from antiquity, and the approaches used to integrate these tenets into scientific study.

Mythical beliefs involving metaphysical elements are insentient and cannot be literally observed. Prior to its inclusion in the modern-day scientific study, evolutionary theory was relegated to the status of philosophy.

Scientific study was the discipline in which empiricists engaged. Empiricists argued that the study of science should only include sentient and observable phenomena. As such, the philosophy of evolution could not be included in scientific study. To overcome this challenge, cosmological philosophers developed a new discipline called the scientific method which facilitated the inclusion of this metaphysical content into scholarly studies.

To facilitate the development of this new discipline, cosmological philosophers developed several philosophical schools of thought. These philosophical schools of thoughts extended rules to include metaphysics and mythical beliefs into the scientific method. There is a discussion of these philosophical tenets and schools of thought in this section.

Section 1 Contents

CHAPTER ONE
PHILOSOPHY AND APR

CHAPTER PREVIEW

Scholarly studies begin with a theoretical framework as the interpretative model for the subject being researched. This study is an attempt to understand the etiology of APR. The aim is to find the answer concerning what causes APR.

The theory of evolution by means of natural selection is the theoretical framework informing service provision, policy, and program development to address APR. Therefore, an analysis of the theory of evolution by means of natural selection and its tenets that are implicated in interpreting APR will be the theory of focus in this study.

Survivability, fitness, and aggression are the foundational tenets of the theory of evolution that impinge on APR. As such, the rationality of these three foundational tenets will be evaluated to assess their applicability for interpreting APR.

Because the theory of evolution by natural selection is the theory that is most often used to interpret and analyze APR, this theory will be the focus of discussion in this text. The focus will be on the major tenets of evolution by natural selection that apply to APR.

In this chapter, there is a discussion of the rationale for the choice of the theoretical framework that will be used as the interpretive model in this study. There will also be an identification of the key concepts derived from evolutionary theory that are pertinent to this study.

PURPOSE AND LEARNING OBJECTIVES

PURPOSE

The purpose of this chapter is to

i. establish the rationale for the discussion of philosophy and APR; and
ii. identify key conceptualizations pertinent to APR.

LEARNING OBJECTIVES

After reading this chapter, the reader should

1. understand the rationale for the discussion of philosophy and APR;
2. perceive the justification for this discussion; and
3. understand key conceptualizations pertinent to this work, viz. APR, DV, IPV, neurodynamics, proximity relationships.

KEY TERMS AND DEFINITIONS:

Aggression in Proximity Relationships (APR)

APR is an all-encompassing definition to include all forms of aggression, including violence and abuse perpetrated by and between persons related through nearness.

Domestic Violence (DV)

DV is:

1) The inflicting of physical injury by one family or household member on another
2) A repeated or habitual pattern of such behavior (Domestic Violence, n.d.).

Intimate Partner Violence (IPV)

IPV describes physical violence, sexual violence, stalking, and psychological aggression (including coercive acts) by a current or former intimate partner (CDC, 2018).

Neurodynamics

Neurodynamics refers to the neurological processes activated through cognitive, emotional, and behavioral interactions between the individual and others. The activation of these neurological processes serves the purpose of self-management.

Proximity Relationship

A proximity relationship is a relationship established based on such ties as biological, geographical, legal, community, or sociocultural. Biological proximity relationships, for example, include such relationships as child/children, parents, siblings, or anyone in a familial relationship based on blood ties.

INTRODUCTION

APR is a redefinition and reconceptualization of violence and abuse in interpersonal relationships between and among persons that are closely or intimately-aligned. Traditional definitions of violence and abuse include concepts such as DV, IPV, and child abuse. Redefining and reconceptualizing violence and abuse in interpersonal relationships among closely or intimately-aligned persons aim to incorporate the range of interpersonal aggression among closely or intimately-aligned persons and extend the range for the inclusion of new types of aggression not thoroughly covered within the ambit of existing concepts and definitions. The aim is to develop a more effective strategy for intervention to address this phenomenon.

THEORETICAL FRAMEWORK

The theory of evolution by means of natural selection of evolutionary theory is an existing conceptual framework applied to explain aggression. Although there are many theories explaining aggression, these theories have their foundation in the theory of evolution by means of natural selection.

Survivability is the primary tenet of evolution by means of natural selection. According to the theory of evolution by means of natural selection, natural selection is a force that exists outside of human control. This unseen force called natural selection set all species on a course of development towards an ultimate goal of orthogenesis.

The principle of orthogenesis states that species will evolve to increasing states of complexities. Survivability is the principle that the most complex and best-suited organism and species will achieve orthogenesis. Aggression is one of the mechanisms that cause species to evolve.

According to the theory of evolution by means of natural selection, aggression is an innate instinct that exists in all species. Aggression exists in all species to serve the purpose of survivability. Therefore, aggression is functional.

However, there is a consensus that APR is dysfunctional behavior. The dysfunctionality of APR raises many questions concerning whether aggression is innate and whether APR is due to some malfunctioning elements. If aggression is innate, then the question relates as to whether an instinct could malfunction and if so, what are the causes of this malfunction.

Often, evolutionary theorists posit divergent explanations for the same phenomenon. If aggression is innate and functional, then APR is functional behavior. If on the other hand, aggression is dysfunctional, then APR is dysfunctional behavior.

Findings from research conducted within the framework of evolutionary theory often present conflicting results. These challenges pose difficulties in applying theory and research to practice.

Of greater concern is the notion that possibly the tenets of the theory of evolution by means of natural selection might not provide a valid explanation for APR. However, the theory of evolution by means of natural selection is the foundation of all theories used to explain this phenomenon.

APR continues to escalate and present in new forms. These escalations and transformations are pointing to the need for more effective strategies for service provision, policy, and program development. As such, there is a need to revisit the undergirding theoretical framework that currently drives theory, research, and practice (UNICEF, 2005; WHO, 2014).

PHILOSOPHICAL ORIENTATION

A plethora of studies continue to provide scientific support for the theory of evolution by means of natural selection. Findings from these studies are being applied to address APR. Despite this, APR is a global problem that continues to exacerbate (UNICEF, 2005; WHO, 2014).

Because theory drives programs, policies, and service provision, a reevaluation of the foundational theory is relevant to increase the understanding of APR. A philosophical orientation undergirds all theory; therefore, the philosophical orientation that undergirds the theory of evolution by means of natural selection should also be evaluated.

The philosophical orientation of the theorist is the theorist's worldview. An individual's worldview is a personal perspective on the way that the world functions and the way things function in the world. As such, the philosophical orientation undergirding evolutionary theory is a perspective or worldview on issues such as aggression and survivability.

Evolutionary theory is an ancient philosophy that has been explicated for more than 2200 years. Moreover, a cosmological, philosophical orientation based on ancient myths and metaphysics undergirds evolutionary theory. Cosmological philosophical tenets form the foundation of evolutionary tenets.

Mythical, metaphysical events, concepts, and phenomenon are integral to cosmology. These mythical, metaphysical events, concepts, and phenomenon are intricately interwoven into evolutionary theory. These mythical, metaphysical events and concepts inadvertently continue to inform research, practice, and policies related to APR. However, mythical, metaphysical events, concepts, and phenomena are impalpable. As such, the fundamental assumptions and premises of evolutionary theory are inconclusive, untenable, and unsubstantiated. Consequently, the interweaving of these impalpable elements to explain aggression might invalidate the applicability of evolutionary theory to explain this phenomenon.

From its earliest inception, there were credible scientists called empiricists that refuted evolutionary theory because of the inclusion of impalpable tenets in its foundational hypotheses. Nevertheless, ardent proponents of evolutionary theory resisted the refutations of empiricists and persisted by developing strategies that would force evolutionary tenets into academic studies.

Philosophy was the main tool that proponents of evolutionary theory used to force the integration of impalpable tenets into academic pursuits. Proponents of evolutionary philosophy developed several philosophical disciplines, rules, and procedures to validate the integration of mythical, metaphysical events, concepts, and phenomena into academic studies. These disciplines, rules, and procedures became known as natural philosophies, which later became known as the natural sciences, and the scientific method.

Due to the ardent work of zealous evolutionary philosophers, the theory of evolution was promulgated to explain ontogeny of life, the ontogeny of species, and human existence. Evolutionary theory became integrated into academic study, and its philosophy promoted as explanations that would provide answers to human challenges.

However, because the foundational myths and metaphysical elements of evolutionary theory have never been inconclusively proven, despite the abundance of scientific evidence to support the theory, the ontogenetic premises remain shaky. This shaky foundation might be at the root of the challenges related to applying and effectively relating theory, research, and practice based on evolutionary theory to APR.

CONCLUSION

Current programs, policies, and services to address APR have their foundations in evolutionary theory. However, APR continues to escalate, new forms and challenges of interpersonal aggression continue to emerge, and programs, policies, and services to address this phenomenon have flaws, weaknesses, and reduced efficacy.

Evolutionary theory is the theoretical framework for theory, research, and practice related to APR. Evolutionary theory has its foundation in myths and metaphysics cosmological philosophy. The mythical and metaphysical foundational tenets of evolutionary theory are untenable and unsubstantiated.

Like all theories, the philosophical orientation that is specific to the theorist is the framework for developing the tenets of evolutionary theory. A philosophical orientation is indicative of the personal perspectives or worldview of the philosopher. The weaknesses and the flaws that manifest when seeking to apply theory and research to practice might be indicative of flaws and weaknesses in the undergirding philosophical, theoretical orientation of evolutionary theory.

CHAPTER REVIEW

REVIEW QUESTIONS

1. What is a philosophical orientation?
2. How do philosophical orientations differ from theory?
3. What are the connections between philosophy and theory?
4. In what ways do the theorist's philosophical orientation impinge on the theory?

CHAPTER TWO
REEVALUATING APR MODELS

CHAPTER PREVIEW

Evolution by means of natural selection is the primary theory undergirding existing models used to interpret, analyze, and explain APR. Theory forms the basis of research and practice related to APR. Philosophies undergird theory. In this chapter, there will be a discussion of the significance of philosophy as an undergirding element of the theories applied to understand, interpret, and analyze APR and the relevance of understanding philosophy when addressing APR.

THE NEED FOR CHANGE

Changing social relations and globalization are resulting in new types of relationships and relational aggression. Existing models inadequately address the needs of some nontraditional and minority groups who are also impacted by APR. There is a need to develop new strategies that would address these newly emerging types of relationships and relational aggression.

New technology, such as neuroimaging technologies, is providing new insights into aggression. New findings are pointing to the need to reevaluate interpretation concerning dysfunctional behaviors manifested in APR. Results from new research should be incorporated into these new strategies.

PURPOSE AND LEARNING OBJECTIVES

PURPOSE

The purpose of this theory is to explore the existing theoretical models and approaches to APR and to establish a case for change.

LEARNING OBJECTIVES

After studying this chapter, the reader should understand the basic elements of the theoretical models and approaches to APR and identify the reasons why finding a new approach is necessary.

KEY TERMS AND DEFINITIONS

Theory

Merriam-Webster Dictionary (Theory, n.d.) provides several definitions of theory

1)
   a. A plausible or scientifically acceptable general principle or body of principles offered to explain phenomena;

2)
   a. a belief, policy, or procedure proposed or followed as the basis of action;
   b. an ideal or hypothetical set of facts, principles, or circumstances —often used in the phrase in theory;

3)
   a. a hypothesis assumed for the sake of argument or investigation;
   b. an unproved assumption: conjecture;
   c. a body of theorems presenting a concise, systematic view of a subject;

4)
   a. the general or abstract principle of a body of fact, a science, or an art;

5)
   a. abstract thought: speculation;

6)
   a. the analysis of a set of facts in their relation to one another (Theory, n.d.).

INTRODUCTION

One of the most voiced criticisms of existing approaches to APR is the skewed approach that focuses on females as victims, to the exclusion of males. This skewed focus is indicative of the philosophical orientation and theoretical foundations that guide approaches to interpreting, analyzing, and addressing APR. Flaws in existing approaches to addressing APR might be indicative of deficiencies in philosophy and philosophical orientation.

SYSTEMS APPROACH AND DYSFUNCTIONAL AGGRESSION

Current approaches addressing APR explain APR as dysfunctional aggression caused by dysfunctional systems, such as family systems. Explaining APR as dysfunctions of systems and institutions is an approach that uses a systems' theoretical framework to understand social problems. Systems theory has its roots in evolutionary theory.

The focus on failed institutions and systems presents several challenges. For example, the concentration on dysfunctional systems reduces the focus and impact of failed neurobiological mechanisms that may be impacting dysfunctional aggression. Additionally, there are several weaknesses related to defining functional and dysfunctional aggression.

APR is also considered within the context of functional and dysfunctional behavioral aggression. Foundational conceptualization of functional and dysfunctional aggression also has its roots in the theory of evolution by natural selection.

THE NEUROBIOLOGICAL BASIS OF BEHAVIOR

New research, facilitated by technological advances, is changing the perception of dysfunctional behaviors. Neuroimaging technology is helping researchers to gain increased insight into the neurobiological basis of behavior and its implications for APR. These new findings are having a positive impact on APR policies, programs, and the development of services.

The neurobiological basis for dysfunctional behaviors is also rooted in evolutionary theory. However, the continued escalation of APR and the emergence of new types of APR behaviors are pointing to the need for continuous research.

THE NEED TO REVISIT UNDERGIRDING INTERPERSONAL AGGRESSION THEORIES

A revision of theories that undergird APR policies, programs, and services remains a critical area that needs focus. Interpretive frameworks that use systems theory, cognitive-emotional, behavioral, and psychological dysfunctionalities have their basis in the theory of evolution by means of natural selection.

Although tenets from evolution theory inform various theories found to be applicable to understanding APR, each theory tends to be presented in isolation of the others. Consequently, there seems to be an absence of a clear-cut theoretical basis for the current approaches to addressing APR.

Different programs and approaches are reliant either on one or on several theories. However, APR is a multifaceted phenomenon. Some theories might address some aspects of APR while ignoring other aspects of the problem. Furthermore, findings from these different evolution-based theories continue to show conflicting results regarding their efficacy in addressing APR.

The establishment of a firm theoretical basis for program development warrants a revisiting of the current theories undergirding existing programs and services. A critical appraisal of these theories might provide insight into the existing shortcomings of current APR policies and programs.

Although existing theories provide some insight into the phenomenon of APR, new theories based on different philosophical orientations are also emerging. These new theories are also pertinent to disciplines that inform policies, program development, and the provision of services for victims and perpetrators of APR. These new theories might offer feasible options for improving APR policies, programs, and services.

NEED FOR INCLUSIONS

There is an increasing need for APR policies, programs, and services that are more inclusive of minority populations[1], such as African-Americans,

Population	2010 Census	2011	2012	2013	2014	2015	2016	2017
White	78.36%	78.08%	77.85%	77.61%	77.37%	77.12%	76.88%	76.64%
Black	13.04%	13.09%	13.14%	13.18%	13.23%	13.27%	13.31%	13.36%
Native Am	1.21%	1.22%	1.23%	1.23%	1.24%	1.25%	1.25%	1.26%
Asian	4.91%	5.05%	5.17%	5.29%	5.43%	5.56%	5.70%	5.83%
Hawaiian	0.22%	0.22%	0.23%	0.23%	0.23%	0.23%	0.24%	0.24%
Multi Race	2.26%	2.33%	2.39%	2.45%	2.50%	2.56%	2.62%	2.68%

Table 2-1   US Minority Population Data

gays, lesbians, and migrants. In addition to revisiting the current approach to addressing APR, there is a need to establish a firm theoretical basis that can address unmet needs of victims and perpetrators of APR. Revisiting

---

[1] Table 2-1   US Census Bureau

these theories should begin with an understanding of the philosophical tenets that undergird existing theories underpinning current APR models.

CONCLUSION

Almost all theories, research, and practice related to human aggression hinge on evolutionary theory. Three fundamental premises *life is a struggle,* aggression functionality, and survivability undergird the theory of evolution by means of natural selection. These tenets undergird research and practice into dysfunctional human aggression. These underlying tenets impinge on the way we understand, interpret, and analyze APR.

The tenets of survivability and aggression as posited under evolutionary theory is a tenuous argument when applied as an explanation for aggression. Many facets of APR remain obscure when these tenets are integrated into systems theory as an approach to interpreting aggression.

Because of the need to find a more applicable theoretical explanation for this phenomenon, there is a need, to begin with, a thorough evaluation of the existing theoretical approach. Other indicators, such as the need for greater inclusion of persons impacted by APR along with new studies that implicate neuro-functionality as being relevant for understanding APR, also points to the need for a revisiting of the existing APR models.

CHAPTER REVIEW

REVIEW QUESTIONS

1. What are the basic philosophical tenets undergirding functional aggression?
2. How adequate are these philosophical tenets for explaining APR?
3. Do you think that existing APR programs should be remodeled for greater inclusion of victims and perpetrators not included in traditional definitions of APR?

CHAPTER THREE
EVOLUTION OF AGGRESSION

CHAPTER PREVIEW

Flaws and weaknesses in the current models used to address APR might be an indication of flaws and weaknesses in the philosophical orientation and theoretical foundation of the current models. These flaws and deficiencies might be pointing to the need for a reevaluation of the philosophical orientation and the theoretical foundation of existing models undergirding APR policies and programs.

Evolution by means of natural selection posits tenets concerning ontogeny. Tenets of ontogeny are pertinent to the nature of being and human aggression. A philosophical orientation concerning life, being, and the nature of life forms the theoretical basis for evolution by natural selection. In this chapter, there will be a review of the fundamental tenets of evolution, such as the origin of life and the origin of species. These tenets impinge on the understanding of APR.

PURPOSE AND LEARNING OBJECTIVES

PURPOSE

The theory of evolution by means of natural selection is the foremost, if not only theory used to interpret and explain aggression. The purpose of this chapter is to establish the importance of understanding the philosophical underpinnings of the dominant theory that shape research, practice, and policies related to aggression.

LEARNING OBJECTIVES

After studying this chapter, the reader should understand the reasons why philosophical tenets and philosophical orientation are pertinent to APR.

KEY TERMS AND DEFINITIONS

Cosmology

Cosmology is a branch of philosophy dealing with the origin and general structure of the universe, with its parts, elements, and laws, and especially with such of its characteristics as space, time, causality, and freedom. Cosmology is also a branch of astronomy that deals with the general structure and evolution of the universe (Oparin, 1957).

Cosmozoë

Cosmozoë is a branch of philosophy that can be traced back to ancient Greece. Cosmozoë philosophers hypothesized explanations of the origin and general structure of the universe. Cosmozoë philosophers believed that stars were gods and that stars were responsible for ontogeny. Cosmozoë philosophers attempted to remove mythical elements from cosmology and establish metaphysics as a scientific discipline. The present-day discipline of cosmology has its origin in cosmozoë (Oparin, 1957).

Epigenetics

Epigenetics is the study of heritable phenotypic changes that do not involve alterations in the deoxyribonucleic acid (DNA) molecule. Epigenetics refers to the process related to or produced by the chain of developmental processes in epigenesis that lead from genotype to phenotype after the initial actions of the genes. Epigenetics also means related to, being, or involve changes in gene functions that do not involve changes in the DNA molecular sequence (Epigenetics, n.d.).

Hypothetical Assumption

A hypothetical assumption is an assumptive statement that forms the basis of a hypothesis. A hypothetical assumption is a statement based on beliefs concerning the way the world and things in the world function.

Hypothesis

1) A hypothesis is a proposed explanation for a phenomenon. It forms the basis of research or experiment that is designed to test whether the hypothetical assumptions undergirding the hypothesis are true. Scientists generally base their hypothesis on previous observations that cannot satisfactorily be explained with the available scientific theories.

2) A hypothesis is a supposition or proposed explanation made based on limited information or evidence as the starting point for further research (Hypothesis, n.d.).

Ontogeny

Ontogeny is the developmental history of an organism, individual, or species (Ontogeny, n.d.).

Ontogenesis, also called morphogenesis, is the study of the origination and development of individual organisms. Embryology is also referred to as ontogeny.

Metaphysical

Metaphysical means pertaining to metaphysics (Metaphysical, n.d.).

Metaphysics

Metaphysics is a branch of philosophy that is concerned with the fundamental nature of reality and being. Metaphysics philosophy includes ontology, cosmology, and epistemology.

In ontology, metaphysical disciplines are abstract philosophical studies: a study of what is outside of objective experience.

"'*Metaphysics* analyzes the generic traits manifested by existences of any kind' J. H. Randall." (Metaphysics, n.d.).

Mythical

Mythical means pertaining to a myth. A myth is a traditional story, especially one concerning the early history of a people or explaining a natural or social phenomenon, and typically involving supernatural beings or events (Myth Def. 1, n.d.).

Philosophy

Merriam-Webster Dictionary (Philosophy, n.d.) provides several definitions of philosophy.

1) Disciplinary

      a. Philosophy underpins all disciplines and subdisciplines, including philosophy, ethics, biology, sociology, law, politics, economics, logic, metaphysics, religion, and aesthetics. Philosophy also refers to a course of higher learning, such as a Ph.D.

2) Beliefs, Concepts, and Attitudes
      a. Philosophy also refers to fundamental beliefs, concepts, attitudes, and practices of individuals and groups, such as religious philosophy.

3) Wisdom
      a. Philosophy also refers to the pursuit of wisdom, a search for a general understanding, or the fundamental beliefs that undergird hypothetical formulations.

INTRODUCTION

Philosophy undergirds all theory. In research and practice, the theoretical underpinning sets the boundaries for interpreting the problem, reviewing existing research and literature on the issue, and analyzing the problem. An understanding of the undergirding philosophy of evolutionary theory will improve understanding of the beliefs and thoughts that impinge on theoretical development and increase the ability to evaluate those theories that are foundational to APR.

Evolutionary theory is the theory that is most often applied to interpret, analyze, and address APR. As such, the theory of evolution by natural selection is the focus of this text.

Cosmozoë philosophy undergirds the theory of evolution by natural selection. As such, a critical appraisal of cosmozoë philosophy is pertinent to this study.

PHILOSOPHY, THEORY, RESEARCH, AND PRACTICE

Despite compartmentalization of disciplines, all disciplines and their subdisciplines converge under the broad umbrella of philosophy. Additionally, all disciplines overlap and integrate with other similar or related disciplines. For example, biology, genetics, and epigenetics are overlapping disciplines. However, scholars integrate these studies with other disciplines, such as statistics, computer analysis, and neuroimaging. These disciplines, subdisciplines, and integrated studies drive research, applied research, and practice pertinent to cognition, emotion, and behavior. Cognition, emotions, and behaviors are central to understanding APR. Theory undergirds every discipline.

Philosophies and disciplines are contextual and reflective of the cultural framework within which philosophies are developed and transmitted. Theories undergird research and practice. Philosophy underlies all theory. Because evolutionary theory undergirds almost all disciplines, evolutionary philosophy is also intertwined in almost all disciplines.

When conducting research, the researcher must choose a theory as the framework upon which to build the study. Philosophical tenets are at the foundation of all theories, research, and practice. As such, an evaluation of philosophy is central to any study seeking to address dysfunctional behavior.

EVOLUTION BY MEANS OF NATURAL SELECTION AS A MAJOR THEORETICAL FOUNDATION OF APR

Studies in genetics, epigenetics, biogenetics, and neuroscience have a basis in evolutionary theory. Moreover, disciplines in the behavioral sciences apply findings from studies in these fields to develop APR treatment and therapy. These studies tend to examine the social, biological, psychological, and neurophysiological variables that correlate with APR. These disciplines apply tenets from evolutionary theory (Brandon, 2014; Buss, 2009).

Studies on human aggression involve tenets of the ontogeny of species, *life*, *being*, and the nature of being. Evolutionary theory heavily influences almost every theory and research into these concepts. Evolutionary tenets concerning life, being, and the nature of being, provide foundational explanations of aggression. Given the preponderance of disciplines, theories, research, and practice undergirded by evolutionary theory, a revisiting of the philosophical tenets undergirding evolutionary theory might shed light on issues pertinent to APR (Adamson, 2017; Colbert & Rowe, 2008; Dall, Bell, Bolnick, & Ratnieks, 2012).

THE RELEVANCE OF PHILOSOPHICAL ORIENTATION

HYPOTHETICAL ASSUMPTIONS AND PHILOSOPHY

Theoretical propositions begin with a speculative, assumptive hypothesis. These hypothetical assumptions reflect the philosophical orientation of the theorist. Consequently, theories are undergirded by theorist's philosophical orientations and beliefs. As such, a critical appraisal of the philosophical orientation and beliefs of the proponents of the theory of evolution by natural selection is relevant for this study (Bradie & Harms, 2017).

Evolutionary theorists posit hypotheses concerning the origin of life and origin of species. These hypothetical assumptions and premises have high applicability for understanding the current structures of APR policies, programs, and the provision of services. These hypothetical assumptions include philosophical thoughts about the origin of life, the nature of life, and the role of aggression (Colbert & Rowe, 2008).

ONTOGENY AND AGGRESSION

Ontogeny is the study of the origin of life and the origin of species. The origin of life and the origin of species are two distinct phenomena. The origin of life refers to the very first existence of any living organism or being on this planet. The origin of species refers to the process whereby different life-forms emerged. According to the tenets of evolution by natural selection, various life-forms or species evolved gradually over time.

However, before organisms evolved into species, the element called life must have existed. Proponents of the theory of natural selection have never proposed an explanation for the origin of life on this planet.

Although the proponents of evolutionary theory never explained the source or appearance of life on the planet, evolutionists conjectured several tenets about life. These tenets are inferences that have become accepted as truths.

Beliefs influence behavior. Behavior, in turn, reinforces and validates beliefs. The conjecture concerning aggression is a fundamental belief that has shaped human behavior.

The struggle for survival and fitness are the foremost premise of evolutionary theory. According to evolutionary theory, aggression is an innate behavior that drives the process of evolution. According to the theory of evolution by natural selection, aggression is an innate quality of life that defines the nature of human beings. Aggression is an innate instinct imparted into humans by the gods.

EARLY PHILOSOPHICAL EXPLANATIONS OF AGGRESSION

Current models addressing APR demonstrate an implicit acceptance of the philosophical thought that aggression is innate and instinctive. The belief that aggression is an innate quality of life and the conceptualization of inherent aggression could be traced back to an ancient Greek philosophical school called cosmozoë.

COSMOZOË

Cosmozoë[2] was an ancient religious philosophy concerned with the origin of the earth and life on earth. According to this theory, "fragments of stars bearing the seeds

Figure 3-1   Cosmozoë

of life reached the Earth and thus impregnate it" (Oparin, 1957, p. 53).

Philosophers from antiquity believed that the stars were gods. The conceptualization that fragments of the stars came to earth bearing the seeds of life is a belief that life on earth is due to the gods. This ancient belief was a religious myth concerning metaphysical entities called stars and gods.

The fundamental beliefs concerning the stars and gods as the explanation of ontogeny of life were the core elements of cosmozoic philosophy. According to Aristotle, a cosmological philosopher, "the stars are gods."

---

[2] Figure 3-1   Anonymous/Unknown author (https://commons.wikimedia.org/wiki/File:Flammarion.jpg), "Flammarion", marked as public domain, more details on Wikimedia Commons: https://commons.wikimedia.org/wiki/Template:PD-old

> *From old – and indeed extremely ancient – times there has been handed down to our later age intimations of a mythical character to the effect that the stars are gods and that the divine embraces the whole of nature. The further details were subsequently added in the manner of myth. Their purpose was the persuasion of the masses and general legislative and political expediency. For instance, the myths tell us that these gods are anthropomorphic or resemble some of the other animals and give us other, comparable extrapolations of the basic picture. If, then, we discard these accretions and consider the central feature, that they held the primary substances to be gods, we might well believe the claim to have been directly inspired. We might also conclude that, while it is highly probable that all possible arts and doctrines have been many times discovered and lost, these ancient cosmologies have been preserved, like holy relics, right up to the present day. It is these, and these alone, that we can know clearly of the ancestral – indeed primordial – beliefs.*
> *(Aristotle, 1999, pp. 380-381).*

Aristotle attempted to extricate myths from metaphysical beliefs. Aristotle believed that ideas concerning ontogeny and the universe were the essence of metaphysical philosophy. However, the masses and the general population engaged in the embellishment of these conceptualizations and produced myths and legends as a part of their interpretation and explanation. Scholars aimed to disentangle these basic conceptualizations from mythical beliefs and present these as a disciplinary study under natural philosophies (Aristotle, 1999).

Even when cosmological philosophers attempted to extricate myths from their metaphysical beliefs, they still could explain the source or origins of life without recourse to using explanations involving insentient, impalpable phenomena. To overcome this challenge, cosmological philosophers conceived of a type of study, a new discipline called natural philosophy.

Natural philosophy or the philosophy of nature is a discipline concerned with nature and the physical universe. Natural philosophy is the precursor of modern-day natural sciences, which includes disciplines such as physics, chemistry, and biology. Prior to the development of the natural sciences, philosophers that engaged in the natural philosophers were called naturalists. In the modern-day era, scholars in these disciplines are called scientists (Del Soldato, 2016).

Cosmological philosophy was a natural philosophy discipline. Imagining and reasoning about incorporeal existence was the foundation of cosmological philosophy. Cosmological philosophers such as Aristotle handed down the methods used in natural philosophy such as the process of imagining and reasoning, to natural philosophers, or naturalists (Bodnar, 2018; Del Soldato, 2016).

COSMOLOGICAL EXPLANATIONS OF AGGRESSION

According to cosmozoë philosophy, the stars in the constellations were gods. These gods seeded life on earth as tiny microscopic organisms. This seeding is responsible for life, being, and the nature of being. As such, aggression in humans is due to the seeding by the gods.

This explanation is based on myths that involve metaphysical elements. This philosophical foundation remains as an implicit mainstay in modern science.

The conversion from mythical origin to science occurred gradually over several centuries. Cosmozoë philosophers understood the ramifications of engaging in philosophical explanations based on intangible, incorporeal constructs, and cosmozoë philosophers aimed to establish their metaphysical, philosophical thought into a sentient reality (Aristotle, 1999; Oparin, 1957).

As early as the fifth century, B. C. Xenophanes, an early Greek philosopher, criticized the reliance on myths as an explanation for the origins of humans and the nature of being. Xenophanes, like Aristotle and later Greek philosophers, argued that metaphysical, ontogenetic explanations represented true knowledge, whereas the mythical content represented beliefs (Aristotle, 1999; Kahn, 2003; Oparin, 1957).

The distinction that these philosophies hoped to achieve in philosophical thought was the difference between myths and the metaphysical. Explanations using myths represented beliefs, but explanations using the metaphysical represented knowledge.

Ascribing the existence of the metaphysical to the work of the pantheon of gods was the religious aspects of cosmology. Early Greek philosophers believed that the metaphysical represented an aspect of reality and human existence. The metaphysical could be used to explain life, being, and the nature of being while ignoring the mythical aspects of the religious philosophy from which these explanations emerged.

Using the metaphysical to explain life, existence, and the nature of being was apart and distinct from the reliance on the pantheon of gods as an explanation of the source of these elements. Cosmozoë philosophers contended that explanations about life, existence, and the nature of being that centered on thoughts about metaphysical elements should be a discipline based on knowledge rather than a philosophy based on beliefs.

This discipline became known as the philosophical method. Cosmozoë philosophers engaged in the discipline called the philosophical method to convert thoughts based on metaphysical elements into a sentient reality. The conversion of philosophical thoughts centered on converting metaphysics into a sentient reality became the foundation of transforming religious philosophy into science. Cosmozoë philosophies became known as the natural philosophies.

Cosmological philosophers engaged in the philosophical methods to study cosmozoë philosophies as a new branch of philosophy called the natural philosophies. Several new disciplines emerged in the natural philosophies. Each new philosophical discipline presented philosophical thoughts that became more removed and remote from the initial religious tenet.

Causation is the foundation of the philosophical method. Philosophers that engaged in the natural philosophy were called naturalists. Naturalists used a causative methodology to establish knowledge that applied beliefs about metaphysical elements as knowledge with epistemic value in their natural philosophies (Adamson, 2017; Aristotle, 1999; Del Soldato, 2016; Oparin, 1957).

GREEK RELIGIOUS PHILOSOPHY AND EVOLUTION

Evolution by means of natural selection involves premises concerning life, the origin of life, and origin of species. These premises are based on religious beliefs from several metaphysical philosophies in antiquity (MacCorquodale & Meehl, 1948; Paternotte, 2011).

In antiquity, evolutionary philosophy was part of a religious belief concerning ontogeny. In antiquity, philosophy and religion were interrelated. In antiquity, philosophers held a religious philosophy or worldview concerning their beliefs about the way life began on earth. Darwin derived his concept of pangenesis from Greek religious mythology (Green, 2018; Smeenk & Ellis, 2017).

Figure 3-2   Greek God Pan

Pan[3] is a god in Greek religious mythology. According to cosmological philosophy, the universe is god (Oparin, 1957). Pan engaged in a battle with the Typhons, and as an outcome of his success in battle, Pan became god of the universe. Pan is the giver of life. Pan was responsible for spreading

---

[3] Figure 3-2   © Marie-Lan Nguyen / Wikimedia Commons
(https://commons.wikimedia.org/wiki/File:Pan_goat_MAN_Napoli_Inv27709_n01.
jpg), „Pan goat MAN Napoli Inv27709 n01",
https://creativecommons.org/licenses/by/2.5/legalcode

pangenomes, pangenes, or pansperms throughout the universe. Pan imparted pangenes to humans. Pangenes are the mechanisms of transmission of heredity (Darwin C., 1872; 1882).

The word pan has emerged to mean all. However, the conceptualization has a basis in the belief that Pan was an all-encompassing god. At the time that Darwin was presenting his theory, cosmozoë philosophers had already become steeped in a tradition of presenting cosmozoë philosophy, but in their philosophical treatise, the mythical aspects remained as an unspoken accepted assumption.

While some may argue that cosmozoë philosophy that integrated Greek philosophy into theories of natural philosophies, such as Darwin's theory of evolution has little or no relevance to modern-day theory, research, and practice; Greek mythical philosophies continue to be a foundational element of current theory, research, and practice. Gene theory, for example, has many facets that came out of cosmozoë philosophies.

Tenets from cosmozoë philosophies persist in the chromosomal theory of inheritance and subsequent theories in genetics. Several concepts from Greek mythology, such as predispositional vulnerability, remain entwined in theoretical interpretations and applications. Predispositional vulnerability is an example of the way that a foundational belief from Greek mythology continues to influence research, theory, and practice.

According to Greek mythology, the gods imparted gifts to humans. These gifts were virtues and vices that the gods possessed. Humans, who were the recipients of these impartations, were predisposed to manifest these virtues and vices in their behaviors. Darwin referred to these virtues and vices as gemmules. The conception of gemmules was the foundation of eugenics or 'good genes.'

The concept of genes emerged from Greek philosophies concerning origin or genesis. Pangenesis theory embodied the philosophical thoughts of ontogeny. These thoughts influenced the conceptualization of predispositional vulnerability.

Gene theory and the chromosomal theory of inheritance were developed from pangenesis theory; the core elements of Greek philosophical thought still influences core elements of modern-day genetic theories. In light of increasing evidence that supports genetic predispositions to vulnerability, scholars must reconsider the validity of the philosophical orientations of evolution by natural selection, genetics, and inheritance.

Darwinism, Cosmological Philosophies, and Aggression

Charles Darwin was steeply influenced by cosmological philosophy (Peretó, Bada, & Lazcano, 2009; Peretó, 2005). Based on cosmological tenets, Darwin posited that life on earth first began as microscopic organisms or microbes. After possibly millions of years, these microbes developed into species. Life originated first, and species originated at a much later date. Today, each plant and animal life represent species that evolved from these simple organisms (Darwin C., 1872).

The theory of evolution by means of natural selection has implied assumptions about aggression founded in cosmozoë philosophy. Although Darwin engaged in the philosophical methods to develop the theory of evolution by natural selection, the foundational tenets from ancient mythical beliefs remained embedded in the theory. For example, the conceptualization that life on earth first began as microscopic organism or microbes stems from cosmozoë philosophy that the stars in the constellation are gods and that these gods seeded the earth with small fragments or microbes (Oparin, 1957).

ANTHROPOMORPHISM AND PERSONIFICATION

Anthropomorphism and personification were key concepts in Darwin's theory of evolution by natural selection. The word anthropomorphism derives from two Greek words *ánthrōpos* (ἄνθρωπος, lit. "human") and *morphē* (μορφή). Anthropomorphism is the attribution of human traits, emotions, and intentions to nonhuman entities. Personification is the attribution of human form and characteristics to abstract, metaphysical concepts (Guthrie, 2008; Hutson, 2012).

Anthropomorphism and personification were key elements in Greek philosophy. The gods possessed human traits and emotions that they imparted to humans. Humans, in turn, personified the gods.

Darwin's conceptualization of life bears elements of personification. Within life are characteristics of the gods. As such, the characteristics of life, existence, and being represented personification of the gods.

According to Darwin, pangenes are the mechanism whereby characteristics transmit to humans. In Greek mythology, the god Pan was the giver of life. Pan imparted life to all living things.

Darwin argued that inside of that abstract concept called *life*, there are different qualities, one of which is aggression. Aggression was one of the characteristics specific to the god Pan. Pan, from which the word panic derives, struck fear in those who opposed him. Pan imparted aggression through the element called life (The Editors of Encyclopædia Britannica, 2018).

Darwin argued that *life is a struggle* and aggression within *life* is a quality that promotes evolution. Therefore, organisms and living beings must struggle to survive. When organisms and living beings struggle to survive, the unfit will die, and the *fittest* will survive. Aggression is an inherent quality of life that enables the fit to survive.

Because aggression is an inherent quality in life, then aggression is an indication of the nature of being. Aggression, therefore, is an essential part of human nature. Aggression is instinctive, self-preservative behavior. Aggression defines the nature of our being. Therefore, to understand aggression, there is a need to study beliefs about the origin of life to assess whether ontogeny of life holds the answer to understanding aggression in humans. There must also be an evaluation of the validity of the evolutionary premise of ontogeny.

An organism must be aggressive to survive because the fittest survive, and the unfit die. Therefore, aggression is a functional element of evolution by natural selection and foundational to survival.

Although there are several evolutionary premises pertinent to APR, these three basic premises continue to inform thought and influence research in nearly all disciplines and their subdisciplines. The underlying philosophical bases of evolutionary thinking are; first, *life is a struggle,* second, aggression is functional, and third, aggression is foundational to survivability. These underlying philosophical premises delimit the boundaries of APR.

CONCLUSION

Almost all theories, research, and practice related to human aggression hinge on evolutionary theory. Three fundamental premises *life is a struggle,* aggression functionality, and survivability undergird the theory of evolution by means of natural selection. These tenets undergird research and practice into dysfunctional human aggression. These underlying tenets impinge on the way we understand, interpret, and analyze APR.

The underlying tenets of the theory of evolution by means of natural selection emerged from cosmozoë philosophy. As such, a cosmological, philosophical orientation is the foundation of the theory of evolution by means of natural selection. Cosmological philosophy implicitly influences the interpretation and analysis of APR.

CHAPTER REVIEW

REVIEW QUESTIONS

1. Why is an understanding of philosophical orientation important for understanding APR?
2. What are the basic philosophical tenets undergirding functional aggression?
3. How adequate are these philosophical tenets for explaining APR?

CHAPTER FOUR
PHILOSOPHICAL ORIENTATION

CHAPTER PREVIEW

In this chapter, there will be a discussion of hypotheses, beliefs, facts, and truths. Hypotheses are beliefs and may not be factual or true.

Theories explaining life, the origin of life, and the origin of species are hypothetical assumptions. As such, theories of ontogeny are not facts or truths but are plausible hypotheses derived from cosmology and natural philosophy.

Additionally, hypotheses are not without bias but reflect the philosophical orientation of the theorists. In this chapter, there will be a discussion of the ways that philosophical orientation influence hypothesis formulation and the risks of bias associated with undergirding philosophical orientation.

Because philosophical orientations influence hypothesis formulations, philosophical orientation influences ontogenetic theories. Currently, existing ontogenetic theories are used to explain APR.

In this chapter, there will be a revision of the likelihood that skewed philosophical orientations might be influencing the interpretation of APR. As such, there is a need to understand the ways that philosophical orientations might be influencing current perspectives on APR.

PURPOSE AND LEARNING OBJECTIVES

PURPOSE

The purpose of this chapter is to explain the philosophical orientation of the theories of origin.

LEARNING OBJECTIVES

After studying this chapter, the reader should understand the origination and development of philosophical thoughts and orientations and their implications for APR.

KEY TERMS AND DEFINITIONS

Antiquities

Matters relating to the life or culture of ancient times (Antiquity, n.d.).

Antiquity

Antiquity is a period of history prior to the Middle Ages. Ancient time (Antiquity, n.d.).

Hypothetical Construct

A hypothetical construct in the philosophy of science is an object that exists in the mind of the theorist. A hypothetical construct is an explanatory variable that is not directly observable (Andersen & Hepburn, 2016; MacCorquodale & Meehl, 1948).

Impalpable Entities and Phenomena

An entity, concept, or phenomenon whose existence, nature, properties, qualities, or relations are not directly observable by humans. Examples of impalpable entities and concepts are atoms, atomic particles, the force of gravity, causation, beliefs, and desires (Impalpable, n.d.).

Nonsensorially Observable Phenomena

Nonsensorially observable phenomena are phenomena that cannot be literally observed using the five senses (see *Impalpable*) (Impalpable, n.d.).

Palpable

Palpable means to be capable of being touched or felt: tangible. Easily perceived: noticeable. Easily perceptible by the mind: manifest (Palpable, n.d.).

INTRODUCTION

All theorists have philosophical thoughts or orientations that form the foundation of their hypotheses (Reiss & Sprenger, 2017). Hypotheses drive theories and form the foundation of all theories. A philosophical thought or orientation is not a truth or a fact. A philosophical orientation or thought is a belief.

The philosophical orientation of a theory is the belief of the theorists. If the philosophical belief is tenuous, then the theory is tenuous.

Evolutionary theory has a philosophical foundation in ancient cosmozoë. Cosmozoë philosophical orientation is the foundation of the three primary evolutionary premises that are pertinent to APR. When considering intervention and APR prevention strategies, because cosmozoë is the underlying philosophical orientation of three evolutionary premises, an understanding of cosmozoë philosophy is contextually relevant.

BELIEF AND HYPOTHESIS

Beliefs and hypotheses are impalpable, or nonsensorially observable. An impalpable concept or entity is one whose existence, nature, properties, qualities, or relations are not directly observable by humans.

A hypothesis does not establish a fact or a law but is indicative of the beliefs, perceptions, and philosophical orientation of the theorists. Aggression and survivability tenets are based on cosmozoë philosophical thought, orientation, or belief.

Cosmozoë philosophers made hypothetical assumptions about aggression and survivability based on a fundamental belief concerning elements such as gods, stars, and attributes of the gods. Currently, these tenets of aggression and survivability are unquestioned, and the foundational cosmozoë philosophy from which these tenets derive are ignored. Because of the tenuity of foundational cosmozoë philosophy, the hypothetical assumptions upon which aggression and survivability are premised should be revisited.

TENUITY AND BELIEFS

In the philosophical disciplines, including the philosophies of the natural sciences, examples of impalpable entities are atoms, atomic particles, the force of gravity, causation, beliefs, and desires. Cosmological philosophy is founded upon impalpable concepts, beliefs, constructs, and elements.

Naturalists and cosmological philosophers created the scientific method to allow impalpable, metaphysical beliefs, elements, concepts, and constructs to be integrated and accepted as a scientific study. Cosmozoë philosophers were instrumental in the development of the scientific method.

Because the tenets and hypotheses presented by cosmozoë philosophers and naturalists involved impalpable events, concepts, and entities, cosmozoë philosophers and naturalists developed philosophies to give tenuity to their beliefs and hypotheses. An undergirding philosophy of the scientific method is that if a belief is valid, then the hypothetical assumptions stemming from the belief is rational. A valid belief is a reasonable belief. As such, cosmozoë philosophers argued that cosmozoë philosophies are valid, reasonable beliefs.

However, because the scientific method requires that hypotheses should be tested, re-tested, evaluated and reevaluated, cosmozoë philosophies could be challenged. Scholars, therefore, should question whether the foundational cosmozoë philosophies concerning gods, the stars, aggression, and survivability are reasonable beliefs. Even after coming to a conclusion that cosmozoë philosophies might be reasonable beliefs, scholars must bear in mind that reasonable belief is neither fact nor truth.

Scholars should bear in mind that foundational tenets of aggression and survivability are based on assumptions and beliefs involving gods, and metaphysics. These foundational elements are impalpable, immeasurable, cannot be observed directly with human senses, and can never be observed sensorially within the existing limitations of human senses. As such, the tenets and hypotheses emerging from these beliefs remain the perception of the believer, the thoughts and imagination of the philosopher, and the philosophical orientation guiding the philosopher's thoughts and imagination.

If the scholar concludes that the three ontogenetic premises that influence current perspectives on APR are rational and reasonable beliefs, these hypotheses might still not be accurate. Considering the challenges in addressing APR, there might be a need to revisit and revise the fundamental beliefs undergirding current ontogenetic hypotheses and theories.

SCIENTIFIC RESEARCH AND VALIDATION

Evolutionary theory has a long-standing ontogenetic history. These tenets have been accepted as truths for more than 2,000 years. Additionally, theorists such as Darwin, have been validated as credible scholars. These two facts make challenging fundamental cosmozoë philosophy about ontogeny a formidable task.

Two polarized camps, Darwinist and anti-Darwinists, seem to exist in academia. Given Darwin's credibility and auspicious work as a scholar, and the longevity of the tenets of evolution, any attempt to question this long-standing firmly entrenched theory is likely to receive resistance.

Researchers who attempt to question long-established theories and hypotheses might see this prospect as daunting and experience intimidation. This intimidation might stem from partial knowledge of the purpose of scientific research in relation to beliefs and hypothetical assumptions.

The purpose of scientific research is to establish that the belief is

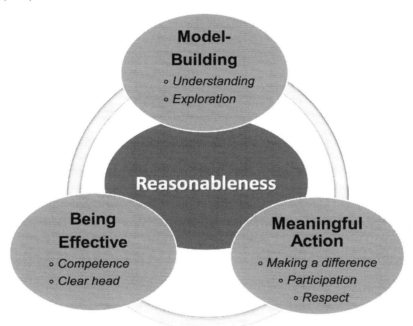

Figure 4-1   Rationality

valid. Scientific research does not validate the belief, but the rationality[4] of the belief.

Scientists validate beliefs when they engage in scientific research that supports hypotheses undergirding the theory. Currently, there are conflicting results from research that seeks to establish the validity of fundamental tenets of aggression and survivability.

Although aggression and survivability are accepted as valid beliefs, when researchers present findings that do not support these tenets, then these tenets are not validated. Because of these conflicting results and the difficulties associated with applying tenets of aggression and survivability to explain phenomena such as APR, theorists are encouraged to develop new theories that integrate different philosophical orientations and beliefs, to explain these phenomena.

---

4 Figure 4-1   Rachel Kaplan
(https://en.wikipedia.org/wiki/File:Reasonable_Person_Model_Diagram_2.png),
„Reasonable Person Model Diagram 2",
https://creativecommons.org/licenses/by-sa/3.0/legalcode

THE INCLUSION OF BELIEFS IN THE SCIENTIFIC METHOD

Scholars are encouraged to question foundational beliefs undergirding theories. During the earlier days of modern scientific research, foundational philosophical beliefs were questioned. Darwin himself encouraged other theorists and scholars to debate his proposals and theories. As such, some of Darwin's foundational tenets were challenged and revised.

Although modern-day scholars accept beliefs as the foundation of hypothesis, before the development of the scientific method, beliefs could not be the foundation of science as a discipline. While it is acceptable practice to apply belief to undergird hypotheses, it is also an acceptable practice in the modern-day scientific method to question the validity of a belief.

Prior to the development of the scientific method, objects and facts were the subjects of scientific studies. Beliefs are insentient and nonsensorially observable and could not be included in scientific studies. Beliefs were the subject matter of philosophies. Philosophies were not included as a discipline in scientific studies.

In antiquity, philosophers acknowledged that objects were facts and beliefs were philosophies. Philosophers' beliefs were merely their philosophical orientation, were insentient, and could not be observed. Insentient beliefs that cannot be observed could not be included in scientific study.

Empiricists were scientists who claimed that science was the study of truth and fact. Based on empiricists' rules, scientists can only validate sentient and sensorially observed phenomena as truth or fact. Therefore, beliefs and philosophies that are insentient and cannot be observed do not fit the criteria for inclusion into the discipline called scientific study.

Consequently, naturalists developed a new discipline, called the scientific method. Because of the ardent work of naturalists, the scientific method replaced scientific study.

One of the rationales for developing the scientific method was to establish rules that would facilitate the inclusion of beliefs as the foundation for hypotheses. Based on these rules, if the philosopher could prove that the belief was logical, then the belief became accepted as a valid belief. Upon validation of the belief, naturalists established additional rules to make the claim that validation of the belief establishes the belief as a fact and a truth.

Beginning in antiquity, cosmozoë philosophers began acknowledging that beliefs were not the subject matter of scientific study. Consequently, cosmozoë philosophers began extricating their philosophies from existing myths. Although their philosophies did not include myths, the core elements of these myths remained entangled in their study.

Core elements of these mythical beliefs remained entangled in evolutionary philosophy. Among these core elements were beliefs concerning ontogeny. Because evolutionary theory forms the basis of many disciplines, these core beliefs continue to impinge on modern-day theories, research, and practice.

It might be that some modern-day scholars may not give thought to beliefs and philosophical orientation undergirding the theories that form the foundation of their research. However, these beliefs inform the hypothetical assumptions of their research. Accepting beliefs and philosophical orientations as the unspoken foundation of hypothetical assumptions were not always customary.

Even today, it is accepted that beliefs are different from facts. During the early philosophical development of the scientific method, empiricists resisted the inclusion of beliefs as an element of the scientific discipline and insisted that facts and truths were sentient, sensorially observable phenomena, such as an object that could be seen and touched. Therefore, facts and truths should be the subject matter of scientific studies.

In antiquity, philosophies, philosophical thoughts, and beliefs belonged to a branch of study called metaphysics. Metaphysics was the study of those things and beliefs that were beyond sentient, sensorially observable objects. Empiricists did not include philosophies into scientific studies (National Academy of Sciences and Institute of Medicine, 2008).

Although philosophy was a traditional discipline standing on its merit, philosophical thoughts and beliefs were not presented or accepted as facts or truths. Development of philosophical thought over several centuries facilitated the inclusion of beliefs and philosophies into scientific research. Nevertheless, it is of ethical consideration that theorists, researchers, and practitioners should not inculcate the assumption that beliefs, thoughts, and inferences are truths and facts.

Philosophical orientations have been used to support theories or hypotheses. Although philosophical beliefs from antiquity have a stronghold in the scientific method, there is space for a reevaluation of these philosophical beliefs.

CONCLUSION

Difficulties in finding relevant and applicable solutions to human challenges might be due to fundamental philosophical orientations that undergird existing theories. In health and medicine, for example, continuous research results in repealing and changing of medical procedures and approaches in which practitioners previously engaged. Scholars contend that ongoing research is necessary to find accurate and relevant solutions for problems.

Problems of aggression continue to plague society. Research indicates ongoing escalations in violence, especially APR. Several theories and hypotheses seek to explain the existence and presentment of aggression in humans. Almost all studies on aggression among humans use evolutionary theory and evolutionary philosophy as the theoretical framework.

To arrive at accurate and relevant solutions to address APR, the true cause of APR should be the premise of programs and services. Inaccurate solutions that cite failed institutions and systems as the cause of APR might stem from research based on beliefs, rather than research founded on truth (Evans, Newstead, & Byrne, 2004).

CHAPTER REVIEW

REVIEW QUESTIONS

1. Distinguish between beliefs and theory.
2. How does philosophy influence theory?
3. How does philosophy from antiquity influence the modern-day theory of genetics?

CHAPTER FIVE
THEORY OF ORIGIN

CHAPTER PREVIEW

Charles Darwin's theory of evolution by means of natural selection has a strong basis in ancient cosmozoë philosophies. Cosmozoë philosophers posited metaphysical explanations for ontogeny.

In this chapter, there will be a discussion of the emergence of cosmological philosophies and their integration into tenets of origin enshrouded in the theory of evolution by natural selection.

The chapter begins with an introduction to the fundamental tenets of natural selection and ontogenesis. In this discussion, there are highlights of several underlying assumptions presented in the theory of evolution by means of natural selection such as the unseen force that directs the natural selection, the concept of natural selection, and hypotheses about life and existence.

These hypothetical assumptions reflect a cosmozoic philosophical orientation. In the acceptance of the evolutionary theory, there is also an implicit acceptance of the underlying philosophical orientation and hypothetical assumptions as truth and fact. However, these assumptions are based on impalpable beliefs and concepts.

Because of the impalpability of these foundational assumptions, scholars should be willing to question the theory or aspects of the theory that appear(s) to be contradictory, or which fail to provide an adequate solution to problems that the theory is addressing. In this chapter, there will be an evaluation of the underlying premises of ontogeny that undergird the theory of evolution by natural selection, and the relevance of these premises for interpreting and analyzing APR.

PURPOSE AND LEARNING OBJECTIVES

PURPOSE

The purpose of this chapter is to explain fundamental ontogenetic tenets relevant to APR.

LEARNING OBJECTIVES

After studying this chapter, the reader should understand

1   the origination and development of theories of origin; and
2   the applicability of theories of origin to current interpretations of APR.

KEY TERMS AND DEFINITIONS

Fatalism

Fatalism is the acceptance of all things and events as inevitable: submission to fate (Fatalism, n.d.).

Natural Selection

Natural Selection is an element that exists outside the control of humans (Darwin C., 1872).

Predeterminism

Predeterminism is the belief that all events that occur have already been determined.

Predestination

Predestination is the belief that the eventual fate is predetermined and willed by a force outside of human control.

INTRODUCTION

Charles Darwin posited the theory of evolution by natural selection. Survival of the fittest is the foundational premise of this theory. Survival of the fittest is a premise that life is a struggle in which the fittest survive. However, survivability is predetermined and predestinated by a force outside of human control. This force directs a natural selection process based on predetermination and predestination.

Predetermination, predestination, survival of the fittest, natural selection, survivability, and the force that directs natural selection are hypothetical premises of the theory of evolution by natural selection. Cosmozoic philosophical orientation and beliefs undergird these premises. However, while these premises are implicitly received, and define the way evolutionary theory is applied in research and practice, they remain hypothetical assumptions based on impalpable premises, which can be modified and reevaluated.

Implicit acceptance of these hypothetical premises defines current interpretations of APR. For example, power and control dynamics imply acceptance of the premises of survivability and survival of the fittest. While aspects of these premises are criticized when applied to power and control, other aspects or different interpretations of these premises seem relevant for biogenetic explanations of aggression.

PHILOSOPHICAL ORIENTATION RELEVANT TO AGGRESSION

Darwin hypothesized that evolution is a natural selection process. Natural selection is an overarching force and process of evolution. The purpose of this overarching process is to achieve orthogenesis. Orthogenesis is a long-term goal of evolution. According to the tenet of orthogenesis, species will evolve to a higher state of complexity.

This theory of orthogenesis is a foundation of genetic research. The concept of natural selection, fitness, and orthogenesis are also the foundational elements of eugenics.

Several aspects of this philosophical thought have specific implications for APR. One fundamental concern is whether APR violates natural selection and orthogenesis. However, prior to answering the question regarding APR, natural selection, and orthogenesis, practitioners must first answer a more fundamental question: whether natural selection and orthogenesis are valid hypothetical premises.

FATALISM AND EVOLUTION BY MEANS OF NATURAL SELECTION

Darwin founded his theory of evolution by natural selection upon principles of fatalism. The central tenets of evolution by natural selection include natural selection, the forces that direct natural selection, predeterminism, predestination, the survival of the fittest, instinct, and aggression. Every aspect of evolution by means of natural selection falls outside the gambit of human control.

NATURAL SELECTION

Natural selection is a belief that a force outside of human control selects some species for survival and others for elimination. The force that directs natural selection endows some species and species members with superior survival qualities and others with vulnerability.

The natural selection process is random and predetermined. The force that directs natural selection randomly chooses the species upon which to bestow superior survival qualities. The force that directs natural selection also predetermines which species will have survivability and which species are vulnerable.

This concept of survivability and vulnerability inadvertently influences thought about vulnerable populations and vulnerable population members. For example, some populations and population members have a greater susceptibility to vulnerability than others. The concept of variability in survivability and susceptibility to vulnerability influence research into genetic predispositions and APR. Research into APR also focuses on variations in susceptibility to vulnerabilities based on differences such as gender and race.

However, natural selection is a philosophical thought and an impalpable belief. There is acceptance of the principle of natural selection, in theory, research, and practice. However, scholars should reevaluate this foundational premise and assess its validity as an explanation for APR.

THE FORCE DIRECTING NATURAL SELECTION

According to Darwin, a force that is outside of the control of humans directs natural selection. Natural selection means to be selectively predestinated or chosen for survivability or elimination (Darwin C., 1872; 1882).

The force that directs natural selection causes natural disasters such as droughts, famines, and hardships. These natural disasters are naturally occurring events which are outside of human control. These natural disasters are mechanisms that cause natural selection to occur.

These natural disasters are random and selective. Natural disasters occur randomly, but the force that directs natural selection causes these natural disasters to occur. As a mechanism of natural selection, natural disasters will result in the elimination of vulnerable species, but, cause superior species to survive (Darwin C., 1872; 1882).

Different survivability and vulnerability are the essence of evolution by natural selection. Differences in survivability and vulnerability explain the evolutionary process, why some species evolve to greater complexities, and why others become extinct.

Darwin used phylogenesis to explain random selection and predetermination of survivability and vulnerability among humans. According to Darwin's cosmological philosophy, humans came from a common progenitor but has diverged into different races or subspecies. Some of these subspecies, such as the European and the Negro, can be categorized as true species.

Phylogeny is the evolutionary philosophy that organisms, driven by innate aggression and the principle of survival, through successive mutational stage emerged into various species. Darwin conceived phylogeny as a random selection, orthogenetic process based on a predetermination of survivability and vulnerability. The existence of different human subspecies such as the Europeans and the Negro is evidence of predeterminism.

Each species is genetically discernible from other species. Survivability refers to a species' resilience in withstanding natural selection events such as famines and hardships. Species with low resilience are vulnerable. Some species have genes that give them higher survivability; other species have a genetic susceptibility to vulnerability (Darwin C., 1872; 1882).

Evolution by natural selection is a hypothesis based on a belief of genetic predisposition to survivability or vulnerability. The force that directs natural selection also by predetermination endows some species with unique qualities and characteristics that make these species fit so that they can survive. Natural selection also predetermines that some species should possess fewer sterling attributes, qualities, and characteristics that would make them vulnerable. The force that directs natural selection is responsible for selecting species upon which to bestow vulnerable genes for their elimination.

Each species has a specific predetermined, predestinated long-term evolutionary goal. This predetermined, predestinated goal is termed orthogenetic evolution. The force directing natural selection predetermined and predestinated some species to survive and become more fit than other species, while other species were predestinated for elimination. These predestinations are the evolutionary orthogenetic goals.

Increased survivability is the predestinated goal of those species endowed with sterling qualities and characteristics, gemmules, or genes. Destruction and extinction are the predestinated goals of vulnerable species. The force that directs natural selection uses natural events such as natural disasters and genes to accomplish orthogenetic goals.

The force directing natural selection functions on a principle of survival of the fittest and uses aggression to achieve orthogenesis. The force directing natural selection causes aggression to be instinctive in species. Aggression in species increases their survivability by promoting self-preservation. Aggression is an instinctive endowment of natural selection. Aggression serves the purpose of orthogenesis.

DICHOTOMOUS TENETS

Geneticists accept the predispositional vulnerability tenet and seek out the genetic basis for predispositional vulnerability. Accepting the conceptualization of predispositional vulnerability also by extension presupposes an acceptance of predeterminism and predestination. However, why would the force that directs natural selection create a species or cause a species to evolve when the orthogenetic goal is the destruction of that species?

Geneticists affirm that research into vulnerability alleles indicates genetic predispositional susceptibility. However, this leaves ethical-philosophical questions unanswered. One question pertains to culpability, another relates to whether the search for cures violates or whether the search for cures supports orthogenetic goals.

Meehan (2009) discussed this dichotomy in relations to preventative medicine. In her discussion of eugenics, Meehan observed that positive eugenics aim to ensure the promotion of good genes, whereas negative eugenics aims to deter the perpetration of "defectives." According to Meehan as eugenics policies advanced abortion, previously accepted as a negative eugenics policy evolved into positive eugenics (Meehan, 2009).

Earlier eugenicists such as Darwin, Herbert Spencer, and Francis Galton argued that the superior races should not engage in practices and policies to preserve the *unfavoured* races. In the search for cures, prenatal genetic screening developed. In the earlier years of its development, prenatal screening was employed to promote feticide of embryos based on whether the parents are believed to have defective genes. In the more recent period, prenatal genetic screening is used to promote gender-biased abortions. Meehan (2009) captured the ethical-philosophical questions regarding whether the philosophy of predeterminism could be a basis for curative medicine, and whether measures to destroy "defectives" were in alignment with predeterminism.

FATALISM AND PREDETERMINISM

Manifested aggression appears to be the only aspect of the tenets of evolution by natural selection that falls within the gambit of human control. Even so, aggression is instinctive and predetermined to function to achieve the orthogenetic goals for species and species members. Further, because aggression is an inherent quality, there is the argument that aggression is genetically predetermined. Based on this rationale, superior races and individuals are better endowed with aggression. To validate this argument, evolutionists distinguish between functional and dysfunctional aggression.

HEREDITARY MECHANISMS OF PREDESTINATION

Pangenes are heredity mechanisms determining predestination. Pangenes allow organisms and species to survive natural disasters, while others will perish (Darwin C., 1872; 1882). Darwin wrote:

> *...there are hereditary carriers, pangenes, which are carried by the blood stream to the sexual organs and the sex cells. Here we have the explanation of heredity. But if a certain organ, on account of changed external conditions, acquires a stronger function and greater development these pangenes may be increased, be multiplied, and they are also transmitted to the sex cells in this multiplied form. Hence, the progeny also obtains this organ more powerfully developed.*
> *(Nilsson H., 1934, p. 228).*

Instinct and aggression are elements inside of pangenes. These elements were placed inside pangenes and influenced the nature of being. Instinct causes aggression for self-preservation.

Favoured races also have an instinct that is directing them into survival of the fittest. Survivability is the product of aggression, and aggression increases survivability. These broad generalizations are fundamental evolutionary philosophical tenets that continue to drive research related to aggression.

LIFE AND EXISTENCE

Evolutionists outline cosmozoë philosophical thoughts of ontogeny as the foundation of evolutionary theory. The premise that life originated because of interaction between the seen and the unseen also has its basis in cosmozoë philosophy. The seen was the sentient observable being or object such as a person. The unseen is the invisible energy or life (Scharf et al., 2015).

These ontogenetic principles are responsible for ascriptions to life. These ascriptions impinge on interpretations of APR.

The unseen element of life is metaphysical. Empiricists, however, did not consider the philosophy of metaphysics to be science. Science was the study of sentient beings and objects. In the past, scientists were empiricists.

Cosmogony is a branch of metaphysics concerned with the origin of the universe. Philosophers of cosmogony ascribed the existence of the universe to gods, spirits, angels, and other spirit beings. Empiricists argued that incorporeal beings such as gods, spirits, and angels, could not be the subject matter of scientific study because they are not sentient, sensorial objects. Gods, spirits, and angels were subjective, impalpable, metaphysical concepts and could not be studied objectively. Three disciplinary approaches, philosophy, physics, and chemistry were used to integrate religious beliefs involving metaphysics into science.

Sir Isaac Newton (1642-1727), engaged in efforts to transform the cosmological philosophy and the natural philosophies into scientific disciplines. Charles Darwin, a naturalist, heavily influenced by Newton's cosmological philosophy, attempted to include its principles into his theory of evolution by natural selection (Bodnar, 2018; Del Soldato, 2016).

Ontogeny was one of the concerns of metaphysics. Very early conceptualizations of ontogeny were found in the writings of the Greek philosopher, Anaximander of Miletus (c. 610-546 BC). Anaximander proposed a cosmological philosophy of ontogeny. Life, according to Anaximander, emerged from moist elements of evaporation (Evans J., 2009).

Cosmozoë philosophers purported that some form of energy was responsible for the creation, formation, or existence of the earth. This involved a mythical, metaphysical explanation of the earth's creation. This energy was metaphysical and implicated gods, and legends derived from Greek mythical religious traditions (Oparin, 1957; Plato, 1905; Smeenk & Ellis, 2017).

These beliefs about energy found its way into the scientific method through various disciplines. These foundational beliefs from Greek mythology became acceptable, scientific explanations concerning the origin of the earth (Oparin, 1957; Peretó, 2005; Smeenk & Ellis, 2017).

FROM BELIEFS TO SCIENCE

In the early modern period, cosmological philosophies became known as natural philosophies. Disciplines referred to as natural sciences were previously known as natural philosophies. The word science derives from a Greek word meaning knowledge. Philosophers argued that knowledge or knowing was intuitive.

Empiricists contended, however, that knowledge cannot be inferred or deduced in the absence of sensorial experience. Sensorial experience is the means of proving evidence. Evidence is a source of knowledge.

Philosophers of metaphysics developed strategies to supplement experiments as a means to provide evidence. The process of experimentation replaced empiricists' process of knowledge based on evidence.

Philosophers of metaphysics used the argument of instrumentalism to support their claims concerning the replacement of experience with experiments. Philosophers of metaphysics argued that impalpable phenomena become observable if the process of instrumentalism is applied. The process of instrumentalism involve testing or passing the unobservable through formalizing apparatus of the senses and the mind.

Formalizing apparatus of the senses causes impalpable concepts, events, or entities to become perceived phenomena. The experimentation process engages the use of formalizing apparatus. The results from the experimentation process are evidence of knowledge (Metcalf, 1940).

Based on the philosophical tenets of the experimentation process, philosophical tenets such as ontogeny became included in modern-day science. This philosophical tenet that the origination and perpetuation of life are due to an interactive process between physical objects and energy as an intangible force is foundational to research in genetics and epigenetics. The underlying assumptions related to a physiochemical process associated with the origin and the perpetuation of life influence thought and research in a plethora of disciplines. Although theoretical development and research proceed based on these underlying assumptions concerning the earth, the origin of life, and perpetuation of life, metaphysics philosophy informs the underlying assumptions of cosmogony (Oparin, 1957; Peretó, 2005; Scharf et al., 2015; Smeenk & Ellis, 2017).

INTEGRATING COSMOLOGICAL PHILOSOPHIES INTO NATURAL HISTORIES

Naturalists developed theories founded on cosmozoë philosophy into disciplines referred to as the natural philosophies. Later these disciplines became known as the natural sciences and included disciplines such as biology, physics, and chemistry.

Mythical beliefs in antiquity included a belief that the gods and beings from the realm of the gods existed in forms of energy such as light. This belief was the starting point of the hypothesis that physiochemical processes caused organic substances to materialize.

According to this postulate, a form or source of energy existed on the earth. This energy might have existed in either gaseous, semi-gaseous form, or a combination of gaseous and semi-gaseous forms. Possibly due to changes in the atmosphere and the environment, gaseous and semi-gaseous materials carbonized, causing organic matter to develop from inorganic matter (Scharf et al., 2015).

The premise that chemical processes caused the origination and perpetuation of life hinges on three basic hypothetical assumptions or inferences. The first assumption is the belief that the earth might have existed in some semi-gaseous or gaseous form. The second assumption is that these semi-gaseous and gaseous forms underwent chemical processes such as thermodynamic, electrodynamic, quantum dynamics, and photodynamic associated. The third assumption is that inorganic and organic matter might have emerged as a mixture of gases formed by the energy (Scharf et al., 2015).

What caused the earth to come into existence, or what is the source of the energy that existed on the earth is a foundational dynamic that remains missing from these premises. Religious, cosmological beliefs are the foundations of these three assumptions. The first of these beliefs centered on Pan and Panspermia. Based on this belief, some type of war among the gods somewhere in the universe precipitated seismic and chemical changes on the earth, causing the earth to exist in some semi-gaseous or gaseous form. The seismic and chemical changes in the planet were responsible for the emergence of life out of rocks, also studied as abiogenesis and spontaneous generation (Oparin, 1957; Peretó, 2005; Scharf et al., 2015; Smeenk & Ellis, 2017).

The mixture of gases and further chemical processes caused the emergence of inorganic materials, such as rocks. Abiogenesis, the theory that living organisms emerged from inorganic substances such as gases and rocks was one of the earlier beliefs in Greek mythology related to life, the origin of life, and the perpetuation of life. However, the assumption that organic matter or that life emerged from inorganic matter has been revisited and restructured (Scharf et al., 2015). These basic hypothetical assumptions remain as foundational elements in evolutionary theory and all its related emergent theories (Scharf et al., 2015; Smith, Petrik, Kimmel, & Kay, 2012).

IMPLICATIONS FOR APR

Darwin's theory of evolution by means of natural selection emerged primarily out of Greek religious philosophy from antiquity. The central tenet of Darwin's theory is survivability. Survivability is the product of natural selection.

Natural selection is a force like gravity that exists outside of human control and functions on principles of predeterminism and predestination. The tenets of natural selection hinge on specific tenets of life based on cosmological beliefs such as the inherency of aggression, predeterminism, and predestination.

Based on this philosophy, there are inherent qualities in life, such as instinct and aggression that serve the purposes of survivability and natural selection. Aggression is believed to be a predetermined, predestinated phenomenon that the gods genetically wired into humans to facilitate survivability.

Another postulate of this philosophical premise is that survivability is the product of fitness. Aggression, as an inherent quality of life, ensures the survival of the fittest. As such, aggression is a favorable trait.

Endowment with aggression determines survivability or vulnerability. Those species and species members with better endowments of aggression will be superior, have higher survivability, and are predestined to achieve higher complexities and forms. The nature and purpose of aggression as an inherent, instinctive, predetermined, predestinated phenomenon, based on the tenets of evolutionary theory, have implications for understanding APR.

APR and Implicit Perceptions of Aggression

Conceptualizations such as inherency, instinctiveness, predeterminism, and predestination can become subliminally and imperceptibly entwined in the worldviews and perceptions of individuals, and groups. For example, there might be an academic, cultural, or religious acceptance of differences in perceptions of will, free will, and destiny based on these conceptualizations.

When addressing APR, there must be a consideration of the perceptions and worldviews of victims and perpetrators. For example, an aggressor might have a worldview that aggression is an inherent behavior. In this case, service providers must understand whether perpetrators think that aggression is an impulsive, instinctive, behavior, or whether aggressions are functional acts of self-preservation.

Beliefs concerning concepts such as predeterminism and predestination also have implications for the individual's perspectives concerning social structures and systems. For example, the victims and perpetrators may have unquestioned beliefs concerning hierarchical social order that facilitates aggression. In some instances, a victim might believe that an aggressor has the authority to engage in aggression.

Service providers should begin by evaluating their perceptions concerning these foundational philosophical tenets. Thought should also focus on cultural perceptions and whether there are social and educational institutions that are reinforcing a specific philosophical orientation about predeterminism and predestination.

Individuals might internalize philosophical orientation about foundational thoughts on such elements as predeterminism and predestination that influence their interpersonal interactions and relationships. Service providers must assess whether some ethnic and cultural groups are more susceptible to APR as Darwin purported in his theory of evolution by natural selection.

Foundational elements of Greek religious philosophies persist in some religious and other cultural traditions and might be still impacting perspectives on APR. Service providers must question whether those beliefs are still foundationally influencing the way that APR is perceived. Service providers should also consider whether these beliefs are now facts or accepted as facts and truths.

While these tenets may not overtly be understood or believed, service providers should assess whether they are underlying assumptions that influence intervention and practice. Further, service providers and practitioners must evaluate whether these tenets are foundational to policy development.

CONCLUSION

Mythical religious beliefs from Greek antiquity concerning the origin and perpetuation of life form the basis of almost all modern-day research and disciplines pertaining to APR (Oparin, 1957; Peretó, 2005; Scharf et al., 2015; Smeenk & Ellis, 2017). Greek mythical beliefs undergird early theoretical premises concerning chemical processes associated with a source of energy.

In modern-day research, scientists apply explanations such as thermodynamics, electrodynamics, quantum dynamics, photodynamics, or nuclear energy as ontogenetic explanations (Dall et al., 2012). The conceptualization of these physiochemical processes is the foundation of almost every modern scientific discipline including molecular biology, physics, chemistry, biochemistry, geography, systems biology, synthetic biology, genetics, neuroscience, psychiatry, psychology, and sociology. Theories and research in these disciplines form the basis of policies, programs, and services and are pertinent for addressing APR (Scharf et al., 2015; Smith et al., 2012).

CHAPTER REVIEW

REVIEW QUESTIONS

1. What are the fundamental tenets of natural selection?
2. What are the distinguishing elements of the theories of cosmozoë, panspermia, and abiogenesis?

CHAPTER SIX
SCIENCE IN ANTIQUITY

CHAPTER PREVIEW

In antiquity, evolutionary theory was part of a mythical religious belief system. The major tenets of these religious beliefs were taken from ancient Greek mythical religion and incorporated into early modern naturalist philosophies. These tenets were the foundation of Darwin's theory of evolution by natural selection. These fundamental tenets persist in almost all modern-day disciplines.

In the modern-day scientific method, insentient phenomena receive validation from a process defined as scientific objectivity. Generally, modern-day scientific methods preclude the inclusion of mythical beliefs as the causation of physical phenomena. While scientific research is now providing evidence for some aspects of metaphysical phenomena, there remains a challenge because of their roots in mythology.

Philosophers engaged in natural philosophies were not able to include elements from mythical religious beliefs into scientific study. Their fiercest opponents were empiricists.

Empiricists were scientists, who believed that philosophers engaging in natural philosophies applied mythical religious beliefs involving metaphysical elements in their philosophies. As such, natural philosophies were not scientific disciplines. Naturalists developed a series of philosophical tenets that facilitated the inclusion of mythical religious beliefs and philosophies into scientific study.

In this chapter, there will be a discussion of some of the philosophies and methods that naturalists used to incorporate mythical religious beliefs and metaphysical elements into scientific studies. Some of these philosophies, including pragmaticism, changed the meanings of commonly used words and the subject matter of scientific study. Understanding that almost all modern-day disciplines have a foundation in ancient Greek mythical religious philosophies might shed light on hypothetical assumptions that guide research and practice related to APR.

PURPOSE AND LEARNING OBJECTIVES

PURPOSE

The purpose of this chapter is to explain the methods used to integrate philosophies from antiquity into scientific research.

LEARNING OBJECTIVES

After studying this chapter, the reader should understand

1   the origination and development of theories of origin; and
2   the applicability of theories of origin to current interpretations of APR.

KEY TERMS AND DEFINITIONS

Empiricism

Empiricism is a philosophy concerning the theory of knowledge. Empiricists claim knowledge can only be achieved through sensorial observation of a phenomenon.

Pragmaticism

Pragmaticism is the philosophic doctrine of C. S. Peirce (Pragmaticism, n.d.).

Pragmatism

1   A practical approach to problems and affairs.
2   An American movement in philosophy founded by C. S. Peirce and William James and marked by the doctrines that the meaning of conceptions is to be sought in their practical bearings, that the function of thought is to guide action, and that truth is preeminently to be tested by the practical consequences of belief (Pragmatism, n.d.).

Scientific Objectivity

Scientific objectivity is a claim that the methods, claims, and results of research or studies that apply the scientific method are free from bias (Steup, 2018).

INTRODUCTION

The evolutionary theory emerged out of cosmological philosophy from antiquity. Empiricists were scientists who argued that metaphysical philosophies, beliefs, and subject matter were insentient phenomena, and should not be included in scientific studies. In response, philosophers engaged in a series of philosophical debates and developed philosophical rules to include mythical religious beliefs into scientific research.

New disciplines in philosophy, the scientific methodology, and scientific objectivity emerged from these debates and philosophical rules. Gradually, the scientific method replaced scientific study. All modern-day scientific research employs the scientific method and scientific objectivity.

Objective scientific research continues to provide an abundance of support for evolutionary theory, which forms the basis of research and practice related to APR. Existing models that inform research and practice associated with APR have inherent weaknesses. These weaknesses might be an indication of flaws in the philosophical orientation that guides theory, research, and practice (Andersen & Hepburn, 2016; Bradie & Harms, 2017).

RELIGION AND EMPIRICISM

Prior to the integration of philosophies of metaphysics into scientific study, empiricists placed restrictions on the subject matter of scientific study. Empiricists argued that objects were the subject matter of science, and science was the objective research of objects. Objects were sentient sensorial things. Empiricists argued that metaphysical concepts and beliefs were impalpable and could not be included in scientific research.

PHILOSOPHIES OF METAPHYSICS

Philosophies of metaphysics posited hypotheses concerning ontogeny. These hypothetical assumptions included a belief in pangenes, which are the mythical seed of the Greek god Pan. Pangenes were metaphysical objects.

Pangenesis theory came under severe criticism leading to a revision of the theory. However, significant aspects of the original pangenesis theory remained. These revisions culminated in the modern-day gene theory of inheritance.

Despite revisions to Darwin's pangenesis theory, some key conceptualizations remained. The chromosomal theory of inheritance was an extension and update of the theory of pangenesis, the concept that each parent contributes equally to the genetic inheritance remained. However, some questions concerning ontogeny remain unanswered, such as the source of genetic inheritance of all species.

Greek religious philosophers believed that pangenes were the internal mechanisms of hereditary transmissions. Greek religious philosophers posited that the god Pan is the source of all genome or the genetic material of all organisms and species. While scientists have not found the source of all genomes, the concept of genes remains a valid hypothesis. In 1900 Karl Pearson, an ardent eugenicist, wrote that pangenesis "is no more disproved by the statement that 'gemmules have not been found in the blood,' than the atomic theory is disproved by the fact that no atoms have been found in the air" (Pearson, 1900, p. 335).

In a letter to one of his colleagues, Asa Gray, in 1867, Darwin wrote that "What I call Pangenesis will be called a mad dream... I think it contains a great truth." The University of Cambridge (1867) concluded that Darwin developed his provisional hypothesis of pangenesis over many years.

The depth of Darwin's philosophical orientation in his explanation of pangenesis is still being debated. However, Darwin suggested that even if his theory of pangenesis is "stillborn," it will resurface in the future. In 1868, Darwin wrote to his colleague J. D. Hooker, "You will surely be haunted on your deathbed for not honouring the great god Pan" (Freeman, 1978).

Darwin purported a mythical, metaphysical source to explain the ontogeny of life and species. Greek mythical philosophy identified a metaphysical source of genes and the existence of atoms. In order to include mythical objects concerning the origin of life, philosophers of metaphysics needed to develop new philosophical thought and strategies. One of these strategies was to create new philosophical rules, including pragmatism and pragmaticism.

Pragmatic philosophy was initially proposed by a group of Harvard-educated men called The Metaphysical Club. Pragmatism is a philosophical school of thought based on the concept that ideology is true if it is practical. Among the strategies employed by pragmatic philosophers involved changing the meanings of words such as physical and creating terminologies such as objectivity and scientific objectivity (Andersen & Hepburn, 2016; Mayes; McDermid, n.d.).

These philosophical development processes and strategies effectively changed the subject matter to include metaphysical concepts based on religious beliefs into the study of science. New disciplines such as physics and chemistry facilitated these inclusions.

These philosophies and metaphysical concepts sturdily undergird theories of origin and being that are focal to understanding aggression. The theory of evolution presents the most scientifically substantiated metaphysical elements into theory and practice regarding aggression.

Philosophical Foundations of Survivability

All theory begins with a hypothesis. A hypothesis is a general statement about a phenomenon. Survivability is a hypothesis of the theory of evolution by natural selection Survivability is a hypothetical assumption. A specific philosophical orientation about the origin of life and the origin of species undergirds this evolutionary hypothesis of survivability.

However, hypothetical assumptions are neither truth nor fact. Hypothetical assumptions are beliefs based on philosophical orientation. The hypothetical assumptions of the evolutionary theory are based on Greek religious philosophy.

According to ancient Greek religious philosophy, there are two kinds of species members among humans, vulnerable members and members with higher survivability. The gods endowed some members of human species with higher survivability and others with vulnerability.

Increased survivability is the product of instinct. The instinct serves the purpose of self-preservation. Aggression is an innate, instinctive element of survivability and self-preservation.

These tenets and their undergirding philosophies became integrated into modern scientific research based on a series of philosophical debates and rules. These rules were handed down in the philosophical traditions of scientific objectivity and scientific methodology. A critical appraisal of the processes involved in these philosophical developments might shed light on the possibility of flaws in philosophical tenets undergirding survivability.

HYPOTHETICAL CONSTRUCTS

Hypothetical construction was a philosophical process developed to include metaphysical beliefs into the scientific method. Empiricists limited the scope of their study to objects with sentient reality. This limitation precluded the inclusion of beliefs in scientific study.

In disciplines of metaphysics, beliefs are philosophies. Beliefs are neither tangible nor real. To give reality to beliefs, philosophers created hypothetical constructs to represent their beliefs. A hypothetical construct does not have a material physical existence because it is only a belief (MacCorquodale & Meehl, 1948; Paternotte, 2011; Reiss & Sprenger, 2017).

To create hypothetical constructs, philosophers and theorists engage in rational thought. Based on rational thought, the theorist proposes characteristics, qualities, and behaviors or representations of their belief. The philosophical tradition of rationalization was also developed from antiquity and incorporated into the philosophical or scientific method.

PHILOSOPHICAL DEVELOPMENT AND SCIENCE

The development of philosophical thoughts was essential for changing beliefs about ontogeny into scientific research. Philosophers could not present their religious beliefs as though they were facts or truths. Empiricists resisted the inclusions of metaphysical elements and constructs into scientific study. Empiricist argued that sensorial observation was the means for establishing facts and truths (Evans et al., 2004).

Philosophers of metaphysics developed several branches of philosophies such as ontology, metaphysics, abstraction, monism, materialism, realism, existentialism, epistemology, and phenomenology to facilitate the inclusion of religious, mythological beliefs into scientific study. Each philosophical branch created new rules that changed religious beliefs from antiquity into modern-day scientific study. These philosophical thoughts aimed to ensure compliance with the empiricist's requirements for the *objective, scientific* study of incorporeal structures and elements (Savitt, 2017).

OBJECT VS. OBJECTIVITY

Changing the meaning of words was one approach that philosophers used to make the adjustment from metaphysics to science. Pragmaticism was one of the philosophical traditions responsible for changing the meanings of words and their applicability to facilitate these inclusions.

Prior to the modern-day interpretation, an object was palpable. Science or empirical study was the objective study of palpable objects. Empiricists were scientists that engaged in the objective study of palpable objects.

PRAGMATICISM

Arising from the Greek word πρᾶγμα, pragma; pragmaticism was the philosophical discipline primarily responsible for changing the meaning of words and their applications to facilitate objectivism.

Pragmaticism, like other philosophical traditions of natural philosophies, has a strong affiliation with eugenics. Skodo (2015) observed that "the relationship between eugenics and the philosophical traditions of the early twentieth century still remains largely unexplored territory." Eugenics and pragmatic philosophies were closely aligned. Eugenics philosophies could explain the pragmatic philosophical rationale. Eugenics was a common theme creating a bond with naturalist philosophies (Skodo, 2015).

> *Pragmatism is the doctrine (1) that truths are logical values: (2) that the "truth" of an assertion depends on its application; (3) that the meaning of a rule lies in its application: (4) that ultimately all meanings depend on purpose: (5) that all mental life is purposive. Pragmatism is (6) a systematic protest against all ignoring of the purposiveness of actual knowing, and it is (7) a conscious application to epistemology (or logic) of a teleological [purposive] psychology, which implies, ultimately, a voluntaristic metaphysics. (Skodo, 2015, p. 4).*

Philosophers in the tradition of pragmatic philosophy, argued that some things could not be proven or disproven. Theories of metaphysics center on phenomena that can neither be proven or disproven. Therefore, it cannot be determined whether the theories of metaphysics are true or false. Pragmatic philosophers contended that it does not matter whether an ideology is true or false. If a theory is practical, then the theory is acceptable (Andersen & Hepburn, 2016; Mayes; Sidorsky & Talisse, 2018).

Pragmatics avouched that it was not necessary to prove whether metaphysical, ontological explanations were valid or not. The eugenicist, Karl Pearson, contended that in the same way atoms cannot be proven to exist, the existence of genes could not be disproven (Porte, 2018). As such, pragmaticism was not concerned whether the theory was true, but whether the theory was applicable.

Theories of metaphysics involve impalpable phenomenon. However, if these theories could be conceptualized and experimented using formalizing apparatuses, then the findings of these experiments become the evidence of the theory, whether or not the theory is true or false. Methodology in the scientific research process became the backbone of the process of experimentation (Andersen & Hepburn, 2016; Mayes).

Scientific objectivity was a new philosophy birthed to reinforce the scientific method. Whereas scientific study involved the study of objects, scientific objectivity referred to the method used to perform the study or the research, rather than the subject of study. Philosophers appealed to scientific objectivity to validate the metaphysical tenets of ontogeny (Plato, 1905; Sidorsky & Talisse, 2018; Smeenk & Ellis, 2017).

Figure 6-1   Alchemy

Objectivity was a method of study that facilitated the inclusion of metaphysics[5] into scientific study. Naturalists argued that although their subject matter was subjective and impalpable, engagement in objectivity as the method of study validated their beliefs.

Scientific objectivity became the method of study of impalpable, subjective, metaphysical philosophies, thereby changing the definition of scientific objective and meaning of objective study to scientific objectivity. This change facilitated the inclusion of metaphysical subject matter as a scientific discipline. Naturalist philosophers now engaged in objectivity as a method to study nonobjective, metaphysical

---

[5] Figure 6-1   Pieter Brueghel the Elder creator QS:P170,Q43270 (https://commons.wikimedia.org/wiki/File:Alchemist-small.png), „Alchemist-small", marked as public domain, more details on Wikimedia Commons: https://commons.wikimedia.org/wiki/Template:PD-old

constructs. Objectivity became the activity of study, rather than objectively studying the objects as the subject matter. Prior to this, objectivity meant the objective study of objects; the definition was changed to mean the method of study (Savitt, 2017).

Naturalist, pragmatic philosophers further argued that the means justified the results. If the method of study was objective, then the findings were facts and truths. Findings might be true and accurate, even though the premise is subjective. As such, religious beliefs that were the premise of mythical, hypothetical constructs from antiquity were elevated to the status of facts and truths (Savitt, 2017).

Eugenicists pragmatics engaged an additional philosophy called metaphysical voluntarism. The metaphysical referred to the unseen force or energy, which pragmatic philosophers of metaphysics believe exist. The will of the individual aligns to this force to engage in activities determined by this metaphysical force.

Voluntarism in metaphysics refers to an irrational unconscious urge to engage in activities to foster the purpose of this metaphysical force. Eugenic policies, eugenic activities, and selection represent voluntarism. Voluntarism in psychology was accepted premise under Freudian conceptualization of the unconscious will and Jungian theory of collective consciousness (Skodo, 2015).

Pragmatic philosophers were also responsible for changing the meaning and conceptualization of the word physical. In antiquity, the study of physics was metaphysics, and the study of chemistry fell under the study of alchemy. These two disciplines were responsible for creating constructs to represent philosophies of metaphysics. The creation of constructs allowed the objectification of mythical, philosophical beliefs involving metaphysical elements to facilitate their integration into scientific objectivity (Scharf et al., 2015).

OBSERVING IMPALPABLE PHENOMENA

Metaphysical tenets of ontogeny persist in the way that APR is understood and interpreted. In the absence of tangible physical evidence, philosophers used religious philosophies and philosophies of metaphysics to explain the origin of life and the origin of species. These tenets provide the basis for the way life as a phenomenon is interpreted and have applicability to premises that might be used to accept or perpetuate abuse.

Ontogenetic events are impalpable because, given the constraints of human senses and technology, ontogenetic events cannot be physically reinvented. Ontogenetic premises, therefore, continue to remain hypothetical constructs. Because of these challenges, empiricists argued that tenets of natural philosophies were unscientific.

APPEALING TO SCIENTIFIC METHODOLOGY

Empiricists in the early modern era, argued that science could only present knowledge as factual if the acquisition of that knowledge involved empirical research of study involving objects. To overcome this empiricists' argument, naturalist philosophers developed the scientific methodology. Methodology in science refers to the means whereby the researcher arrives at knowledge.

Naturalists argued that research that uses the scientific methodology that applies objectivity in the research process validates the hypothesis. Although hypotheses based in metaphysics cannot be ascertained to be true or false, research that engages the scientific method validates the hypothesis and the belief undergirding the hypothesis.

In its strictest sense, empiricism refers to knowledge acquired through sensorial observations of objects. Although naturalists claimed that using the scientific method made their findings factual, they still faced two grave empiricist's objections. Empiricists argued against the biasness of naturalists' hypothetical assumptions and their philosophical orientation. Empiricists also rejected the inclusion of impalpable phenomena into scientific study.

CONCLUSION

Naturalists faced serious challenges from empiricists related to their explanations of life, the origin of life, the origin of species, and the nature of being. These empiricists' challenges related to philosophical biases and the inability to sensorially observe hypotheses founded in metaphysics.

Naturalists developed philosophical traditions such as pragmaticism and rationality to address empiricists' rejection of the inclusion beliefs based in into scientific study. Scientific objectivity as the method of study emerged as a result of these new philosophical traditions.

These metaphysics underlays have remained as the mainstay for current scientific research. However, they were established through rational philosophical processes. Similarly, rational processes could be used to address some of the unanswered questions, such as the ontogeny of pangenomes.

CHAPTER REVIEW

REVIEW QUESTIONS

1. Research Greek mythology concerning Pan and pangenomes.
2. Why was the concept of pangenes revised?
3. What elements of pangenesis remain in the theory of pangenome?

CHAPTER SEVEN
THEORY AND APR

CHAPTER PREVIEW

In his theory of evolution by means of natural selection, Darwin posited that aggression, vulnerability, and reproductive advantage were the products of natural selection. Additionally, pangenes were the internal hereditary mechanisms that determined the transmission of these characteristics.

The conceptualization of the differential distribution of innate qualities is the basis of superior and vulnerable species and species members. By inference, White male hegemony became a fundamental tenet of Darwin's theory of evolution by natural selection.

Several of Darwin's tenets formed the foundation of patriarchalism, sexism, gender-biasness, eugenics, and racial discrimination. Darwin contended that these differences and vulnerabilities were the products of natural selection and genetic transmissions. These conceptualizations continue to inform studies in such disciplines as biology and genetics that undergird APR interpretations.

PURPOSE AND LEARNING OBJECTIVES

PURPOSE

The purpose of this chapter is to introduce the philosophies underpinning theories pertinent to APR.

LEARNING OBJECTIVES

After studying this chapter, the reader should understand the challenges in establishing the philosophical underpinnings to APR.

KEY TERMS AND DEFINITIONS

Patriarchy

Patriarchy is a social system in which males hold primary power and predominate in roles of political leadership, moral authority, social privilege, and control of property.

INTRODUCTION

Existing programs addressing APR are community-based[6]. Community-based programs have a sturdy foundation in systems theory. Systems theories implicate aggression as a functional instinctive, self-preservative, survivability behavior. Aggression that serves these functions delimits the definition of APR (McAdams, Foster, Dotson-Blake, & Brendel, 2009; Paymar & Barnes, 2017; Wallpe, 2010).

Figure 7-1   Community

PATRIARCHAL-CLASS BASED PHILOSOPHICAL ORIENTATION

Patriarchal systems were common in antiquity and the ancient world. Patriarchal systems were also common in medieval and early modern Europe. The patriarchal system in medieval Europe was founded on White male superiority. White male patriarchal supremacy received a boost because of colonization. Philosophers such as Galton, Spencer, and Darwin expounded on the theoretical rationale of male superiority (Albee, 1996).

---

[6] Figure 7-1   https://svgsilh.com/image/304353.html: CC0 1.0 Universal (CC0 1.0) Public Domain Dedication

Darwin's conceptualizations male superiority was incorporated into the tenet of life as a struggle and functional aggression. These conceptualizations are common elements in social systems theory, genetics, eugenics, and epigenetics. These elements continue to inform policies and practices related to APR (Darwin C., 1872; 1882).

THE BIOLOGICAL ORIGINS OF MALE SUPERIORITY

Darwin contended that hierarchical structures were of biological origins. Darwin propounded, especially on the role of males and the biological endowments that gave males reproductive advantages over females (Albee, 1996; Darwin C., 1872; 1882).

The social environment were critical elements in creating this reproductive advantage or higher survivability for men. The social environment reinforced male reproductive advantage (Albee, 1996; Darwin C., 1872; 1882).

Applying tenets of evolution by natural selection, social distresses have a biological origin. Therefore, core elements of APR such as sexism, racism, homophobias, and polygamy are the products of biological mechanisms. For example, a person's race is the product of heritable qualities via biological mechanisms involving human pangenome. Darwin assigned survivability and vulnerability to the different races and concluded that the force that directs natural selection accomplished this assignment by predestination. Genetic defects are sources of vulnerability.

As such, research into genetics is a hunt for the source of vulnerability. In the last century, eugenicists spear-headed the hunt for the source of vulnerability. Eugenicists also implored scientists to engage in genetic research to facilitate and accelerate this hunt. Success in finding vulnerability genes was a triumph for eugenics (Albee, 1996; Darwin C., 1872; 1882).

CONCLUSION

Darwin's theory of evolution by natural selection has implications for APR. The fundamental tenets of predestination and aggression undergird perceptions, conceptualizations, and definitions of APR.

The tenet of predestination by natural selection undergirds thoughts concerning genetics and susceptibility to vulnerability. The tenet of aggression regarding instinct suggests that aggression is functional. Functionality and aggression are determinants of the perception of APR.

CHAPTER REVIEW

REVIEW QUESTIONS

1. How does modern-day empirical study differ from an early modern-day natural approach to study?

2. Trace the philosophical development of the scientific method from its inception to the current day.

CHAPTER EIGHT
PHILOSOPHIES OF APR

CHAPTER PREVIEW

Empiricists resisted the inclusion of naturalists' philosophies into scientific study. Empiricists argued that natural philosophies were not the study of objects and are unscientific. Naturalists argued that metaphysics could be studied using the philosophical method. The philosophical method involved a process of reasoning called rationality.

Rationality is a process of reasoning that uses arguments such as deductive and inductive reasoning. Evolutionary philosophers referred to their disciplines as natural philosophies. Empiricists argued that beliefs were impalpable and should not be included in scientific studies. Because of empiricist's objection to the inclusion of beliefs into scientific study, evolutionary philosophers developed the scientific method of study.

The scientific method of study employed objectivity rather than the study of sentient objects. Scientific objectivity as the method of study rather than the object of study facilitated the inclusion of metaphysics as the subject matter of scientific study.

In this chapter, there is a discussion of the rationalization for the use of hypothetical assumptions as to the rational premise of the scientific method. Rationalization validated the inclusion of hypothetical assumptions based on metaphysics and naturalists' philosophies concerning the origin of life and the ontogeny of species into a scientific discipline.

PURPOSE AND LEARNING OBJECTIVES

PURPOSE

The purpose of this chapter is to explore the process of hypothetical developments of tenets relevant to APR.

LEARNING OBJECTIVES

After studying this chapter, the reader should understand

1   the fundamental philosophical tenets concerning APR; and
2   the processes involved in developing these tenets and their implications for APR.

KEY TERMS AND DEFINITIONS

Rationality

Rationality is the rational process that refers to the steps involved in arriving at a reasonable, logical thought or belief.

1   the quality or state of being rational,
2   the quality or state of being agreeable to reason, or
3   a rational opinion, belief, or practice—usually used in the plural (Rationality, n.d.).

Validity

Validity is the extent to which a concept, conclusion, or measurement is well-founded and likely corresponds to the real world based on probability. The quality or state of being valid such as

1   the state of being acceptable according to the law; or
2   the quality of being well-grounded, sound, or correct (Validity, n.d.).

INTRODUCTION

Naturalists studied metaphysics using the philosophical method. Philosophers engaging in the philosophical method used rational arguments to develop their hypotheses (Andersen & Hepburn, 2016).

There emerged two types of study, naturalist philosophy, where philosophers used the philosophical or scientific method and empirical scientific study. Although empiricists contended that their studied objects objectively and this was the subject matter of scientific studies, naturalists argued that the method they engaged in their study was objective and therefore their subject matter was scientific (Andersen & Hepburn, 2016).

PHILOSOPHICAL THOUGHT AND THE SCIENTIFIC METHOD

Empiricists contended that hypotheses are not statements of facts. Evolutionary naturalists counterargued that hypotheses are merely assumptive and need not be factual or based on evidence. As such, evolutionary hypotheses concerning life, the origin of life, and the origin of species are assumptive propositions that need not be factual or based on evidence (Andersen & Hepburn, 2016).

PHILOSOPHICAL BIAS

Superiority and vulnerability are not new concepts. The conceptualization of superiority and vulnerability was a structural bias in the ontogenetic premise that applied arguments based on ancient myths and metaphysics. Among philosophers from antiquity was the thought that the gods created two types of humans, the children of the gods and the sons of men. The children of the gods had gemmules imparted to them from the gods. The sons of men were the inferior servants to the sons of God.

In modern-day genetics, the conceptualization of predispositional genetic vulnerability persists. Predispositional genetic vulnerability resulted in a focus on hereditary transmissions of vulnerability related to aggression.

OVERCOMING THE ARGUMENT OF PHILOSOPHICAL BIAS

Naturalists presented arguments of reason and logic to overcome the empiricists' criticisms related to philosophical bias. Naturalists claim that although a hypothesis is only a proposition made as a basis for reasoning without any assumptions of its truth, a premise is valid if it is based on logical reasoning. This philosophical argument became known as rationality or the rational process (Hypothesis, n.d.).

Philosophers of metaphysics referred to the philosophical methods as natural philosophies or natural histories. These disciplines became known as the natural sciences. Scholars in natural sciences disciplines incorporated the philosophical method like the scientific method. Currently, the scientific method is the methodology used in scholarly work in almost all disciplines (Andersen & Hepburn, 2016).

Philosophical orientations are the guiding principles for theoretical formulations in the scientific method. Philosophical orientations represent the belief theorists hold concerning the world and the way things function in the world (Andersen & Hepburn, 2016).

RATIONALITY

Rationality, in thought, refers to the alignment between beliefs and reasons for the beliefs. The rational process relates to the steps involved in arriving at a reasonable, logical thought or belief. Scientific rationality is founded on the principle that fact or truth is not dependent on history or substantive evidence[7].

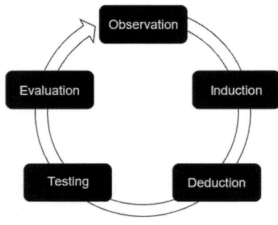

Figure 8-1   Empirical Cycle

If theory and research stem from rational reasoning such as inductive or deductive logic, then the hypothetical assumptions are facts and truths. Hypothetical assumptions are not facts or evidence of facts. As such, the ontogenetic premises undergirding evolutionary tenets are not facts or evidence of facts. Although hypothetical ontogenetic assumptions are not facts or evidence, they are accepted as valid because they stem rational reasoning. As such, the two underlying tenets of survivability and functional aggression are rational arguments. Elements of these hypothetical assumptions might be questionable and open to further research and reevaluation (Nickles, 2017).

CONCLUSION

Evolutionary theorists posit that aggression is a functional element of self-preservation and natural selection. Early modern-day evolutionary theorists used these foundational philosophies to validate such factors as patriarchalism, male hegemony, eugenics, and minority population vulnerability. When considering APR, researchers and practitioners should be aware of these underlying assumptions of evolutionary tenets.

Additionally, researchers and practitioners should remain aware of the philosophical foundations of these tenets. Heightened awareness of these tenets and their philosophical underpinnings might show up subtle weaknesses in understanding, interpreting, and addressing APR.

---

[7] Figure 8-1   By Empirical_Cycle.png: TesseUndDaanderivative work: Beao (talk) - Empirical_Cycle.png, CC BY 3.0, https://commons.wikimedia.org/w/index.php?curid=7968500

CHAPTER REVIEW

REVIEW QUESTIONS

1. Develop an alternative hypothesis to explain the origin of life.
2. How does the theory of evolution by natural selection impinge on APR?

CHAPTER NINE
EPISTEMIC VALUE

CHAPTER PREVIEW

Epistemic value is a branch of philosophy concerned with the nature of knowledge. In this chapter, there will be a discussion of the epistemic philosophy and the nature of knowledge.

Naturalists argued that although hypothetical ontogenetic assumptions are neither facts nor truth; their beliefs have epistemic value. Epistemologists contend that if the belief is rational, then the belief is justifiable.

PURPOSE AND LEARNING OBJECTIVES

PURPOSE

The purpose of this chapter is to explore the development of philosophical thought on epistemic value.

LEARNING OBJECTIVES

After studying this chapter, the reader should understand

1   the concept of epistemic value; and
2   the application of epistemic value to research.

KEY TERMS AND DEFINITIONS

Epistemology

Epistemology is a branch of philosophy concerned with the origin, nature, methods, and scope of human knowledge (Steup, 2018).

INTRODUCTION

Naturalists encountered a significant hurdle associated with the justification of beliefs and philosophical orientations underpinning metaphysical ontogenetic explanations. Empiricists argued that biased and unsubstantiated philosophical beliefs undergirded evolutionary ontogenetic premises.

Empiricists arguments centered on the way the researcher gain knowledge. Empiricists posit that knowledge could only be attained through sentient experiences. Epistemology is a branch of philosophy that philosophers of metaphysics developed to address empiricists' arguments concerning the way that the researcher acquired knowledge.

SCIENTIFIC STUDY VS. SCIENTIFIC METHOD

In the scientific method approach to study, belief is the foundation of the hypothesis, whereas fact or truth is the product of the search for truth. Evolutionary foundational ontogenetic hypotheses based on philosophies of metaphysics such as pangenes, predispositional fitness, and vulnerability are neither absolute fact nor truth. However, evolutionary philosophy is natural philosophy, and therefore, has epistemic value. Epistemological, philosophical tenets facilitated the maintenance of some elements of metaphysics while removing other facets from the theory, such as elements of religion and god. Despite this, elements of gods, religion, and metaphysics remained as overt, implicit assumptions of evolutionary theory (Bradie & Harms, 2017; Steup, 2018).

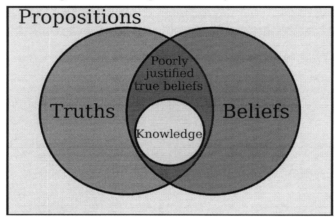

Figure 9-1   The Definition of Knowledge

EPISTEMOLOGY

Epistemologists are philosophers who investigate the origin, nature, scope, methods, and limits of human knowledge[8]. Knowledge about the inherent quality of life, the origin of life, and the origin of species at the time of their origin are limited. This limited knowledge is primarily due to the inability to reconstruct, revisit, or observe these phenomena sensorially.

As such, ontogenetic hypotheses are only rational beliefs. Epistemologists claim that, if theorists can prove their beliefs are rational, then those beliefs can be accepted as truths, and rational beliefs have epistemic value.

---

[8] Figure 9-1   Krishnavedala
        (https://commons.wikimedia.org/wiki/File:Classical_definition_of_Kno.svg),
        „Classical definition of Kno",
        https://creativecommons.org/publicdomain/zero/1.0/legalcode

Rational thoughts and rational processes provide epistemic value that justifies impalpable ontogenetic premises. Epistemologists contend that there is a fundamental difference between belief and truth. If the theorist uses the scientific methodology, the belief is justifiable, then the conclusions or findings from the research render the belief to be facts and truth. Epistemologists explore the justifications for the belief and the philosophical orientation that undergirds theoretical assumptions (Aho, 2014; Bradie & Harms, 2017).

THEORIES OF KNOWLEDGE AND EPISTEMOLOGY

Theories of knowledge is a branch of philosophy concerned with the nature of knowledge and the way that philosophers acquire knowledge. Knowledge theorists contend that some knowledge falls outside the ambit of sentient reality. Knowledge theorists propose that knowledge can contain several elements. Knowledge can be based on the physical existence of a property, in which instant knowledge is deemed to be factual.

On the other hand, knowledge might imply conscious experiences that involve nonphysical properties, such as empathetic understanding or metaphysical properties. Knowledge can also be propositional or probabilistic. Most importantly, knowledge should be reliable. Naturalists applied tenets from the theory of knowledge to validate their hypothetical assumptions stemming from insentient reality (Ichikawa & Steup, 2018).

EPISTEMIC VALUE

Because beliefs are insentient and are neither fact nor truth, beliefs are assessed based on its epistemic value. Epistemic value is assessed based on the reasonableness or unreasonableness of the belief (Grimm, 2008).

A belief has epistemic value if it is like truth, approximates truth, is close to the truth, has empirical adequacy, and predictive accuracy. The epistemologist evaluates the theorist's underlying beliefs and perceptions to assess the plausibility and logic of the theorist's premises, hypotheses, and theories based on whether the belief has the criteria required to assign epistemic value. Epistemologists assign a value to the theorist's premises and hypotheses based on the epistemologist's evaluation of the justification for the theorist's beliefs (Bourget & Mendelovici, 2017; Smith D. W., 2018; Wynn, 2016).

The evolutionary theory stems from hypotheses based on beliefs concerning the origin of life. Two fundamental philosophical tenets of survivability and adaptation are the bases for these beliefs. The undergirding premises that life is a struggle and that aggression is a functional aspect of life are beliefs that support the premises of survivability and adaptation. These hypotheses are propositional and probabilistic.

Evolutionary epistemologists accept these propositions and ideologies as rational, reliable, knowledge (Ichikawa & Steup, 2018).

CONCLUSION

Epistemic value refers to cognitively justified beliefs of the possessor of the beliefs. Although the evolutionary theory is grounded in an interpretive framework that implicates the metaphysical, evolutionary tenets are deemed to have epistemic value (Ichikawa & Steup, 2018).

Although some aspects of survivability theory might be relevant and rational, some facets remain questionable, for example, those elements associated with patriarchy, superiority, and vulnerability. Although these tenets might have epistemic value, the epistemic value does not create truth.

CHAPTER REVIEW

REVIEW QUESTIONS

1. What is the difference between belief and fact?
2. Relate epistemic value to belief and fact.
3. Trace the origin and development of the concept of epistemic value.

CHAPTER TEN
SCIENTIFIC OBJECTIVITY

CHAPTER PREVIEW

Naturalists argued that epistemic value establishes the rationality of their beliefs. Naturalists philosophers further argued that their beliefs are rational and exist outside the minds of the philosopher. Phenomena that exist outside the minds of the philosopher are real.

Naturalist philosophers developed scientific objectivity, one of the processes of the philosophical or scientific method was to establish that rational beliefs with epistemic value exist outside the minds of the philosopher. Scholars that engage in the scientific method achieve the objective of objectivity. In this chapter, there will be a discussion of scientific objectivity.

PURPOSE AND LEARNING OBJECTIVES

PURPOSE

The purpose of this chapter is to explore the development of philosophical thought that facilitated the process called scientific objectivity in research involving impalpable phenomenon.

LEARNING OBJECTIVES

After studying this chapter, the reader should understand the process involved in attaining scientific objectivity.

KEY TERMS AND DEFINITIONS

Worldview

The term worldview refers to any ideological, philosophical, theological, or religious perspective that provides an overarching understanding of God, the world, man's relations to God and the world.

1   A comprehensive conception or apprehension of the world, especially from a specific standpoint (Worldview, n.d.).

INTRODUCTION

Epistemic value receives its credibility based on the cognitively rational processes in which the possessor of a belief arrives at that belief. Epistemic value is also attained based on the rational philosophical processes in which the theorist engages to justify the belief. In addition to granting epistemic value to the naturalists' ontogenetic premises, the logical philosophical processes that naturalists employ to justify their belief grant scientific objectivity to naturalists' theories (Ichikawa & Steup, 2018).

The philosophical processes, also called the scientific method, are the methods that theorists use to validate their philosophical persuasions. Naturalists contended that if they used the philosophical methodology that achieved objectivity, then, the methodology made their research objective. Although the philosophers of the metaphysics traditions used the scientific method as an argument of scientific objectivity, it still did not remove the empiricist's argument concerning the philosophical bias of evolutionary theory.

As a philosophy, the argument of scientific objectivity served the purposes of cosmological philosophers, naturalists, and philosophers of the metaphysics traditions. Scientific objectivity is a process or method used to study impalpable beliefs, constructs, and elements. The process of scientific objectivity did not objectify the impalpable beliefs, constructs, and elements of philosophers of the metaphysics tradition, it did not cause palpability, neither did it make mythical, metaphysical beliefs, constructs, and elements objective or free from bias.

SCIENTIFIC OBJECTIVITY AND HYPOTHETICAL ASSUMPTIONS

Scientific objectivity is a claim that the methods, claims, and results of research or studies that apply the scientific method are free from bias. Although researchers apply the scientific method and engage in scientific objectivity in the methodological processes that they use in their research, the hypothesis or the hypothetical assumptions undergirding their theories might not be free from bias. A new hypothesis might be based on a previous hypothesis. A new hypothesis might also stem from a hypothetical assumption, which may also be not free from bias.

The hypothesis is the premise or statement about the phenomenon under investigation in the scientific observation. The hypothetical assumptions are the philosophical thoughts that undergird the hypothesis. The philosophical orientation of theorists underpins their hypothetical assumptions. The theorist's experiences and worldview might color the theorist's philosophical orientation and the philosophical underpinnings of the theory. As such, the methodology can be objective, but the philosophy undergirding the hypothetical premises upon which the research is founded might remain biased (Reiss & Sprenger, 2017).

THE SCIENTIFIC METHOD

Philosophers of metaphysics accepted the scientific method as the pathway to objectively assess and analyze the hypothesis or theory to determine its validity. The scientific method is a modern terminology for the philosophical method (Andersen & Hepburn, 2016).

Philosophy is the rational investigation to uncover truths and principles of being, knowledge, or conduct. In the study of philosophy, the philosopher engages the philosophical method[9] in the rational observations of a phenomenon. The philosopher applies principles of logic and can use either inductive or deductive reasoning as a part of the process of rational observations (Zelenkov et al., 2011).

The Scientific Method as an Ongoing Process

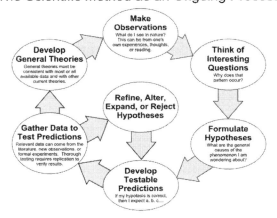

Figure 10-1 The Scientific Method

Deductive reasoning, also called deductive logic or logical deduction, is the process of reasoning that begins with one or more general statement(s) to reach a logically certain conclusion. This general statement is the hypothesis or premise. Theorists use the scientific method of observation to engage in hypothesis testing. When researchers use the inductive method of observation, they begin with a specific statement and engage in observation to arrive at a broad statement or generalization. These specific statements are the hypotheses that undergird the theory (Evans et al., 2004).

Naturalists engage in the philosophical method to substantiate the epistemic value of their ontogenetic philosophical tenets. Although the ontology of life remains elusive, scientific objectivity validates metaphysical ontogenetic philosophy. Although there is a dearth of tangible, corporeal, evidence to support impalpable ontogenetic philosophical beliefs, these tenets are determined to be justified objective beliefs. The assignment of epistemic value status and objectivity are the products of epistemological and rational philosophies (Ichikawa & Steup, 2018; National Academy of Sciences and Institute of Medicine, 2008).

Scientific research serves the purpose of the search for truth. Scientific research involves the use of the scientific method. The scientific method is the sequence of steps the researcher uses to gain objective knowledge and arrive at the truth. Because the researcher engages in the

---

[9] Figure 10-1 ArchonMagnus (https://commons.wikimedia.org/wiki/File: The_Scientific_Method_as_an_Ongoing_Process.svg), https://creativecommons.org/licenses/by-sa/4.0/legalcode

scientific method, it creates justification for the belief or hypothesis, even though the belief or hypothesis is based on philosophical orientations. Truth or fact is established based on the reliability or the validity of the scientific process. For example, metaphysical, philosophical orientations may undergird the hypothesis, but scientific objectivity and the scientific method provide these beliefs with reliability and validity (Bradie & Harms, 2017; Steup, 2018).

Therefore, current ontogenetic hypotheses derived from philosophies of metaphysics are neither facts nor truths within the context of physiological sensorial experience but based on beliefs upon which hypothetical assumptions were made. Although metaphysical ontogenetic premises are neither true nor factual, these premises are accepted as fact and truth because the researcher engages in scientific objectivity in the philosophical method. The scientific methodology and scientific objectivity are deemed to be the conveyors of truth in ontogenetic theory. Within this context, the ontogenetic tenets are deemed to be truth and fact.

CONCLUSION

The justification for ontogenetic philosophical belief concerning life, the origin of life, and the origin of species based on philosophies of metaphysics are based on the credibility of the objective scientific method used in studies undergirded by ontogenetic theories. Even so, knowledge is still subjective and likely to change when new information presents. Keeping theory and knowledge as contextual elements in research and continuous theoretical reevaluation is crucial in maintaining objectivity in the scientific methods (Ichikawa & Steup, 2018; Reiss & Sprenger, 2017).

Because of the significance of ontogenetic theory to tenets that are relevant for understanding APR, researchers, philosophers, and practitioners should continue to keep in mind that the foundational tenets are still only based on beliefs. If ontogenetic premises are not providing thorough answers to explain APR, then researchers, philosophers, and practitioners should be willing to revisit the ontogenetic philosophical tenets.

CHAPTER REVIEW

REVIEW QUESTIONS

1. What is the difference between objects, objectively, objectivity?
2. Trace the philosophical development of scientific objectivity.
3. Evaluate the validity of the process of scientific objectivity for discovering truths and facts.

CHAPTER ELEVEN
CAUSATION

CHAPTER PREVIEW

Naturalists use a cause-effect epistemic methodological approach to explain ontogeny. Establishing a cause-effect relationship validates hypothetical assumptions. Concerning the cause of aggression in humans, evolutionary theorists propose that a force directing natural selection determines genetic inheritance. Aggression might be due to genetics. In this chapter, there will be a discussion of cause-effect as an epistemic approach to natural philosophies.

Cause and effect are principles of rational natural philosophies. Life is a metaphysical principle. Philosophers posited a metaphysical ontogenetic physiochemical interaction as the cause of life. This ontogenetic explanation for the origin of life and the origin of species is also used to explain the physiochemical processes of hereditary transmissions. However, Naturalists have been unable to identify the source of physiochemical materials or the first cause responsible for the ontogenetic process.

The first cause is what caused the physiochemical interaction that caused the origin of life and the origin of species. Although Naturalists apply a cause-effect relationship as the epistemic approach, naturalists ignore the first cause.

Purpose and Learning Objectives

PURPOSE

The purpose of this chapter is to explore the identification of cause, life, being, and the nature of being in relation to APR.

LEARNING OBJECTIVES

After studying this chapter, the reader should understand

1   the process of identification of cause as a step in the scientific process; and
2   the implications of identification of cause for the study of APR.

Key Terms and Definitions

Causation

Causation is anything that causes an effect.

1   The act or process of causing.
2   The act or agency which produces an effect (Causation, n.d.).

Intervening Variables

An intervening variable is a hypothetical construct used to measure differences and explain causal relationships between other variables (Andersen & Hepburn, 2016; MacCorquodale & Meehl, 1948).

Introduction

Natural philosophers apply causation to explain life, the origin of life, the cause of the origin of life, and the nature of being. Empiricists contended that ontogenetic premises based on metaphysics involve nonphysical, intangible, incorporeal, impalpable elements, and these types of studies were unscientific Naturalists included causality into the philosophic method to validate their claims for inclusion of these premises as scientific.

The Natural Approach

Evolutionary theorists apply a natural approach to epistemology. According to naturalists, a natural approach engages explanations based on a cause-effect relationship. However, even when evolutionary theorists engaged in the natural approach to scientific research using a cause-effect relationship, there was still another troubling ontogenetic reality: the first cause. Naturalists could not answer the question of the first cause of what caused the very first cause.

Philosophers of metaphysics addressed this challenge by ignoring the first cause. Although naturalists ignore the first cause, which is what caused the origin of life or the existence of earth, naturalists presented premises of explanations for what caused life, the origin of life, and the origin of species. Evolutionists contend, for example, that chemical processes caused the earth to form and genes cause heredity.

Although the arguments presented by naturalists was extended beyond the emergence of life, the extension of this argument still did not address the question concerning what might have caused the chemicals to be present to be the cause of the origin of life. Additionally, naturalists ascribed the origin of genes to the existence of metaphysical beings but still could not explain the origin of these metaphysical beings (Oparin, 1957).

ONTOGENETIC CAUSAL RELATIONSHIPS

Based on the natural approach to epistemology, ontogenetic premises have causal relationships with each other. Knowledge is gained by studying the cause-effect relationship that produced the phenomenon. For example, one or several chemically-related processes caused the origin of life and the origin of species. The ontological premises of these theories are valid knowledge based on cause and effect mechanisms. Nevertheless, establishing causation of the first cause presents challenges for researchers at both the ontogenetic and the phylogenetic level (Bradie & Harms, 2017).

Evolution-based theories continue to face fundamental ontological challenges (Nilsson H., 1934). To overcome the difficulties associated with the first cause of the origin of life and human existence, evolutionary theorists purport ontogenesis within the context of existing life (Bradie & Harms, 2017). Evolutionary theorists seek to establish a causal relationship by applying principles of ontogeny and phylogeny using current research. Findings from current research are extrapolated to support hypothetical assumptions about life, the origin of life, and the origin of species (Hall, 2016; Hofweber, 2018).

IDENTIFICATION OF CAUSE

Studies in human behavior, including aggression, raise questions concerning human nature and the nature of being. Understanding the nature of being can provide insight into the inherent cause of human behavior. The nature of being encompasses specific characteristics, traits, and behaviors that distinguish an organism, individual, or species from others. Theorists contend that an understanding of the cause of the origin of species might shed light on the nature of being and those characteristics, traits, and behaviors that distinguish one species from another.

To explain an event or a phenomenon requires the identification of its cause. Identification of cause[10] is foundational to hypothesis testing and research development. These processes are critical to objective scientific methodology.

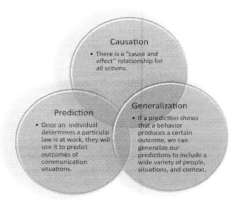

Figure 11-1 Causation

Identification of cause facilitates objective scientific observation that can establish or lend support to theoretical hypotheses and assumptions. Literal observation of some events is not possible. Theories of explanations emerged as a philosophical study to address the requirements of establishing causation in objective scientific studies and have relevance for studies related to phenomena that cannot be literally observed (Beebee, Hitchcock, & Menzies, 2012; Mayes).

Cause and effect are the ontological principles of evolutionary theory. In addition to developing hypothetical constructs which were fundamental to the theory, intervening variables were also hypothesized. Intervening variables are hypothetical variables used to explain a causal link between other variables (Andersen & Hepburn, 2016; Cook, Bookstein, & Gennari, 2011).

APR also involves behavioral studies that require the establishment of constructs that act as organizing principles to explain the phenomenon. For example, constructs that define behavior might include emotional boundaries, physiological manifestations, and physical actions. Cause and effect are principles used to understand the phenomenon within the context of the organizing principles.

Causation is a fundamental element in evolutionary epistemology. Evolutionary theory is established on the conception of natural philosophy defined as cause-effect mechanisms. Genomics, genetics, and epigenetics research are pertinent for understanding survivability. Findings from these studies should seek to identify the causal factors associated with failed survival mechanisms (Bradie & Harms, 2017).

---

[10] Figure 11-1 Spaynton (https://commons.wikimedia.org/wiki/File:Graphcause.png), https://creativecommons.org/licenses/by-sa/4.0/legalcode

CONCLUSION

Evolutionary researchers thus far, have yielded evidence of association, but have experienced difficulties in establishing causal relationships. The difficulties evolutionary researchers encounter in establishing causal relationships, except in very specific controlled experiments, might be closely aligned with identifying troubling etiology related to survivability. These challenges might also be related to weaknesses in evolutionary, ontogenetic premises (Dall et al., 2012).

CHAPTER REVIEW

REVIEW QUESTIONS

1   What is the natural approach to science?
2   How does the natural approach to science differ from the natural sciences?
3   Trace the philosophical development of the natural sciences?

CHAPTER TWELVE
HYPOTHESIZING

CHAPTER PREVIEW

Naturalists engaged in hypothetical formulations and hypothetical constructions to concretize intangible, impalpable, metaphysical phenomena to facilitate their inclusion in research that used the scientific method. In this chapter, there will be a discussion of the process of hypothesis formulation and hypothesis testing that facilitated the inclusion of beliefs based on metaphysics into the scientific method.

PURPOSE AND LEARNING OBJECTIVES

PURPOSE

The purpose of this chapter is to explore the development of theoretical formulations for studies involving the origin of life and being.

LEARNING OBJECTIVES

After studying this chapter, the reader should be familiar with formulating hypotheses and hypotheses testing.

KEY TERMS AND DEFINITIONS

Etiology

Etiology is a branch of knowledge concerned with causes (Etiology, n.d.).

INTRODUCTION

Solid theoretical underpinning should be the foundation of effective programs, policies, and intervention for APR. The purpose of developing theories and engaging in research is to find answers to questions about problems and challenges related to human existence. The applicable theory that best answers questions relating to the etiology of APR should undergird current and future models for programs, policies, and services to address APR. Evolutionary theory posits ontogenetic premises that seek to answer questions about the etiology of challenges facing humanity and are therefore applicable to several disciplines relevant for developing policies, programs, and interventions to address APR.

Genetic, epigenetic, neuroscientific, and behavioral theories are only a few of the theories applicable to APR policies, programs, and intervention implementation. Studies related to life, the nature of life, the origin of life, and the origin of species have relevance for theories used in these disciplines. However, due to the challenges associated with researching ontogeny of life and species, scientists presenting theories related to these phenomena can only propose hypotheses or plausible explanations of the possible ways life and species might have originated.

Theorists positing theories or hypotheses concerning the origin of species encounter challenges due to the nature of research involving ontogeny of species. These challenges involved the inclusion of impalpable elements and principles. Including impalpable elements and principles into objective scientific study involved overcoming the specific requirement of empiricism that scientific study can only involve tangible objects and sentient experiences (Bradie & Harms, 2017).

HYPOTHESIS AND THEORETICAL FORMULATIONS

Theorists engage in contemplative thought to develop their hypotheses. These contemplative thoughts are reflections of the theorist's beliefs, perceptions, and philosophical orientation concerning the nature of life and the way things function within the context of life. For example, evolutionary tenets of organism-environmental interactions and survivability are hypotheses and hypothetical assumptions based on ontogenetic evolutionary philosophical orientation (National Academy of Sciences and Institute of Medicine, 2008; Reiss & Sprenger, 2017).

In addition to making a statement about the nature of things, hypotheses also include predictive, propositional, or probabilistic elements. Hypotheses become the platform for research into the validity and reliability of the theory.

A premise is the basis of a hypothesis. A premise is a statement about a belief or observation that guides the theorist through the hypothesis formulation process. In hypothesis formulation, the theorist evaluates all the possible explanations for the belief or the phenomenon which is under contemplation and incorporates these as elements of the hypothesis. After hypothesis formulation, the theorist engages in the process called hypothesis testing (Andersen & Hepburn, 2016).

HYPOTHESIS TESTING

Hypothesis testing[11] involves scientific research to establish the justification for the hypothesis or hypothetical assumptions. The purpose of

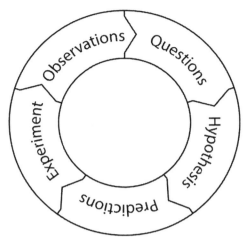

Figure 12-1 Hypothesis Testing

hypothesis testing is to seek out evidence to validate a theory. Validity is not absolute. Validity refers to the extent to which a concept or measurement corresponds or the closeness with which it aligns to the real world.

Validity is measured in degrees or on a continuum. As such, validity is identified based on its strength. The strength or validity of a measure or concept is an indication of the accuracy of the measure or concept. A measure or concept is strong if it accurately describes, measures, or is a very near approximate of reality (Andersen & Hepburn, 2016).

Hypothesis testing is not conducted to support a theory but to test the validity of the theory. If the researcher begins with a premise that the outcome will support the theory, then there is the risk that the practice of the research might be skewed. If the research is skewed, the results will support the theory rather than validate the theory. The risk of using hypothesis testing to support a theory that stems from vagueness in understanding the difference between fact, theory, and hypothesis (Reiss & Sprenger, 2017).

CONCLUSION

Hypotheses are neither truth nor facts but are rational assumptions based on the philosophical orientation of the theorist. The process of hypothesis testing is to assess the validity of the hypothesis. Hypothesis testing can establish the validity of the hypothesis, but it might not establish the validity of the philosophical orientation.

Research findings might provide support for the premises and hypotheses related to APR. However, the philosophical orientation might not have total validity. Foundational to the philosophical orientation are ontogenetic explanations that are applicable to APR, which might require reevaluation.

---

[11] Figure 12-1 Sarah Greenwood
(https://commons.wikimedia.org/wiki/File:Scientific_Method_Graphic.png),
https://creativecommons.org/licenses/by/4.0/legalcode

CHAPTER REVIEW

REVIEW QUESTIONS

1. Why was hypothesis testing included in the scientific method?
2. Does hypothesis testing establish truth and fact?
3. Provide support for the arguments you presented in response to the above question.

CHAPTER THIRTEEN
TRUTH AND FACTS

CHAPTER PREVIEW

Empiricists argue that the origin of life and the origin of species are impalpable phenomena. Even though Naturalists used epistemic value, the natural approach of cause and effect, and scientific methodology to justify and validate their beliefs, empiricists argued that beliefs are neither truth nor fact.

In this chapter, there will be a discussion of two philosophical schools of thought, existentialism, and phenomenology. Naturalists developed these schools of thought to validate their beliefs as truths and facts. Theories of explanation is another philosophical approach used to bridge gaps in ontogenetic theories.

PURPOSE AND LEARNING OBJECTIVES

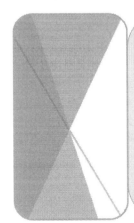

PURPOSE
The purpose of this chapter is to explore the basic ontogenetic existentialist, phenomenological, and theories of explanation tenets.

LEARNING OBJECTIVES
After studying this chapter, the reader should be familiar with the basic existentialist, phenomenological, and theories of explanation tenets.

KEY TERMS AND DEFINITIONS

Existentialism

Existentialism is a chiefly 20th-century philosophical movement embracing diverse doctrines but centering on analysis of individual existence in an unfathomable universe and the plight of the individual who must assume ultimate responsibility for acts of free will without any certain knowledge of what is right or wrong or good or bad (Existentialism, n.d.).

Phenomenology

Phenomenology is the study of the development of human consciousness and self-awareness as a preface to or a part of philosophy (Phenomenology, n.d.).

INTRODUCTION

Although ontogenetic premises developed from metaphysics are based on impalpable phenomena, a plethora of studies have been and are being conducted to substantiate these ontogenetic tenets. The credibility of the findings from these studies is dependent on the researcher's adherence to the processes involved in scientific methodology (Andersen & Hepburn, 2016).

Figure 13-1 Truth

ESTABLISHING METAPHYSICAL BELIEFS AS TRUTHS AND FACTS

The establishment of evolutionary, ontogenetic tenets as truth[12] and facts involved long philosophical, historical developments. Philosophical tenets emerged to facilitate the concretization of impalpable phenomena of metaphysics that were used to explain ontogeny. Concretization of these elements is foundational to the explanations concerning life, the origin of life, being, the nature of being, and causation, that have implications for human behavior.

Metaphysics and ontological philosophies and theories, for example, were used to extricate genes, a fundamental evolutionary tenet, from religion. Abstraction, modal abstraction, and realism were philosophies used to conceptualize, concretize, and assign properties to metaphysical concepts. After using these philosophies to grant physical existence to these metaphysical concepts, they became facts. Because knowledge derives from the physical existence of characteristics and properties, constructs designed to represent metaphysical constructs are real and therefore, based on knowledge (Ichikawa & Steup, 2018).

---

[12] Figure 13-1 English: Artist is Olin Levi Warner (1844–1896). Photographed in 2007 by Carol Highsmith (1946–), who explicitly placed the photograph in the public domain. Español: El artista fue Olin Levi Warner (1844–1896). El autor de la foto del año 2007 fue Carol Highsmith, quien explícitamente ubicó esta imagen en el dominio público. (https://commons.wikimedia.org/wiki/File:Truth-Warner-Highsmith.jpeg), „Truth-Warner-Highsmith", marked as public domain, more details on Wikimedia Commons: https://commons.wikimedia.org/wiki/Template:PD-US

EXISTENTIALISM

Existentialism is a philosophical tenet about human beings and their existence. Existentialists posit that full comprehension of an individual's reality is unachievable within the existing range of science. Existentialists do not deny the validity and applicability of the sciences, but, contend that science alone does not provide an adequate explanation for the range of human experiences.

Current technology is limited, and therefore, science is limited to the extent of its applicability to human experiences. Using abstractions is one of the ways that some human experiences are measurable within the scientific methods (Aho, 2014; Crowell, 2012; 2017).

Phenomenological research explores the lived experiences of the subjects. Phenomenologists conduct their research from the first-person perspective. Phenomenological analysis lends itself to existentialist philosophy. Participants in phenomenological research ascribe meaning to their lived experiences. Existential-phenomenological studies have been used as a scientific method to increase the understanding of religion and spirituality as elements in the lived experiences of humans (Bourget & Mendelovici, 2017; Wynn, 2016; 2017).

The philosophical underpinnings of theory establish the boundaries for conducting studies. For example, evolutionary theorists adhere to a worldview and a philosophical tenet that a heredity-environment interaction is elemental to adaptation and survival. This fundamental evolutionary tenet establishes the boundaries in all research, studies, and disciplines undergirded by evolutionary theory.

Evolutionary theory undergirds several theories related to aggression and human interaction. The evolutionary theory presents a broad, general statement about survival. Survival is the product of adaptation to environmental cues. Organisms adapt by producing the best characteristics, traits, and behaviors to ensure survival. These broad generalizations are fundamental evolutionary tenets. These tenets reflect a philosophical perspective of life (Andersen & Hepburn, 2016; Brandon, 2014).

CONCLUSION

The origin of life remains an unobservable event and therefore, presents challenges associated with hypotheses and theories to explain this phenomenon. However, the cause of the origin of life might provide explanations concerning aggression among species. These explanations might also shed light on the nature-nurture debate concerning aggression, survivability, and APR (Nilsson H., 1934). Theories of explanation emerged to present philosophical tenets that facilitated scholarly research into nonsensorially observable phenomena (Andersen & Hepburn, 2016; Mayes; Monton & Mohler, 2017).

CHAPTER REVIEW

REVIEW QUESTIONS

1. Trace the development of the concept of validity.
2. What is the significance of developing the concept of validity?
3. What is the difference between truth, fact, validity, and probability?

CHAPTER FOURTEEN
MAKING IT REAL

CHAPTER PREVIEW

Within the last two centuries, evolutionary theories made great strides in validating and including specific aspects of religious, mythical, metaphysical philosophies from antiquity into a credible scientific method. Physics, chemistry, and biology are among the foremost disciplines benefitting from these inclusions.

Several philosophical schools of thought and scientific processes were developed to facilitate the conversion of metaphysics into scientific disciplines. In this chapter, there will be a brief review of philosophical thoughts, such as ontology, structuralism, and dualism, that made the conversion of metaphysical constructs into the scientific method possible.

Concretizing incorporeal structures such as genes also involved the integration of thoughts from metaphysics and new research processes. Abstraction and modal abstraction were some of the methods developed to elucidate metaphysical constructs in the research process.

New disciplines and subdisciplines such as system biology and synthetic biological engineering, also emerged. Synthetic biological engineers design and create artificial biological devices, such as synthetic DNA, and protocells to engage in the elucidation of constructs from antiquity previously considered to be mythical and metaphysical.

PURPOSE AND LEARNING OBJECTIVES

PURPOSE

The purpose of this chapter is to explore the development of philosophical thought to concretize impalpable phenomenon.

LEARNING OBJECTIVES

After studying this chapter, the reader should

1. possess knowledge of fundamental philosophical tenets devised to facilitate the incorporation of metaphysical concepts into scientific study; and

2. understand the application of these philosophical tenets to APR

KEY TERMS AND DEFINITIONS

Abstraction

The act of considering something as a general quality or characteristic, apart from concrete realities or beings.

Abstraction in scientific research often pertains to things that do not have a concrete existence, such as atoms and molecules. Things such as atoms and molecules that do not have a concrete existence are given specific identifying properties and qualities. These characteristics are used to study hypothetical constructs of phenomena.

1. The act or process of abstracting: the state of being abstracted.
2. An abstract idea or term.
3. Abstract quality or character.
4. An abstract composition or creation in art (Abstraction, n.d.).

Ontology

Ontology is a branch of philosophy concerned with the nature of being (Ontology, n.d.).

Quantum Mechanics

Quantum mechanics is a field of study dealing with the behavior of matter and light on atomic and subatomic scales (Lewis P. J., 2016).

INTRODUCTION

Challenges associated with researching impalpable phenomena present significant concerns for theorists wishing to engage in objective scientific analysis related to ontogenesis. Theorists bridged the ontogenetic gap by using hypothetical formulations, constructs, and assumptions to explain the origin of life and ontogeny of species. Several philosophies were developed to facilitate these inclusions (Andersen & Hepburn, 2016). Philosophies in metaphysics, epistemology, ontology, existentialism, realism, and metaphysical realism were critical developments in evolutionary and emergent theories such as survivability, genetics, epigenetics, and molecular sciences (Bliss & Trogdon, 2016).

METAPHYSICS

Metaphysics is a branch of philosophy that proposes tenets to explain

intangible, incorporeal concepts. Philosophy is a discipline where scholars[13] and thinkers present their thoughts and ideas concerning the way the world works and the way things function in the world.

DEVELOPMENT OF THE PHILOSOPHY OF METAPHYSICS

Although naturalists attempted to extricate religious elements from the

Figure 14-1 Pompeii - Villa del Cicerone

scientific method, some troubling realities remained. The very nature of life involves metaphysical elements. Moreover, the cause of the origin of life remained elusive. Religion provided several types of explanations, even though religion did not present a means to validate these explanations (Oparin, 1957).

THE PARTING OF WAYS

There was a shunning of studies and disciplines that employed religious ontogenetic explanations. However, because metaphysical

---

[13] Figure 14-1 WolfgangRieger (https://commons.wikimedia.org/wiki/File:Pompeii_-_Villa_del_Cicerone_-_Mosaic_-_MAN.jpg), „Pompeii - Villa del Cicerone - Mosaic - MAN", marked as public domain, more details on Wikimedia Commons: https://commons.wikimedia.org/wiki/Template:PD-old

existence was crucial to any interpretation of life and existence, philosophers presented new philosophies and principles that resulted in the emergence of subdisciplines of metaphysics such as abstraction, modal abstraction, epistemic value, and ontology.

Naturalists created concepts to define, research, and study impalpable phenomena, such as emotions and aggression to transcend the constraints of integrating metaphysics into the scientific method. Scientific disciplines, including psychology, physics, mathematics, statistics, quantum mechanics, and theology, apply these concepts (Garson, 2016; Yang, 2014).

Scientists hypothesize about the existence[14] of phenomena they perceived of which reality and elements of human existence comprise, such as atoms, genes, and molecules. The next step involves creating

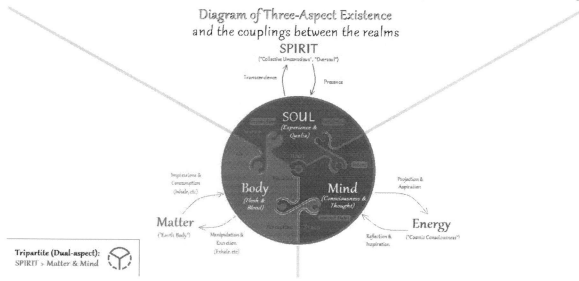

Figure 14-2 Body Mind and Soul

hypothetical constructs to explain their perceptions of reality. Theorists also create hypothetical constructs, such as intelligence and emotions as explanations of intangible elements of human existence. Scientists then define their perceptions of reality as hypothetical constructs. After defining these constructs, scientists assign characteristics, traits, and behaviors to these constructs. These characteristics, traits, and behaviors help to concretize the hypothetical constructs

---

[14] Figure 14-2 Dustin Dewynne (https://commons.wikimedia.org/wiki/File:Body-Mind-SOUL--Matter-Energy-SPIRIT.png), „Body-Mind-SOUL--Matter-Energy-SPIRIT", https://creativecommons.org/publicdomain/zero/1.0/legalcode

THE NATURE OF BEING AND HUMAN EXISTENCE

Human existence involves both a physical, corporeal existence and an incorporeal or metaphysical existence. Research and practice in the life sciences, specifically, involve the integration of physical and impalpable aspects of human existence, for example, physical characteristics and genes. Chemistry and physics are disciplines that facilitated the concretization of impalpable concepts. These impalpable concepts are used to explain aggression (Bliss & Trogdon, 2016; Craver & Tabery, 2017).

Geneticists are seeking out the genetic pathways that predispose an individual to aggression. Evolutionary theorists contend that the predisposition to aggression is due to inherent elements in life. As such, aggression is a quality or characteristic of life. These intrinsic qualities of life reside in genes.

Genes comprise atoms. However, atoms are intangible, incorporeal, impalpable concepts. To overcome the hurdle of researching constructs such as atoms and genes, physicists gave defining qualities to these constructs. Scientists hypothesize that DNA is a molecule. The chemical composition and behavior of the molecule are the defining qualities of the DNA molecule.

The hypothetical DNA molecule is representative of DNA, an acid that exists in the nucleus of cells in all living organisms. DNA and the attributions on the hypothesize chemicals that make up DNA and their behaviors are conceptualizations and are also impalpable.

Genome researchers study the construct of the DNA molecule as a chemical based on its atomic composition and structure. DNA and genes are hypothetical constructs based on impalpable attributes (Bliss & Trogdon, 2016; Craver & Tabery, 2017).

Despite the troubling element of impalpability of attributes such as genes, and although researchers will never be able to optically view the DNA molecule because the DNA molecule is only a conceptual model, its' existence and use in genetic analysis are proposed to be valid. Pragmaticism is the basis of this validity. Pragmaticism allows modern-day researchers to engage in DNA research by conceptualizing and thereby concretizing the atom (Bliss & Trogdon, 2016; Craver & Tabery, 2017).

Biochemical processes form the basis of theory, research, and practice in many disciplines, including medicine, biology, genetics, psychology, and psychiatry. Concretization of intangible, incorporeal, or metaphysical concepts is the backbone of these modern-day disciplines (Bliss & Trogdon, 2016; Craver & Tabery, 2017).

Mechanisms and systems, aided by technological advancement, were developed to promote research and experiments in those disciplines that involve the integration of the physical and the metaphysical. Theories that undergird research and practice engage philosophical tenets, such as pragmaticism, existentialism, dualism, phenomenology, metaphysics, epistemology, realism, and new mechanisms, as interpretive frameworks to bridge the gap between the physical and metaphysical aspects of human existence (Bliss & Trogdon, 2016; Craver & Tabery, 2017).

ONTOLOGY

Ontology is a branch or subdiscipline of philosophy involving the way people experience their reality. Ontologists are philosophers who study being, the nature of being, becoming, existence or reality, and their relations with being or existence. Ontological philosophy provides the framework for researchers to engage in the studies involving subjective, intangible incorporeal impalpable phenomena.

Religion is one of the ways that people experience their reality. In antiquity and among early modern-day evolutionary theorists, religion was a primary influence of the evolutionary philosophy. Ontological philosophy enabled the extrication of religion from objective scientific research involving evolution. While god and religion were used to explain life, the origin of life, and the origin of species, religious philosophies involved intangible, incorporeal, impalpable concepts. These conceptualizations did not lend themselves to empirical observations and therefore, were not included in objective scientific research. However, scientific research continues to include intangible, incorporeal, impalpable concepts, and phenomena (Bliss & Trogdon, 2016; Craver & Tabery, 2017).

Ontology involves studies that are based on the abstraction of reality. Emotions are some of the ways that people experience their reality. Emotions are abstract terms used to describe intangible, incorporeal subjective experiences. The study of metaphysics involves analysis of generic traits, such as emotions.

Emotions are manifestations of existence and being. Emotions, for example, distinguish humans from other animals. Emotions, therefore, are states of being. However, emotions are distinguishing characteristics of the nature of being, such as the nature of humans when compared with the nature of cats.

In ontological studies, the theorist assigns qualities, characteristics, and properties to life to describe the fundamental nature of reality and being, based on the theorist's perception of life. These qualities, properties, and characteristics are intangible, abstract principles, and elements. For example, well-being is a quality of life. States of being, such as happiness are used to determine well-being (Bliss & Trogdon, 2016; Hall, 2016; Being, n.d.).

The ontological aspect of metaphysics informs theory and practice through the creation of abstractions to hypothesize about the nature of being that exists outside of objective experience. These qualities, characteristics, and properties are abstract, nonconcrete elements and principles. Usually, phenomenological studies are used to explore these abstract elements (Brigandt & Love, 2017).

Figure 14-3 Abstraction

ABSTRACTION AND MODAL ABSTRACTION

Hypothetical assumptions have philosophical grounding referred to as the first principle. The first principle is the hypothesis or underlying theoretical assumption. A hypothesis usually begins with a logical premise based on things believed or observed. Hypothetical assumptions are abstractions of reality. The ontogenetic premises of life and species are hypothetical assumptions. Abstraction is the philosophical process used to concretize hypothetical assumptions (MacCorquodale & Meehl, 1948).

Abstraction[15] of reality is the focus of ontology. Abstraction is the process of assigning characteristics and qualities to objects and thoughts of nonbeing. Abstraction and modal abstraction are used to create operational definitions of variables that represent nonbeing, intangible objects and thought, such as intelligence, atoms, energy, or genes (Colbert & Rowe, 2008; Hall, 2016; Hofweber, 2018).

Abstraction of energy involves defining concepts such as atoms, elements, and molecules. Atoms, elements, and molecules do not have concrete, tangible existences. However, scholars assign qualities and characteristics to these concepts. The assigned qualities and characteristics are measurable. As such, energy, which is an incorporeal phenomenon, is measured based on abstractions of concepts such as atoms, elements, and molecules.

Energy is metaphysical. Abstractions of reality involve assigning qualities to metaphysical phenomena. As such, evolutionary theory is rooted in hypothetical assumptions about an intangible, incorporeal, impalpable, metaphysical phenomenon, *viz.* energy and the source(s) of power critical to the emergence of the earth, life, origin of life, origin of species and the perpetuation of life (Bliss & Trogdon, 2016).

---

[15] Figure 14-3 UnknownUnknown author (https://commons.wikimedia.org/wiki/File:Leviathan_by_Thomas_Hobbes.jpg), „Leviathan by Thomas Hobbes", marked as public domain, more details on Wikimedia Commons: https://commons.wikimedia.org/wiki/Template:PD-old

Given the limitations of technology and human sciences, scientists continue to engage in abstraction to premise hypothetical assumptions concerning the ontogeny of species or the origin of life on the earth. The process of abstraction applies philosophical tenets of ontology. The subject matter of ontology is an abstraction that exists outside objective experiences. The creation of abstractions is the basis of study in every natural science discipline. In essence, the natural sciences involve the abstraction of metaphysical elements and principles (Bliss & Trogdon, 2016; Brigandt & Love, 2017).

DISTINGUISHING BETWEEN MATTER, TANGIBLE, AND INTANGIBLE

As a fundamental philosophical approach to studies in physics and chemistry, the nature of matter is of significance. The modern approach in science to matter, tangibility, and intangibility relates to individualism and composition in form. One such hypothetical abstraction is the atom (Robinson, 2017; Stoljar, 2017).

An atom is a hypothetical construct developed to represent aspects of existence. An atom is a metaphysical construct. As a metaphysical construct, atoms bridge the gap between incorporeal and corporeal existence. To bridge this gap, the earlier conceptualization of the atom as an intangible metaphysical hypothetical abstraction has since changed. Philosophers developed additional rules of philosophy to change an atom from being an intangible, metaphysical construct into a tangible form (Chalmers, 2014).

A fundamental philosophical tenet in modern sciences is that all things, that we could experience with senses such as sight, and touch are made up of atoms. A chair is an example. If a chair is a tangible, sensorial object and the chair is made up of atoms, then atoms are tangible and sensorial. Therefore, an atom is a physical, tangible entity (Chalmers, 2014).

DISCIPLINES IN MATTER, INTANGIBILITY, AND TANGIBILITY

Physics as a discipline developed differently from chemistry as a discipline. In antiquity, chemistry referred to the practices of apothecary and alchemy. Both alchemy and metaphysics were religious disciplines or subdisciplines in religion. Physics developed as a discipline to establish metaphysical elements as physical elements and to extricate religion from metaphysics (Chalmers, 2014).

One of the steps in creating the discipline of physics was to change the meaning of physical. In antiquity, physical meant anything that was sentient or could be experienced by one or more of the senses. For example, a chair can be seen and touched, so a chair is physical. However, atoms could not be seen and touched. Therefore, atoms were not physical entities.

The meaning of the word physical had to be changed to include impalpable constructs such as atoms. Pragmatists changed the meaning of the word physical to include impalpable, metaphysical elements. Pragmatic philosophers proposed that an impalpable, metaphysical construct is physical if it consists of properties, qualities, and characteristics that distinguish the construct from other things with physical or metaphysical properties. This simple change in the definition of the word physical facilitated the inclusion of impalpable, metaphysical elements, and structures into objective scientific study.

Changing the meaning of the word physical facilitated the development of the modern-day scientific discipline called physics. Changing the meaning of the word physical and the assignment of characteristics, traits, and behaviors to these metaphysical concepts, changed these impalpable, metaphysical concepts into constructs in physics. The word metaphysical means to be beyond or outside physical existence (Chalmers, 2014).

Several philosophical approaches to matter such as physicalism, materialism, dualism, and monism apply to the debate concerning matter, tangibility, and intangibility. Monists contend that all things, including abstract elements of thoughts, have physical properties and existence. Monist philosophy influences scientific research into consciousness, being, god, the collective consciousness, and thoughts about the universe (Schaffer, 2016; Stoljar, 2017).

Geneticists, genomics, and DNA researchers continue to seek out evidence to substantiate the hypothesis that instinctive survival behaviors are the products of evolutionary adaptation. These studies promise to shed light on dysfunctional aggression (Colbert & Rowe, 2008).

GENES, ATOMS, AND DEOXYRIBONUCLEIC ACID

Genes, atoms, DNA, and fields are hypothetical constructs of scientific beliefs concerning the way the world works. As hypothetical constructs, these constructs and processes are impalpable. Geneticists, genomists, related researchers, and scientists hold a realist interpretation of these hypothetical constructs, in that they accept these entities and processes as having a real existence (Lakadamyali & Cosma, 2015; Lewis & Kattmann, 2004).

Principles of structural and metaphysical realism facilitated the development of these hypothetical impalpable constructs. These principles were critical in genetic studies and the conceptualization of hypothetical constructs such as chromosomes, genes, the genetic code, and DNA. These constructs form the basis of research in several disciplines including molecular biology, systems biology, biological design creations, and statistical analysis (Ladyman, Ross, Spurrett, & Collier, 2007; Lakadamyali & Cosma, 2015).

Evolutionary theorists apply these hypothetical constructs to support the gene theory of inheritance. Genome researchers and geneticists postulate that DNA is an acid that exists in cells and that this acid is the mechanism for the transmission of evolutionary adaptive behaviors. Geneticists use complex hypothetical assumptions and calculations in their research. These hypothetical assumptions and calculations emerge from previous and existing theories in disciplines such as physics and chemistry, and human statistics that were gathered earlier primarily from the eugenicists. Based on these constructs and calculations, biologists, called synthetic biological engineers, create synthetic biological designs to represent these constructs. These synthetic designs are used in research and practice.

Genetic research is ongoing. Currently, however, support for the hypothesis that genes are causative elements in adaptation, mutation, or hereditary transmission of behavior is based on extrapolations and speculations from the initial premise of evolutionary theory (Liu, Du, Xie, & Gui, 2013).

Dualism

Dualism is another philosophical school of thought that developed to facilitate the inclusion of metaphysical philosophies, constructs, and concepts into the scientific method. Dualists make a distinction between mind and matter. Metaphysical dualists philosophers contend that there are two kinds of realities: material or physical and immaterial or spiritual. Dualist philosophy presents challenges in science and physics. Dualists separate substance (chemical properties) and properties, such as the physical properties of atoms that make up the unit (Robinson, 2017).

In science and physics, chemical and physical properties make up the unit, whether visible and corporeal or invisible and incorporeal. This conception of physical and chemical properties of atoms based on dualism is foundational to theoretical development and research in genome, genetics, and epigenetics (Chalmers, 2014).

QUANTUM MECHANICS AND METAPHYSICAL

Quantum mechanics[16] is a branch of knowledge that also helps to bridge the gap between the metaphysical and the physical. Metaphysical phenomena exist outside of physical reality. In metaphysics, two kinds of realities are defined, physical and nonphysical. In physics, chemistry, and quantum mechanics, measurable, intangible constructs are deemed to have physical characteristics and properties. As such, metaphysical constructs are deemed to be physical entities because of their measurability (Cook et al., 2011; Lewis P. J., 2016).

Quantum mechanics[17] theory is foundational in several disciplines. Quantum mechanics make a distinction between abstractions, measurability, and theory of mind.

Figure 14-4 Albert Einstein

These distinctions are based on the assignment of properties to intangible elements that are crucial to evolutionary theory and research. Quantification bridged the gap between hypothetical ontological assumptions undergirding evolutionary theory that cannot be established as either factual or true, and acceptance of evolutionary conclusions that validate evolutionary

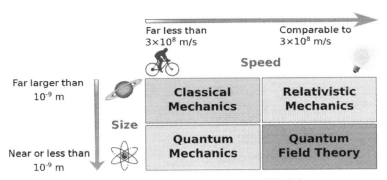

Figure 14-5 Mechanics Fields

theory. For example, aggression, as an abstract construct, can be measured using a Likert scale (Lewis P. J., 2016).

Quantum mechanics theory is used in biochemistry, molecular biology, and genetics. These disciplines are concerned with survivability and are relevant for APR. Tenets from several different philosophical orientations including realism, structural realism, and dualism were

---

[16] Figure 14-4 Photograph by Orren Jack Turner, Princeton, N.J. Modified with Photoshop by PM_Poon and later by Dantadd. (https://commons.wikimedia.org/wiki/File:Albert_Einstein_Head.jpg), „Albert Einstein Head", marked as public domain, more details on Wikimedia Commons: https://commons.wikimedia.org/wiki/Template:PD-US

[17] Figure 14-5 GYassineMrabetTalk This W3C-unspecified vector image was created with Inkscape. (https://commons.wikimedia.org/wiki/File:Modernphysicsfields.svg), „Modernphysicsfields", https://creativecommons.org/licenses/by-sa/3.0/legalcode

integrated to facilitate and develop epistemological and ontological bases that undergird studies in quantum mechanics (Lewis P. J., 2016).

Cook et al. (2011, p. 2) contend that "The measurement, analysis, and simulation of biological processes depend on observable physical and thermodynamic quantities such as force, charge, and energy." New philosophies and processes developed to facilitate the observation of these hitherto impalpable phenomena.

REDUCTIONISM

Reductionism is the theory that every complex phenomenon, especially in biology and psychology is explainable. Explanation of complex phenomenon is achieved by analyzing the simplest, most basic physical mechanisms that are in operation.

The theory of reduction and the reduction process are commonly used in biology, physics, molecular biology, psychology, and developmental biology research. The theory of reduction is pertinent to integrating phylogeny and ontogeny. Reductionism is applied in genetic research to ascertain stable developmental functional characteristics, traits, and behaviors as gene expression. Gene expression represents both phylogenetic and ontogenetic elements (Brigandt & Love, 2017).

Reductionism in genetics applies theories and findings from phylogeny to explain and understand ontogeny. Phylogenetic theories and findings which explain evolutionary genetic developments in humans as a species are applied in research to increase understanding of the effect of genetic influence and development in the individual. Reductionism also permits findings from ontogeny to be applied to phylogeny. Findings concerning genetic influence at the individual level are employed to increase understanding at the group or species level (Brigandt & Love, 2017).

REALISM

Realists contend reality exists independently of the observer.

Figure 14-6 Realism

Realism[18] in scientific methodology is an attempt to establish the reality or existence of an abstract principle or hypothetical metaphysical construct. Although the original concept of genes emerged from religious thought, several philosophical ideas and approaches brought these abstract concepts into reality. Even though, for example, genes and the DNA molecule are not optically visible, in science they are concepts taken to represent real things because they are measurable and purported to behave characteristically (Bliss & Trogdon, 2016).

Research in system biology and synthetic biology harks back to a basic empiricists' philosophical concerns related to metaphysics, realism, and metaphysical realism. The central issue pertained to things that are physical and things that are real.

Although Naturalists were successfully able to change the meaning of physical to conceptualize metaphysical constructs, the concern of realism remained. Empiricists argued whether metaphysical constructs with physical properties and characteristics are real elements and structures (Bliss & Trogdon, 2016).

Metaphysics pertains to abstractions based on hypothetical constructions of a belief about the nature of some element. Abstraction is the process of assigning qualities to ideas or concepts. Abstraction is one of the processes in hypothetical formulations (Bliss & Trogdon, 2016).

ABSTRACTION AND REALISM IN GENETICS

In the case of natural selection, Darwin proposed pangenes to solve gaps in his theory of evolution by natural selection. The most significant gap related to the cause of the origin of life. Darwin contended that the Creator breathed life into one form or many. Contending that life emanated from a specific source other than the form itself, Darwin suggested the god

---

[18] Figure 14-6 Jean-François Millet creator QS:P170,Q148458
(https://commons.wikimedia.org/wiki/File:Jean-François_Millet_-_Gleaners_-_Google_Art_Project_2.jpg), „Jean-François Millet - Gleaners - Google Art Project 2", marked as public domain, more details on Wikimedia Commons: https://commons.wikimedia.org/wiki/Template:PD-old

Pan was responsible for life on earth. Therefore, humans possessed pangenes (Darwin C., 1872).

Survivability is a product of gene-environmental interaction and functionality. Systems biologists, with a recently emerging subdiscipline called evolutionary systems biology, focus their research on functionality (Green, 2018).

Based on the process of abstraction, qualities, and properties were assigned to genes. Biological engineers create synthetic devices to measure the qualities and properties of genes and to establish a causal relationship between genes and inheritance (Cook et al., 2011; Green, 2018).

Systems biology and synthetic biological engineering are two disciplines involved in practices relevant to behavioral studies. Synthetic biological engineers design and create synthetic designs such as DNA-based devices, genome-driven cell engineering, and protocell creation. Systems biologists and synthetic biological engineers go beyond abstraction and metaphysical conceptualizations inherent in pangenesis and genetics to create physical representations of hypothetical evolutionary constructs initially perceived as intangible and incorporeal (Cook et al., 2011; Green, 2018).

Similar to the processes involved in the creation of synthetic DNA, synthetic biological engineers create artificial cells, called protocells. One of the approaches to creating these artificial cells is to provide support for early evolutionary premises. Schrum, Zhu, and Szostak (2010) asserted that protocells creation aims at understanding the origins of cellular life on earth.

> *The integration of a dynamic fatty-acid compartment with robust, generalized genetic polymer replication would yield a laboratory model of a protocell with the potential for classical Darwinian biological evolution, and may help to evaluate potential pathways for the emergence of life on the early Earth. (Schrum et al., 2010, p. 1).*

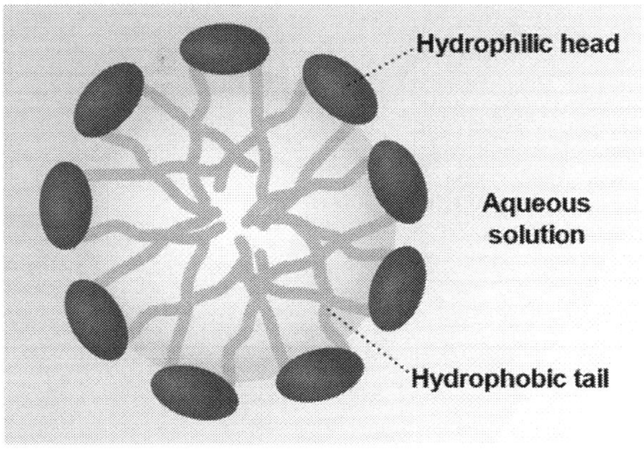

One of the aims of protocell[19] creation is to test the validity of the spontaneous generation theoretical tenet that life originated in a hydrothermal environment. Protocell creation involves the use of organic and inorganic materials to facilitate spontaneous generation in laboratory conditions (Schrum et al., 2010; Xu, Hu, & Chen, 2016).

Figure 14-7 Scheme of a Micelle

CONCLUSION

Explanations of APR apply theoretical deductions based on the origin of life, the ontogeny of species, life, being, and the nature of being. These theories concern intangible, insentient, impalpable, hypothetical constructs. Philosophers posited several philosophical tenets and related philosophies that impact modern perspectives on these intangible, impalpable, hypothetical constructs.

Scholars now perceive these hitherto intangible, impalpable, hypothetical constructs as tangibles. Technologies and other related processes were also developed to lend credence to the tangibility of these elements, structures, and phenomena. The arguments posited to substantiate their tangibility are philosophical tenets currently accepted as foundational to objective scientific research and methodology.

CHAPTER REVIEW

REVIEW QUESTIONS

1. Select two philosophical developments that facilitated the inclusion of metaphysical constructs into scientific research.
   a. Trace their historical development to the present.
   b. Evaluate the validity of these developments for understanding APR.

---

[19] Figure 14-7 Micelle_scheme-en.svg: SuperManu derivative work: ZanderZ (talk) (https://commons.wikimedia.org/wiki/File:Micelle_scheme-nl.svg), „Micelle scheme-nl", https://creativecommons.org/licenses/by-sa/3.0/legalcode

CHAPTER FIFTEEN
LIFE AND AGGRESSION

CHAPTER PREVIEW

In this chapter, there will be a discussion of the theoretical propositions concerning the source(s) of aggression. There will be a discussion of three possible sources of aggression; inherent or innate, functional, and ecological.

Innate aggression points to a specific quality inherent in life that causes humans to be aggressive. Inherent aggression is due to natural selection. Aggression is determined to be functional for self-preservation and survival. Aggression emerged because of the interaction of genes with the environment.

There are several broad general theories of origin, spontaneous generation, creationism, intelligent design (ID), evolution, and ecological theories. While these theories appear to be different, there are similarities and overlaps in their tenets.

PURPOSE AND LEARNING OBJECTIVES

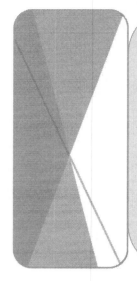

PURPOSE

The purpose of this chapter is to explore the emergence of theories of explanation concerning the origin of life.

LEARNING OBJECTIVES

After studying this chapter, the reader should understand

1. the fundamental philosophical tenets concerning life; and
2. the implications of these tenets for APR.

KEY TERMS AND DEFINITIONS

Genotype

The genotype is all or part of the genetic constitution of an individual or group (Genotype, n.d.).

Phenotype

A phenotype is the observable properties of an organism that are produced by the interaction of the genotype and the environment (Phenotype, n.d.).

Phylogeny

A phylogeny is a hypothetical reconstruction of the evolutionary relationships or the sequential evolutionary steps of a group of organisms. These sequences (nucleotide or amino acid) can explain the origin of a species and its development to its current state of existence or being. The phylogeny of species is often represented graphically in the form of a tree and enables scientists to find new relationships between organisms (Phylogeny, n.d.).

Spontaneous Generation

Spontaneous Generation is a hypothetical construct that living organisms developed from nonliving objects. Another aspect of this hypothesis is that several types of organisms or species appeared at the same time (Oparin, 1957).

INTRODUCTION

Philosophical orientations concerning life and the origins of life undergird hypotheses and theories that seek to explain behaviors defined as innate, instinctive, or survival behaviors. An understanding of the ontogenetic philosophical underpinning is foundational to APR. Fundamental tenets pertaining to life might shed light on being and the interaction of humans with the environment (Peretó, 2005).

SOURCES OF AGGRESSION

According to the theory of evolution, there are three likely sources of aggression; inherent or innate, environmental, or an interplay between inherent and environment. Several worldviews undergird philosophical tenets associated with the three possible sources of aggression. These worldviews of life, heritability, and gene expression include spontaneous generation, creationism, evolution, and ecological theories of the origin of life.

INHERENT OR INNATE AGGRESSION

Theorists contending that aggression is inherent also contend that genes contain inherent characteristics of life. Inherency in life suggests there is a core functional element of aggression within life. Consequently, this core functional element exists in every species. Although the evolutionary process causes the genotype to be different in each species, the foundational features of aggression within life persist (Darwin C., 1872; 1882).

FUNCTIONAL AGGRESSION

Darwin conceived of life as being a struggle for existence in which the fittest survive. The conception of life as a struggle drives the orthogenetic evolution by the natural selection process. Aggression is instinctively implicated in the struggle for survival (Darwin C., 1872; 1882).

AGGRESSION AND ECOLOGY

Aggression is a genetic expression designed to fulfill the predestinated goals of natural selection. Aggression is an innate, instinctive, functional survival mechanism. Aggression serves the functions of self-preservation and inequity among species and species members. Aggression is a mechanism of natural selection that serves the purposes of hegemony and control among groups and species, thereby fulfilling the predestinated goals of orthogenesis (Darwin C., 1872; Oparin, 1957; Peretó, 2005).

Functional characteristics, traits, and behaviors that serve the purpose of survival become heritable. Geneticists define these heritable characteristics, traits, and behaviors as genotypes and phenotypes. Genotypes are those characteristics, traits, and behaviors common to the group, family, or species. Phenotypes are those characteristics, traits, and behaviors sensitive to natural selection. Functional and dysfunctional gene expression is a contextual adaptation process in the struggle to exist (Oparin, 1957; Pereló, 2005).

Although evolutionary theorists argue that aggression is functional, APR is dysfunctional aggression. The presentment of aggression as contextual functional or dysfunctional behavior is due to the organisms or individuals genotype and phenotype. The individuals or organisms responses to environmental conditions mediate gene expression and might be the process responsible for either functional or dysfunctional aggression expressions (Oparin, 1957; Pereló, 2005).

THEORETICAL BASIS FOR INNATE FUNCTIONAL AGGRESSION

The argument that aggression expression is the organisms or individuals predetermined response due to natural selection suggests that aggression is latent within the genes and might express as functional or dysfunctional behavior because of the pangenome. This perspective of gene expression can is traceable back to Aristotelian philosophy (Oparin, 1957).

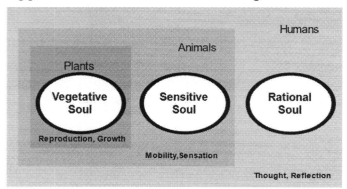

Figure 15-1 Aristotelian Soul

Some scholars claim Aristotle[20] was an early geneticist. Aristotle contended that living organisms were the product of substance and form. Substance was inorganic, such as matter, whereas, form represented life or energy. Substance and form combined to form living organisms. Scholars contending Aristotle was an early geneticist claim that form represents genes and DNA (Oparin, 1957).

Form, which represents life or energy determines the type and nature of the life or organism that emerges. As such, gene expression is the product of form and therefore represents qualities and characteristics inherent in form (Oparin, 1957; Vinci & Robert, 2005).

Darwin also suggested that life is an inherent quality or element common to all species. To Darwin, this inherent quality is the breath "breathed by the Creator" into various forms (Darwin C., 1872, p. 429). To Aristotle, form was the energy that gave life to matter. Speciation is the

---

[20] Figure 15-1 Ian Alexander (https://commons.wikimedia.org/wiki/File:Aristotelian_Soul.png), https://creativecommons.org/licenses/by-sa/4.0/legalcode

process whereby matter and form combine to adapt to changing environments (Oparin, 1957; Vinci & Robert, 2005).

THEORIES OF ORIGIN

Several theories of origin seem to suggest life is an inherent quality and the element from which genes derive. These theorists also purport that aggression is an instinctive element of pangenomes. Aggression is a mechanism imparted into the pangenomes of species to fulfill the predestinated goals of natural selection.

SPONTANEOUS GENERATION

Spontaneous generation theorists contend that species emerged from nonliving or inorganic substances. Spontaneous generation is one of the hypotheses of panspermia. Rocks or meteoroids from exploding planets bore the seeds of life, which were transmitted to the earth. Life, originating from this source might have been preserved in the water. This life sprung out of the water. Original thoughts of abiogenesis were intertwined in this belief.

Some evolutionary theorists contend that life on earth began in a hydrothermal environment. However, some spontaneous generation theorists believe that unique conditions in the earth's environment caused a variety of species to come into existence spontaneously. These spontaneous generation theorists believe that these species appeared in their existing form (Darwin C., 1872; 1882; Oparin, 1957).

CREATIONISM

Creationists contend that a variety of species emerged on earth because of the deliberate action of an intelligent being or cause. Creationists may use religious arguments, nonreligious arguments, or a mixture of both, to support their theory of origin. Some creationists would be included among spontaneous generation theorists. Some creationists are also evolutionists (Darwin C., 1872; Oparin, 1957).

INTELLIGENT DESIGN

ID refers to a community of scientists, philosophers, researchers and other scholars engaged in scientific research to seek and examine evidence of design in nature. ID theorists contend that an intelligent cause and directed processes best explain the origin of life and species. ID theorists apply knowledge from many disciplines, including molecular biology and genetics to substantiate ID theories (Darwin C., 1872; Meyer, 2013).

Evolutionists and Ecologists

Evolutionists, ecologists, and spontaneous generation ecologists contend that life originated because of changes in the earth's environment. These broad categories of origin of life theorists include the influence of ecology regarding the origin of life, the existence of species, and gene expression. Evolutionary phylogenetic theorists, contending that speciation is the product of natural selection are also ecologists. Spontaneous generation ecologists include those evolutionists who posit theories of cosmozoë, panspermia, and abiogenesis (Bradie & Harms, 2017; Oparin, 1957).

Some evolutionists ignore the origin of life and focus on the origin of species. These evolutionists focus on the study of embryology and phylogeny[21]. Other evolutionists concerned with the original cause of life on earth are ecologists who posit theories of cosmozoë, panspermia, and abiogenesis. Creationists also posit theories concerning the original cause of life on earth. Creationists identify the Absolute Principle or the First Cause as their explanation for the original cause of life on earth.

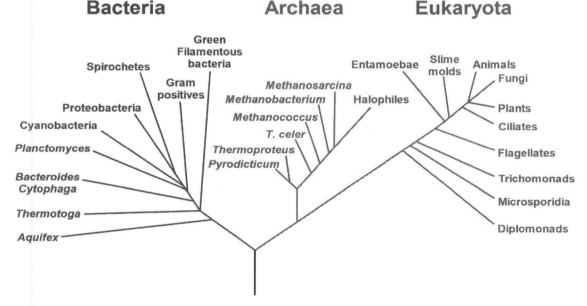

Figure 15-2 Phylogenetic Tree

Evolutionary- creationists also accept adaptation as a developmental process among species (Darwin C., 1872; Meyer, 2013; Oparin, 1957).

---

[21] Figure 15-2 Eric Gaba (Sting - fr:Sting) (https://commons.wikimedia.org/wiki/File:Phylogenetic_tree.svg), „Phylogenetic tree", marked as public domain, more details on Wikimedia Commons:

CONCLUSION

Causes of the origin of life do not lend themselves to literal, sensorial observations. However, ontogenetic theories are pertinent to understanding aggression as a behavioral expression. Ontogenetic premises are the foundations of theories linking genes and aggression.

There are two broad approaches used to explain the link between genes and aggression. The first approach is being taken by those theorists positing theoretical explanations for the origin of life. The second approach is being taken by those theorists who ignore the initial cause of the origin of life.

Because the origin of life remains an insentient impalpable phenomenon, philosophers developed theories of explanations for the origin of life. These philosophers postulate innate or inherent, functional, or integrative innateness and ecological factors as explanations of aggression in species. These postulates continue to delimit the interpretive parameters of APR (Mayes).

CHAPTER REVIEW

REVIEW QUESTIONS

1. What is life?
2. Explore your personal perception of life and the cause of APR.
3. Identify at least five elements that influenced your worldview concerning life and aggression.

CHAPTER SIXTEEN
EMBRYOLOGY AND PHYLOGENY

CHAPTER PREVIEW

Evolutionists ignore the question of the first cause or the origin of life on earth. However, the origin of life on earth holds information that might explain aggression in humans.

In this chapter, there will be a discussion of two branches of ontogenetic studies, embryology, and phylogeny. Scholars in these two disciplines aim to explain the origin of life.

Embryology is a branch of study that examines fetal development to explain behavior. Genetic embryology is a branch of study that seeks to explore the role of genes in fetal development and its implications for predispositions during the lifetime of the organism. In the study of embryology, presuppositions are made concerning the origin of species related to the pangenome.

In the study of phylogeny, aggression is linked to the evolutionary process of speciation. Phylogenetic scholars presuppose that ecological factors influenced speciation.

PURPOSE AND LEARNING OBJECTIVES

PURPOSE

The purpose of this chapter is to explore evolutionary theory and research in embryology and phylogeny as explanations of innateness and their implications for genetics and aggression.

LEARNING OBJECTIVES

After studying this chapter, the reader should understand the applicability of theories of ontogeny to understanding APR.

KEY TERMS AND DEFINITIONS

Biogenesis

Biogenesis originally meant the emergence of life from nonliving things. This conceptualization was aligned with some theories that original life-form or organic life-form emerged from inorganic or nonliving life-forms, such as rocks (Bastian, 1887).

The term biogenesis was redefined to mean the biochemical processes whereby living organisms emerged as an outcome of molecular evolution over millions of years (Sharov, 2006).

Embryology

Embryology is a branch of biology where the focus of the study is on the fertilization process of gametes, and prenatal development of fetuses (Barnes, 2014).

Germline Theory

Some cells, such as sperms and eggs, are called germline cells. Germline cells are purported to be involved in transmitting genetic materials. Germline theory is an emergent theory from Darwin's pangenesis (Brücher & Jamall, 2016; Gyngell, Douglas, & Savulescu, 2017).

Recapitulation

The biogenetic law is a theory of recapitulation. According to the theory of recapitulation, the embryo goes through stages of development that the adult organism underwent throughout the evolutionary process. Each stage of embryonic development from fertilization to birth is reflective of a different stage of evolution (Barnes, 2014).

The Biogenetic Law

Ernst Haeckel, an ardent eugenicist, posited the biogenetic law [22] in the 1860s. According to Haeckel, the chronological development of the embryo is indicative of stages in the evolutionary development. The biogenetic law is often stated as ontogeny recapitulates phylogeny (Barnes, 2014).

Figure 16-1 Ernst Haeckel

INTRODUCTION

Evolutionary theories make assumptive hypotheses concerning the origin of life and the origin of species. Ontogeny is the study of the origin of life and the origin of species. Ontogenetic researchers are seeking to establish whether there is a relationship between ontogeny and behavior. The concern is whether behaviors such as aggression are inherent and whether this inherency is linked to the ontogeny of life and species. Another concern is whether specific aspects or elements of ontogeny cause aggression. Ontogenetic studies, therefore, have relevance for providing insights into the challenges associated with interpreting, analyzing, and addressing APR.

ONTOGENY

Ontogenesis refers to the development or developmental history of an organism, while phylogenetic studies focus on the developmental history of the species. Ontogenetic and phylogenetic studies place their focus on genetics and related disciplines. Research and practice involving these disciplines, for example, seek to determine whether aggression is due to genetic or environmental influences.

Two branches of ontogeny; embryology and phylogeny, are relevant for understanding the neurophysiological and socio-moral characteristics, traits, and behaviors implicated in APR. These two conceptualizations of ontogenesis resulted in divergent scholarly approaches to the study of ontogeny (Colbert & Rowe, 2008; Love, 2015).

Theorists of one perspective consider ontogenesis as the developmental history of the organism within its lifetime. Theorists of the second perspective consider ontogenesis as the developmental history of

---

[22] Figure 16-1 Nicola Perscheid (https://commons.wikimedia.org/wiki/File:ErnstHaeckel.jpg), „ErnstHaeckel", marked as public domain, more details on Wikimedia Commons: https://commons.wikimedia.org/wiki/Template:PD-old

the species. The first perspective entails the study of embryology, and the second perspective includes the study of phylogeny. The study of phylogeny extends the discussion to the theories or explanations of the first cause of the origin of species (Colbert & Rowe, 2008; Love, 2015).

Both ontogeny and phylogeny are ontogenetic perspectives seeking to explain being and the nature of being. Although ontogenetic and phylogenetic studies ignore the origin of life, evolutionary theory from which these studies branched make assumptions and premises about the origin of life that are pertinent to ontogenetic and phylogenetic research (Colbert & Rowe, 2008; Love, 2015).

EMBRYOLOGY

The origin of species, the origin of life, and studies about the nature of life are different and distinct disciplines. Embryology is the study of ontogeny that focuses on the beginning of life of the individual or organism. Some scholars include infancy and early developmental stages in the lifespan as a part of ontogenetic studies (Colbert & Rowe, 2008; Morimoto, Nakatsukasa, Ponce de León, & Zollikofer, 2018; Tomasello & Gonzalez-Cabrera, 2017).

Genetic embryologists apply findings from embryonic research to make extrapolations about the origin of species. The premise that the embryo can provide information about the ontogeny of the species, or the origin of life stems from germline theory (Colbert & Rowe, 2008; Moritomo et al., 2018; Tomasello & Gonzalez-Cabrera, 2017).

GERMLINE THEORY

Germline theory is a hypothetical construct applied in genetics to explain hereditary transmissions. A fundamental hypothesis in germline theory is that billions, possibly trillions of characteristics, traits, and behaviors reside within the sperm and the egg. Geneticists posit that specific genes mediate each characteristic, trait, and behavior. Current research into the cause of aggression is seeking to determine whether there are specific genetic pathways that cause predispositions to aggression (Brücher & Jamall, 2016; Colbert & Rowe, 2008; Dall et al., 2012; Gyngell et al., 2017).

Researchers trace neurological dysfunctions that cause aggression to embryonic neurological development. There is comparatively more research into the impact of embryonic developmental experiences on aggression than research into the possible genetic influence on aggression. Despite the comparative paucity of research into the possibility of genetic influence on aggression, genetic embryology has limitations regarding whether aggression is an innate quality of life (Colbert & Rowe, 2008; Love, 2015).

One of Darwin's fundamental premises is that life is the source of genes and that life has inherent qualities. Identifying whether genes cause aggression does not address the premise of inherency of aggression in life (Bradie & Harms, 2017).

APPLICATION OF FINDINGS IN EMBRYOLOGICAL THEORY AND RESEARCH

Developmental ontogenesis or embryology forms the basis of developmental and stage theories. Freudian developmental stages and Bowlby's attachment theory are founded in developmental ontogeny. Developmental ontogenesis has implications for genetic, phylogenetic, and epigenetic studies, including studies in evolutionary molecular biology, and epigenetic twin-studies, which are applicable to understanding APR (Love, 2015).

BIOGENESIS

The biogenetic law also referred to as "ontogeny recapitulates phylogeny" is a hypothesis used to explain embryonic development as an evolutionary process. According to the biogenetic law, the embryonic development stages[23] are a replication of the evolutionary process. Each embryonic developmental stage is indicative of evolutionary epochs in the development of that species (Barnes, 2014).

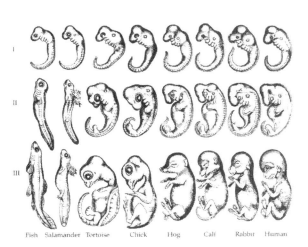

Fish Salamander Tortoise Chick Hog Calf Rabbit Human

Figure 16-2 Drawing of Embryo's by Haeckel

Although the ontogeny recapitulates phylogeny hypothesis has lost credibility, the biogenetic law still has implications for germline theory, phylogenetics, and epigenetic studies. The conceptualization of a biogenetic element in the transmission of observable characteristics, traits, and behaviors stems from early evolutionary conceptualization of *natural selection, reproductive advantage,* and *gemmules* (Darwin C., 1882).

---

[23] Figure 16-2 Romanes, G. J.; uploaded to Wikipedia by en:User:Phlebas; authors of the description page: en:User:Phlebas, en:User:SeventyThree (https://commons.wikimedia.org/wiki/File:Haeckel_drawings.jpg), „Haeckel drawings", marked as public domain, more details on Wikimedia Commons: https://commons.wikimedia.org/wiki/Template:PD-old

PHYLOGENESIS

According to germline theory, the conglomerate of all the genetic materials exists in the egg and sperm. Upon fertilization, the organism draws from the genetic material to grow and to develop into a mature individual (Systematics Association, 1964).

Germline researchers, like other scholars of microbiology, engage in hypothetical constructs and the observation of processes deemed to substantiate the validity of the hypothetical construct. Germline theory is a product of phylogenetic theory. According to phylogenetic theory, different species branched off to become distinct and different from other species. Phylogenetic theorists infer that heredity is the product of an interaction between genetic influence and ecological processes (O'Dwyer, Kembel, & Green, 2012).

Environmental or ecological processes are the influencers of genetic variations. Studies in phylogenetic diversity are a subdiscipline of microbiology involving microbe research. Phylogenetic researchers examine characteristics, traits, and behaviors that distinguish one species from another. Due to their focus on the interplay between genes and the environment, concepts, and theories in phylogeny influence research in epigenetics and the nature-nurture debate (O'Dwyer et al., 2012).

Currently, behaviorists continue to debate the genetic basis for behavior. Some neuroscientists emphasizing neurophysiological impairments and inefficacy as the root of dysfunctional behaviors such as APR, seek to establish a genetic basis for these impairments and inefficacies. Other behaviorists contend that dysfunctional behaviors such as APR are the product of the environment, and yet others contend that characteristics, traits, and behaviors are a complex interplay between genes and the environment (Lewkowicz, 2011; Peretó, 2005; van Ijzendoorn & Bakermans-Kranenburg, 2015).

CONCLUSION

Embryologists and phylogenetic theorists avoid or ignore questions pertaining to the origin of life. To avoid this question and to overcome the challenges associated with providing an explanation for the origin of life on earth, evolutionary onto-geneticists focus solely on embryology. However, genetics is a branch of embryology. The study of genetics is based on assumptions about the origin of life. Therefore, the ontogeny of species or the origin of life should be included in studies related to the nature of being. These studies can give insight into dysfunctional behaviors such as APR (Bradie & Harms, 2017; Dall et al., 2012).

CHAPTER REVIEW

REVIEW QUESTIONS

1. Evaluate the applicability of embryology and phylogeny as means that explain APR.
2. What are the philosophical bases of these branches of knowledge?

CHAPTER SEVENTEEN
ONTOGENY OF SPECIES AND BEING

CHAPTER PREVIEW

In this chapter, there will be a brief discussion of being as the characteristics that define organisms and species. The ontogeny of being holds answers concerning the origin of characteristics that define being.

Being is intangible, and so is life. Although empiricists claim that scientific study could only be concerned with observable sentient phenomena, the inherent nature of life does not readily lend itself to such investigations.

In this chapter, there will also be further discussions concerning the hypotheses of the origin of life. Evolutionists suggest a physiochemical process that explains how life began and an external source as the first cause of this physiochemical process.

PURPOSE AND LEARNING OBJECTIVES

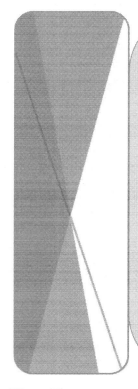

PURPOSE

The purpose of this chapter is to explore the philosophical basis of the nature of being pertaining to APR.

LEARNING OBJECTIVES

After studying this chapter, the reader should

1 understand that being refers to inherent nature;

2 understand that being refers to qualities that make organisms, individuals, and species distinct and different from others; and

3 increase their understanding of the tenets of empiricism and its implications for studying being and the nature of being.

KEY TERMS AND DEFINITIONS

Being

Being is the fact of existence. The substance or nature of living organisms.

INTRODUCTION

Being refers to the substance or nature of living organisms. Being, or what makes a person human, encompasses those characteristics, traits, and behaviors that make an organism, individual, or species distinct and different from others. Humans possess characteristics, traits, and behaviors that make humans distinguishable from other species. Geneticists contend that genes distinguish humans from other species. A discourse on being addresses those substantive qualities in humans that might or might not cause an individual to engage in APR and therefore, is pertinent to the current study.

ONTOGENY AND BEING

Being refers to the existence of all physical, nonphysical, tangible, and intangible things, substances, and qualities. Darwin contended aggression is an inherent quality of life. As such, the origin of life has a bearing on the substantive nature of species. The study of ontogeny has applicability to increasing understanding regarding those characteristics, traits, and behaviors that facilitate the engagement in APR among humans (Savitt, 2017).

Neurophysiological and socio-moral characteristics, traits, and behaviors differentiate humans from other species. Physical appearance, intellectual ability, and emotional characteristics, for example, distinguish humans from other mammals. These neurophysiological and socio-moral characteristics, traits, and behaviors combined, provide the framework for defining being, or the nature of being.

INTANGIBILITY OF BEING

Studies in both ontogeny and the nature of being, involve intangible, immaterial, impalpable elements. However, empiricists remained bound to the philosophy that objective scientific research should involve sensorial observations. Consequently, philosophers developed several philosophical tenets to facilitate objective scientific research into those intangible, immaterial, and impalpable elements that comprise being.

EMPIRICISM

Empiricists contend that phenomena in scientific observation should be tangible, literal, objects, and entities. Nevertheless, unobservable entities, such as atoms, fields, and genes, are insentient phenomena researched and studied in many disciplines. Theories of explanation is a philosophical approach that facilitates the integration of empiricism and scientific rationality, both of which undergird scientific objectivity, into studies of insentient phenomena (Mayes).

Evolutionary theorists use two approaches, realism, and epistemic value, to address impalpable phenomena that preclude literal observation, such as the cause of the origin of life. Realists contend that impalpable phenomena, such as atoms, fields, and genes, are a literal description of an external reality. Consequently, realists conceptualized these phenomena. Realists claim that conceptualization of these intangible phenomena made them tangible (Mayes).

Evolutionary theorists also apply epistemic value to validate theoretical suppositions and postulates. According to evolutionist theorists, a theoretical supposition is valid if it is based on logical propositions involving deductive-nomology and inductive statistics (Mayes).

LIFE

Questions concerning life center on the nature of life and being. The nature of life[24] is a foundational question of genetics, survivability, and heritability.

Ontogeny, phylogeny, and the first cause are approaches to exploring life and the nature of being (Darwin C., 1872; Oparin, 1957).

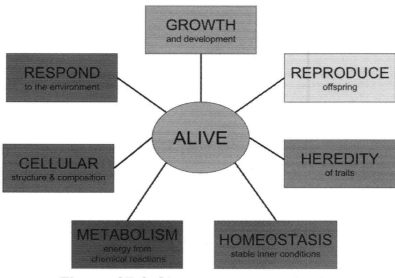

Figure 17-1 Characteristics of Life

Hypotheses and theories about the origin of life on earth are based on the premise that life existed and continues to exist as an intangible element. Life on earth originated from nonphysical, intangible elements. If ontogeny impinges on the nature of being, then the nonphysical, intangible elements of life also have a bearing on the nature of being.

The nonphysical, intangible elements of life are metaphysical or beyond physical existence. Studies that involve perceptions and perspectives on life such as, genomics, genetics, epigenetics, and molecular biology explore life as an incorporeal, nonphysical, intangible phenomenon (Bliss & Trogdon, 2016; Savitt, 2017).

The study of life, perceived as energy in an incorporeal form, involves the study of metaphysics. However, metaphysics is considered to be philosophical studies related to such disciplines like religion, spirituality, and ontology. These disciplines are believed to be nonscientific and do not belong to the natural sciences. The natural sciences are considered to be objective and studied within the context of concrete observable traits, properties, or characteristics. The study of ontogeny or the origin of life, because of its impalpability, does not readily lend itself to the concretized observation required in the natural sciences. Although these studies apply concepts and characteristics descriptive of living organisms, these concepts and characteristics do not explain the essential, inherent element

---

[24] Figure 17-1 Chris Packard
(https://commons.wikimedia.org/wiki/File:Characteristics_of_life.svg),
https://creativecommons.org/licenses/by-sa/4.0/legalcode

referred to as life. As such, philosophers developed different philosophical tenets to overcome this hurdle (Bliss & Trogdon, 2016; Hall, 2016).

Conclusion

The philosophical tenets applied to explain the origin of life posed special challenges to empiricists. Empiricists reject studies involving unobservable entities and processes. Philosophers developed theories of explanation that facilitated the inclusion of intangible, metaphysical entities, and processes that are not literally observable (Mayes).

Chapter Review

REVIEW QUESTIONS
1. What is being?
2. What elements of being might explain APR?

SECTION TWO
THEORIES

SECTION SUMMARY

The theory of evolution by means of natural selection is based on the premise that aggression is a functional element of natural selection, survivability, and orthogenesis. However, APR is a maladaptive phenomenon. It could also be argued that APR does not serve the functions of survivability or orthogenesis. In this section, there will be a discussion of the main tenets of the theory of evolution by means of natural selection and their applicability to understanding, interpreting, and analyzing APR.

Darwin's theory of evolution by means of natural selection is built on Newton's cosmological philosophy. Darwin contended that a force outside the control of humans directs natural selection. Through predetermination and predestination, this force selected some species and species members to have higher survivability and other species and species members to have a greater vulnerability.

Darwin identified pangenes, mutations, gemmules, and instinct as some of the heredity mechanisms responsible for differences in survivability and susceptibility to vulnerability in species and species members. Differential survivability and susceptibility to vulnerability became the foundation of racially-motivated cultural movements such as social Darwinism and eugenics.

Although there has been a movement away from different survivability and susceptibility to vulnerability based on race and ethnicity, the conceptualization of predispositional vulnerability still remains as a core tenet of evolutionary theory.

Research in genetics and epigenetics continue with the aim of identifying specific vulnerability genes and risk alleles. Based on research findings, geneticists posit that there might be predispositional vulnerabilities to mental health that increase the likelihood of phenomenon such as APR.

The conceptualization of predispositional vulnerability is the basis of several diathesis models. Theorists of these models posit that vulnerability might be the product of variants of genes, environment, and stress. Two major disciplines, genetics, and epigenetics are concerned with the gene-environment interaction and their implications for phenomenon such as APR.

In this section, there is a discussion of two alternative theories, panspermia, and ID. Panspermia theorists posit ontogeny due to activities from outside the earth. ID theorists posit that natural selection cannot account for the complexities and synchronization of different parts observed in living organisms.

SECTION 2 CONTENTS

CHAPTER EIGHTEEN
THEORETICAL RATIONALE

CHAPTER PREVIEW

In this chapter, there will be a proposition that evolutionary theory is relevant as the theoretical interpretive framework for understanding APR. Tenets from evolutionary theory are used to explain behaviors at the individual, group, and societal level. Almost all the disciplines that inform service provision, policy, and program development addressing APR use evolutionary theory as their theoretical interpretive framework.

PURPOSE AND LEARNING OBJECTIVES

PURPOSE

The purpose of this chapter is to explore the widespread use of evolutionary theory in disciplines relevant to APR.

LEARNING OBJECTIVES

After studying this chapter, the reader should

1. have an increased understanding of the widespread use of evolutionary theory in disciplines relevant to addressing APR concerns; and
2. determine the applicability of evolutionary theory for addressing the concerns of APR.

KEY TERMS AND DEFINITIONS

Maladaptive Aggression

According to evolutionary conceptualization, aggression can be either functional or dysfunctional behavior. While functional aggression is adaptive, dysfunctional aggression is maladaptive (Bowlby, 1984). Maladaptive aggression is harmful behaviors that violate social conventions. Maladaptive aggression is any behavior that is an intentional and deliberate choice to cause harm and hurt to another person (Suris et al., 2004).

INTRODUCTION

Researchers engage in scholarly work and theoretical development to find solutions for challenges existing in human society. Evolutionary theory is the foundation of research in many disciplines that seek to answer questions concerning problems related to interaction and functioning in human society. Evolutionists posit hypotheses used as explanations of biogenetic, neurological, social, and psychological dysfunctionalities and disordered states in individuals, groups, and the species. Evolutionary tenets used to explain human behaviors center on hypotheses concerning life, the origin of life, and ontogeny of species.

THE RELEVANCE OF EVOLUTIONARY THEORIES

A United Nations (UN) report (2015), describes APR as maladaptive, dysfunctional behaviors that sometimes result in loss of lives. APR is a threat to the survival of self, offspring, and species. Because survivability is a major tenet of evolutionary theory, evolutionary premises of survivability are highly relevant to any study of the real roots of APR.

Evolutionary theory is the backbone of almost all survivability studies. Survivability is a fundamental concept of APR. A review of survivability conceptualizations is pertinent to a better understanding of APR. Because survivability is a central tenet of evolutionary theory, there will be a focus on evolutionary theory and the broad categories of disciplines relevant to survivability and APR in this study.

The theoretical frameworks used to understand and explain dysfunctionalities and disordered states focus on these behaviors and conditions on three basic levels, the individual, group, and species. At the species level, evolutionary theory informs studies related to phylogeny and the human genome.

Social, genetic, and ecological theories place the focus on maladaptive aggression at the group level. Evolutionary theory is the most used theory to explain human interactions and relations at the group level, such as systems theories. APR has implications for sociocultural interactions, hegemony, control, and social cohesion at the group level.

At the individual level, APR presents as dysfunctionalities and disordered states. Evolutionary theory underpins studies such as ontogeny. Ontogeny is the study of the origin of life and the origin of species. These studies seek to examine the qualities and characteristics inherent in life and the nature of being. Findings from ontogenetic studies are applied to explain behaviors at the individual level. Researchers and practitioners apply ontogenetic premises to explain the role of genetics, heredity, and survivability in the manifestation of dysfunctionalities and disordered states.

Theories used to explain individual behaviors inform disciplines such as psychiatry and psychiatric disorders. Clinical definitions of psychiatric disorders that are pertinent to aggression, such as depression, anxiety, and personality disorders, are defined within the context of failed biological mechanisms (de Almeida, Cabral, & Narvaes, 2015).

New imaging technologies are facilitating the integration of theories from disciplines, such as chemistry, molecular biology, and physics to improve understanding and increase insight into the neurophysiology of dysfunctional behaviors and disordered states. The evolutionary theory forms the backbone of these disciplines. As such, theories of evolution are pertinent for improved understanding, management, and development of programs to address APR.

CONCLUSION

Evolutionary theory is a well-developed theory that is used to explain key elements pertaining to life, the origin of life, and the origin of species. Evolutionary tenets inform a plethora, if not all, studies related to survivability and aggression, and are therefore of high relevance in understanding APR.

Despite its widespread use in research and practice, several challenges exist concerning the applicability of findings from studies based on evolutionary tenets. Results from studies undergirded by evolutionary theory tend to have high specificity of applicability, are applicable only under particular conditions, and often cannot be used to make generalizations concerning human behaviors. Despite its shortcomings, the evolutionary theory remains the main theoretical framework used to inform research and practice related to APR (Brandon, 2014; Buss, 2009).

CHAPTER REVIEW

REVIEW QUESTIONS

1. Why is the theory of evolution pertinent to studies of APR?
2. Identify two branches of studies with their roots in evolutionary theory that address concerns related to APR?
3. How do evolutionary tenets drive assumptions in these disciplines?

CHAPTER NINETEEN
THEORY OF EVOLUTION

CHAPTER PREVIEW

In the last chapter, there was a discussion of the relevance of evolutionary theory to the understanding of APR. In this chapter, there will be a discussion of some of the central tenets of Darwin's theory of evolution.

Evolutionary theory can be traced back to philosophical thoughts from antiquity. The basic tenets of the evolutionary theory emerged from cosmological philosophy. Cosmological philosophy emerged from an ancient Greek religious philosophy.

Charles Darwin, who is considered to be the father of modern-day evolutionary theory, was heavily influenced by cosmological philosophy. Darwin replicated cosmological, philosophical beliefs to explain evolution and heredity.

In his theory of evolution by natural selection, Darwin discussed several key concepts such as variation, selection, reproductive advantage, and orthogenesis. These concepts form the basis of research and practice relevant to APR. For example, reproductive advantage is an explanation for vulnerability and susceptibility to APR.

PURPOSE AND LEARNING OBJECTIVES

PURPOSE

The purpose of this chapter is to understand the basic tenets of evolutionary theory and its implications for understanding dysfunctionalities and disordered states as evident in APR.

LEARNING OBJECTIVES

After studying this chapter, the reader should

1. an increased understanding of the basic tenets of the theory of evolution; and

2. an improved understanding of the philosophical basis of evolutionary theory.

KEY TERMS AND DEFINITIONS

Common Descent

According to the common descent hypothesis, species descended from either one or a few common ancestors (Darwin C., 1882).

Orthogenesis

Orthogenesis is a combined form of two Greek words ὀρθός orthós, meaning straight, and γένεσις genesis meaning origin.

Orthogenesis is one of the hypothetical tenets of evolution by natural selection. The orthogenesis premise states that successive generations of some organisms, species, subspecies, and species members become increasingly modified or progressively evolve into higher forms and complexities. The governing force of natural selection has an orthogenetic straight-line goal (Orthogenesis, n.d.).

INTRODUCTION

Evolutionary theory is not new. Evolutionary philosophy can be traced back to several ancient cultures, including ancient Greece and China. Philosophers in antiquity developed the major tenets of the theory of evolution. Charles Darwin[25], the father of modern-day evolutionary theory, expounded on these tenets and added new dimensions to existing evolutionary theories. Evolution by natural selection theory informs the majority, if not all, modern-day science, education, and research disciplines; including physics, psychology, biology, genetics, religion, neuropsychology, neuroanatomy, and spirituality.

Figure 19-1 Charles Darwin

Natural selection is a fundamental evolutionary tenet. Charles Darwin, the father of modern-day evolution, explained that a force outside of human control directs natural selection. Natural selection causes differential survivability that results in a reproductive advantage for some human subspecies and susceptibility for other human subspecies. Due to natural selection, some organisms, species, subspecies, and species members have developed and will continue to evolve to greater complexity and fitness (Darwin C., 1872).

THE EVOLUTIONARY TENET OF SURVIVABILITY

Survivability is a foundational tenet upon which evolutionary theory hinges and is a principal tenet used to explain APR. Due to its emphasis on survivability, evolutionary theory is the theoretical framework used in this study.

According to Darwin's theory of evolution by natural selection, aggression is a mechanism of natural selection. Aggression serves the primary functions of self and species preservation. Groups and institutions such as the family evolved to serve preservation functions for the individual and species. As such, aggression is relevant to the group and institutional functionality.

---

[25] Figure 19-1 J. Cameron (https://commons.wikimedia.org/wiki/File:Charles_Darwin_01.jpg), „Charles Darwin 01", marked as public domain, more details on Wikimedia Commons: https://commons.wikimedia.org/wiki/Template:PD-old

Groups and institutions must have mechanisms of hegemony and control to perform their preservative functions. Aggression, power, dominance, and control are foundational elements of societal institutions. Aggression also serves the functions of evolutionary orthogenesis.

DARWIN'S THEORY OF EVOLUTION

Evolutionists use ontogenetic premises to explain the relationship between aggression and the nature of being. Charles Darwin epitomized his conceptualization of the origin of life and the origin of species in the following quotation:

> *There is grandeur in this view of life, with its several powers, having been originally breathed by the Creator into a few forms or into one; and that, whilst this planet has gone cycling on according to the fixed law of gravity, from so simple a beginning endless forms most beautiful and most wonderful have been, and are being, evolved.*
> *(Darwin C., 1872, p. 429).*

DARWIN'S PERCEPTIONS OF LIFE

Darwin proposed that life was "...originally breathed by the Creator into a few forms or into one" (Darwin C., 1872, p. 429). Philosophical orientations from antiquity influenced this conception of life. Early Greek philosophers purported that life on earth originated from a source outside of earth. In Greek religion, the god Pan was credited as being the creator. This philosophical thought influenced Darwin's conceptualization of life, the origin of life, and the origin of species.

Darwin founded his gene theory from his conception of life. Darwin conceived that the emergence of life was a phenomenon that occurred before the origin of species (Alexandria, 1981; Oparin, 1957; Peretó et al., 2009; Vinci & Robert, 2005). Gene and chromosomal theory are foundational theories in almost all modern-day disciplines and practices. These theories are integral to the way modern-day scholars address problems related to life.

NEWTONIAN PRINCIPIA AND NATURAL LAWS

Natural selection is the core tenet of Darwin's theory of evolution. Darwin embodied his conception of the origin of life, the ontogeny of species, life, being, and the nature of being in his natural selection hypothesis. Natural selection functions on principles of predeterminism, predestination, and preferentialism (Peretó, 2005; Peretó et al., 2009).

Life has inherent qualities or elements. Darwin referred to these inherent qualities and characteristics as pangenes. Pangenes determined the organism's nature. The force that directs natural selection causes interactions between the environment and pangenes. The force directing natural selection predetermines environmental conditions as well as the organism's pangenes. The interactions between the organism and the environment result in the predetermined and predestined orthogenetic goals.

Buss (2009) cited literature and research that concur with Darwin's conceptions of life, struggle, and aggression. Buss reported that DNA studies, paleontological, archaeological, ethnographic records, as well as psychological studies, support "the hypothesis that humans have evolved adaptations for killing other humans, along with evolved defenses for preventing getting killed" (Buss, 2009, p. 142)

PREDETERMINED PREDESTINATION

The force that directs natural selection preferentially predetermined and predestined some species to achieve higher forms, complexities, and fitness than other species. Other species were predestined for destruction and extinction. The force directing natural selection predetermined that some organisms, species, and subspecies would be susceptible to vulnerability. It is the destiny of some species to be superior, and the destiny of others to be susceptible to vulnerability (Darwin C., 1872).

GENETIC DETERMINISM AND AGGRESSION

Some scholars consider genetic determinism as an indication of Darwin's conceptualization of predeterminism. Several studies indicate a correlation between genetic pathways and aggression. In their longitudinal research of physical aggression during early childhood, Lacourse et al. (2014) studied 667 monozygotic and dizygotic twins to examine the developmental roles of genetic and environmental factors in physical aggression. The researchers concluded, "Genetic factors always explained a substantial part of individual differences in physical aggression" (Lacourse et al., 2014).

In their discussion of genetic determinism, Resnik and Vorhaus (2006) identified three philosophical positions related to determinism, hard determinism, indeterminism, and compatibilism. Hard determinism philosophers hold that humans cannot make free choices. Indeterministic philosophers posit that human actions result from spontaneous acts of the will that break free from the world's causal nexus. Philosophers who assert compatibilism contend that free will is compatible with determinism (Resnik & Vorhaus, 2006).

Resnik and Vorhaus (2006) explained that some compatibilists consider actions to be free if they are the product of reasoning and deliberation rather than the product of external force. Darwin's conceptualizations of predeterminism, predestination, and orthogenesis indicate a philosophy of hard determinism because predeterminism, predestination, and orthogenesis are products of the force that directs natural selection.

Resnik and Vorhaus (2006) further argued that genetic determinism is probabilistic, not deterministic. Additionally, genetic determinism might be strong, moderate, or weak. However, advances in behavioral genetics indicate that genetic determinism has implications for psychological determinism (Resnik & Vorhaus, 2006).

Resnik and Vorhaus (2006) concluded:

> *To seriously claim that a gene linked to aggression invalidates the free will of a person with that gene, one would need to show that the gene both strongly determines aggressive tendencies in people and, in addition, that people with these tendencies are not free to act differently. Such a person would truly be a puppet controlled by his/her genes (Resnik & Vorhaus, 2006, p. 4).*

NEWTONIAN COSMOLOGICAL PHILOSOPHY

Darwin applied Newtonian principles of natural philosophies to his theory of natural selection (Peretó, 2005; Peretó et al., 2009). Newton applied cosmological philosophy concerning life to develop three fundamental concepts of physics-- law, forces, and gravity. Darwin's theory of evolution was an application of these three Newtonian laws of physics (Brandon, 2014; Darwin C., 1872; Vinci & Robert, 2005).

Sir Isaac Newton

Figure 19-2 Sir Isaac Newton

Newton developed his cosmological philosophy from ancient mythical Greek philosophy of cosmozoë. According to the Greek philosophy of cosmozoë, the universe plunged into Chaos following a war among the gods. The forces set in motion continued by the hands of the gods. Newton named one of these forces gravity. According to Newton, the laws of gravity are fixed universal principles that function above the governance or interference of man (Hesiod, 1914; Kragh, 2017; Wolfram, 2002).

Newton[26] propounded his thesis concerning natural laws in his thesis "Philosophiæ Naturalis Principia Mathematica" Darwin applied Newtonian conceptualization of natural philosophies to Darwin's theory of evolution by natural selection. Darwin conceived of natural

[26] Figure 19-2 From: Arthur Shuster & Arthur E. Shipley: Britain's Heritage of Science. London, 1917. (https://commons.wikimedia.org/wiki/File:SS-newton.jpg), „SS-newton", marked as public domain, more details on Wikimedia Commons: https://commons.wikimedia.org/wiki/Template:PD-old

selection as a natural law akin to the laws of gravity. According to this conception, natural selection is a fixed and universal natural law (Brandon, 2014; Darwin C., 1872).

Like Newtonian philosophy of fixed, universal, natural laws, Darwin contended that natural selection occurs outside the control and efforts of humans. Selection and variability were the principles of natural selection. According to Darwin, selection was predetermined by natural selection, and therefore, selection is also a fixed universal law.

Darwin identified two aspects of selection, natural selection, and selection. Selection embodied predetermined predestination for orthogenetic fitness and vulnerability based on genetic inheritance that is inherent in life. Selection is an inherent instinct causing species and subspecies to engage in choices that would result in orthogenesis.

Selection produces variability. In their natural habitat, species instinctively engage in selection through selective mating. Selective mating, selective breeding, and interbreeding are choices that produce variability. Humans engage in selective mating to ensure the reproduction of desirable qualities. Even though humans can influence variability in species, though, for example, purposeful mate-choice, these efforts are weak when compared with selection, which is a product of natural laws.

Selection, which is the product of natural laws will cause species members with superior qualities to naturally, and inherently, seek out mates with superior qualities. Species members with lower survivability will also seek out mates with lower survivability. This type of selection, although it employs individual choice, is a product of the natural laws of selection (Darwin C., 1872; Smith G., 2008).

MATTER AND FORM

Aristotle's matter and form, and Newton's metaphysical conceptualizations influenced Darwin's thoughts on the ontogeny of life and species. The sentient materialization of species involves the combination of matter and form. Humans and other living organisms, therefore, consist of two elements, matter, and form.

Aristotle referred to matter as the corporeal structures of species. For example, the manifestation of bodies or organisms, which could be seen and touched, whereas, intangible metaphysical elements, such as breath and life were forms (Janiak, 2016; Oparin, 1957). Darwin, on the other hand, referred to form as the corporeal structures of living organisms and matter as the intangible elements such as life and breath (Darwin C., 1872; Oparin, 1957).

Newton conceived of the forces of gravity as metaphysical elements. Darwin conceived of life as energy. The energy components of humans, for example, consist of insentient elements such as the breath. According to Darwin, the unification of matter and form resulted in the manifestation of living organisms with a corporeal structure (Chalmers, 2014).

LIFE AND EVOLUTION

Life is a metaphysical element that serves the purposes of evolution. Life contains the forces of natural selection, selection, and variations. Pangenes are the mechanisms through which life works.

Pangenes facilitate natural selection, selection, and variations. Variations are the products of natural selection and selection. Variations are responsible for speciation. Pangenes are responsible for differences in characteristics, traits, and behaviors.

Darwin's concept of pangenes was a convergence of the panspermia hypothesis, spontaneous generation, and the belief that life possessed inherent qualities transmittable as pangenes. Inherent qualities in pangenes are responsible for speciation and differentiation in each species (Alexandria, 1981; Oparin, 1957; Peretó et al., 2009; Vinci & Robert, 2005).

SEVERAL POWERS

Darwin conceived of life like form. Life consists of several powers. "There is grandeur in this view of life, with its several powers," (Darwin C., 1872, p. 429). According to Darwin, life comprises several powers or according to Newtonian philosophy, different types of forces (Janiak, 2016).

Life is a metaphysical element "originally breathed by the Creator into a few forms or into one" (Darwin C., 1872, p. 429). According to Darwin, selection and variation were the products of these several powers (Janiak, 2016). Life was breathed into a few forms, or one and "from so simple a beginning endless forms most beautiful and most wonderful have been, and are being, evolved" (Darwin C., 1872, p. 429).

The concept of a "few forms" implies an element of spontaneous generation. According to this tenet, several species and differentiated species emerged at the time that the creator breathed life into these few forms. Darwin wrote, "From passages in Genesis, it is clear that the colour of domestic animals was at that early period attended to" (Darwin C., 1872, p. 25).

FIXED UNIVERSAL LAWS

Newton's first law states: "Every object persists in its state of rest or uniform motion in a straight line unless it is compelled to change that state by forces impressed on it" (Smith G., 2008). Darwin contended that natural selection proceeds as a straight line. Referred to as orthogenesis or straight-line evolution, Darwin contended the goal of evolution is to increase the complexity of species upon a progressive straight-line principle based on natural selection. Evolution, therefore, is the product of a fixed universal law of natural selection or predestination set in motion to cause species to evolve into higher and more complex forms (Darwin C., 1872).

NATURAL SELECTION PROCESSES

Darwin made a distinction between the term natural selection and selection. Selection is an instinctive choice or practice in which humans or other species engage. There are two types of selections, instinctive selection driven by natural selection, and conscious effort or decision. Agriculturists, for example, use crossbreeding to improve the quality of their stock. Also, some species in their natural habitat engage in different forms of selective mating. Selection processes driven by natural selection are the product of inherent instinct to fulfill orthogenesis. However, because purposeful selection fulfills the cause of orthogenesis, purposeful selection is also a natural selection process (Darwin C., 1872).

Darwin contended the causes of this predeterminism and predestination within the natural selection processes are not known. This predeterminism is above and beyond the control of man. "...Natural Selection, we shall hereafter see, is a power incessantly ready for action, and is as immeasurably superior to man's feeble efforts, as the works of Nature are to those of Art." (Darwin C., 1872, p. 49). Natural selection, therefore, is a guiding principle occurring at a higher level of fixed universal laws and is superior to human efforts of selectivity.

ORTHOGENESIS

Orthogenesis is a combined form of two Greek words, ὀρθός orthós, meaning straight, and γένεσις genesis, meaning origin (Liddell & Scott, 2007). Darwin contended that orthogenesis was determined when life originated. Life, within the context of human existence on the planet, began at the time the Creator breathed life into "a few forms or into one" (Darwin C., 1872, p. 429).

Darwin posited that from the inception of creation, species continue to evolve. Darwin wrote that: "...whilst this planet has gone cycling on according to the fixed law of gravity, from so simple a beginning endless forms most beautiful and most wonderful have been, and are being, evolved..." (Darwin C., 1872, p. 429).

In modern evolutionary thought, this straight line of evolution or orthogenesis is the evolutionary pathway the force that directs natural selection causes species to move through automatically. This orthogenetic pathway of evolution has a fixed, predetermined goal. The force behind natural selection directs species to this goal (Darwin C., 1872).

This orthogenetic process occurs because species have instinctive biological sensitivity to environmental conditions. These environmental conditions include the geophysical environments as well as the sociocultural and moral environment (Belsky et al., 2009).

Humans, for example, according to Darwin, will not evolve into a different species, but will become increasingly complex to increase survivability. However, there are several human subspecies. Subspecies are evolving to their orthogenetic goals. Some subspecies are vulnerable, while others have more advantages to increase their survivability.

Applied to APR, APR is an example of predestined orthogenesis. APR is instinctive aggression directed toward less-fit members of species. As such, gender-biased aggression might be part of this orthogenetic process. Additionally, this conceptualization of differential survivability has been applied to outline differential rates of APR using criteria such as ethnic, grouping, and regional location.

Based on these tenets, APR could be interpreted as an interplay between self-preservation and orthogenesis. Self-preservation is an instinctive higher principle. As such, when considering APR, practitioners must bear in mind that both the perpetrator and the victim might be viewing their behaviors within the context of self-preservation. Practitioners must consider the relevance and applicability of self-preservation vis-à-vis APR.

According to evolutionary theory, APR is an orthogenetic natural selection evolutionary development process. The higher principles of natural selection to orthogenesis will prevail. In the long-run APR will cause unfit members of the species to be eliminated (Belsky & Pluess, 2009; Darwin C., 1882).

The implications of orthogenesis for practitioners include considerations whether the perpetrator views the victim as weak, unfit, or vulnerable. Further, practitioners should analyze the internalized worldview of perpetrators and victims, to assess their perspectives on elements such as predestination, predetermination, and orthogenesis.

According to Darwin, orthogenesis is intertwined in the variation and predestination processes. Darwin presented additional hypotheses that included accidental random mutation, pangenesis, gemmules, reproductive advantage, selective mating, and differential evolutionary rates to advance his theory of evolution by means of natural selection (Darwin C., 1872).

The orthogenetic hypothesis comprises two elements, innateness as a driving principle and orthogenesis or evolutionary directedness toward fixed goals. According to the internal or innate driving law, the organism seeks to perfect itself through selective variations of its constituent parts. These constituent parts work together and are involved in the orthogenetic process through directed random mutations (Darwin C., 1872; Thieme, 1952).

ELEMENTS OF NATURAL SELECTION

Darwin's conception of Common Descent has two plausible interpretations. Either each species emerged from a single genus or few genera, or all species came from a single genus or a few genera. Darwin continues his discussion of common descent in his later publication (Darwin C., 1882). In his title, "Common Descent," Darwin proposed that humans emerged from a common progenitor. Based on this work, evolutionists apply the second conception that all species emerged from a common genus and developed several theories to substantiate this application (Darwin C., 1872).

Darwin conceived of species of birds as coming from the same genus. In his earlier works, Darwin implied that each race was a subspecies originating from the same genus. Darwin applied this conception to human races, differentiating between barbarians, savages, and the favoured races.

According to Darwin, each race could be a distinct species. Although all humans came from the same progenitor, some races had attained higher complexities because they were at a higher stage of evolution. Some human subspecies were superior because of natural selection (Darwin C., 1868; 1882).

NATURAL SELECTION, ADAPTATION, AND VARIATION

Darwin engaged in observations of animals, which he believed adapted. Based on his observations, Darwin determined that adaptation involved natural selection, selection, and environmental conditions (Darwin C., 1872).

The power to engage in variation serves two purposes, to facilitate adaptation to environmental conditions, and more importantly, to allow variations to improve fitness for survivability. In the long-term, variation is an orthogenetic mechanism.

Adaptation to environmental conditions can be viewed as a micro level alteration, while adaptation for fitness serves the purpose of long-term overarching evolution. This long-term overarching evolutionary process occurs due to orthogenesis (Darwin C., 1872).

VARIATION FOR ADAPTATION

Darwin discussed adaptations and variations as two elements of evolution. Darwin wrote: "For natural selection acts by either now adapting the varying parts of each being to its organic and inorganic conditions of life; or by having adapted them during past periods of time" (Darwin C., 1872, p. 166). Organic conditions refer to the sentient physical conditions, and inorganic refers to insentient or metaphysical conditions.

The forces of natural selection, therefore, cause the different parts of each being to adapt to both the physical and metaphysical conditions to which the organism or being is exposed. Adaptation causes variations among species and can occur in specific parts of the organism according to the law of growth (Darwin C., 1872).

Some modern-day scientists accept that the inorganic conditions influence genetic inheritance. For example, indirect fetal exposure to inorganic conditions could lead to congenital disorders (Gong et al., 2017).

As such, genetic research involves the study of changes or adaptations due to inorganic or metaphysical conditions that occurred in the past. The species' genome is indicative of changes or adaptations due to past conditions. The individual's phenotype implicates physical and metaphysical conditions to which it is currently exposed.

Within life, there is a power that causes variation. Life, which was breathed into a few forms or one, has inherent power. This intrinsic power which resides in life endows the form or forms with the ability to differentiate. The power to variate resulted in speciation (Darwin C., 1872).

Peacocks and pigeons are variations of species of birds. Darwin wrote that different races might be distinct species, but they can more aptly be described as subspecies that came from a common progenitor. The common progenitor had distinctive qualities that characterized humans (Darwin C., 1882).

At the time of writing, Darwin appears to have thought that different racial and ethnic groups were subspecies of humans in the same manner that he described subspecies of birds or dogs. Variations distinguished the different subspecies. Assorted colors in birds were examples of these variations. In humans, intelligence could be used to distinguish variations among the various human subspecies.

All human subspecies have intelligence. Although intelligence is beneficial to all species, the force that directs natural selection determines that some species and subspecies will be endowed with intelligence while others will not have this endowment. For example, intelligence is present in humans but not in some nonhuman species.

Intelligence tests were once thought to demonstrate differences in intelligence among human subspecies. Intelligence is one of the qualities inherent in life or pangenes that causes variation in human subspecies. Because there are different human subspecies, some human subspecies will have higher intelligence than other human subspecies. However, even among those human subspecies with lower intelligence, there will be members of those human subspecies with higher intelligence than other members in that subspecies (Darwin C., 1872).

Darwin contended that a broad range of intelligence and intellectual capacity exist among human subspecies. Within each subset of the population, there exists a range between high and low intelligence.

Intelligence, however, is cultivated through habit and environmental conditions. As such, the range of intelligence among savages and barbarians is lower when compared with the favoured races. Differences in the distribution of intelligence among human subspecies are due to natural selection. Additionally, differences in intelligence can only imply differences in brain power (Darwin C., 1882).

The cause or driving element behind natural selection that causes speciation and variation is not known (Darwin C., 1872).

> *Why have not apes acquired the intellectual powers of man? Various causes could be assigned; but as they are conjectural, and their relative probability cannot be weighed, it would be useless to give them. A definite answer to the latter question ought not to be expected, seeing that no one can solve the simpler problem, why, of two races of savages, one has risen higher in the scale of civilisation than the other; and this apparently implies increased brain power.*
> *(Darwin C., 1872, p. 181).*

INSTINCT AND VARIATION

Two innate qualities, instinct, and variability aid the processes of natural selection (Darwin C., 1872). Darwin defined instinct as "an action... when performed by an animal, more especially by a very young one, without experience, and when performed by many individuals in the same way, without their knowing for what purpose it is performed, is usually said to be instinctive" (Darwin C., 1872, p. 205).

Darwin identified instinct as different from learned behaviors. Aggression is instinctive and serves self-preservation and orthogenetic purposes. The instinct that promotes the purpose of natural selection and straight-line evolution is as "important as corporeal structures for the welfare of each species" (Darwin C., 1872, p. 206).

According to Darwin, instinct can vary because of different conditions of life. Natural selection is the originator of instinct. Instinct is a principle which guides species to engage in reproductive and survivability behaviors to promote straight-line evolution. Making a distinction between instinct and habit, Darwin argued further "that the effects of habit are in many cases of subordinate importance to the effects of the natural selection" (Darwin C., 1872, p. 206).

UNITY OF TYPE AND SPECIATION

The orthogenetic process occurs within species so that each species is proceeding to increased survivability within the fixed context of that species. Darwin contended "that all organic beings have been formed on two great laws—Unity of Type, and the Conditions of Existence" (Darwin C., 1872, p. 166).

The Unity of Type is a natural law responsible for speciation. The unity of type is one of the several powers that reside in life. Because the unity of type resides among the several powers of life, one species will not evolve into another species (Darwin C., 1872).

While the unity of type determines the boundaries or limits of the characteristics and traits that define a species, the force directing natural selection assigns characteristics, traits, and behaviors differentially to species or groups within the species' limits (Darwin C., 1872). For example, distinguishing characteristics and traits differentiate one species of birds from another species of birds. These characteristics or traits might be things, such as beaks and wingspan. A bird, for example, may speciate or differentiate in ornithological characteristics and traits, but will not develop human characteristics and traits (Darwin C., 1882).

MUTATION

Speciation or the development of species was a necessary step that caused organisms to adapt to unique environmental conditions. Speciation occurs because environmental conditions trigger a random mutation. Mutations are random and accidental. According to Darwin, mutations[27] cause slight variations in genera to produce different species. Over time, these slight variations accumulated causing complex life-forms to develop from either a single genus or relatively few genera (Darwin C., 1872).

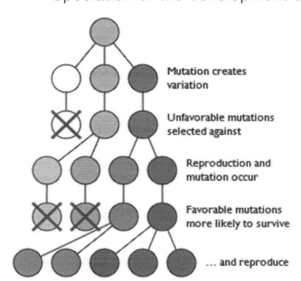

Mutation creates variation

Unfavorable mutations selected against

Reproduction and mutation occur

Favorable mutations more likely to survive

... and reproduce

Figure 19-3 How Adaptations Develop

ACCIDENTAL GENETIC MUTATION

Some species and subspecies have better survivability than others because of random mutation. According to Darwin, the random mutation process is essential to the natural selection orthogenetic process (Sawyer, Parsch, Zhang, & Hartl, 2007).

Darwin contended that chance, and not choice enabled some species to have better survivability than others. This chance is an element of natural selection. Harsh environmental conditions cause some species or species

---

[27] Figure 19-3 Elembis
(https://commons.wikimedia.org/wiki/File:Mutation_and_selection_diagram.svg), „Mutation and selection diagram", https://creativecommons.org/licenses/by-sa/3.0/legalcode

members to die. The same harsh condition will cause mutational changes in those species and species members that survive harsh environmental conditions.

The force that directs natural selection causes harsh environmental conditions that would wipe out weaker species and species members and force the better fit species and species members to survive. The force that directs natural selection causes harsh environmental conditions to occur randomly. Natural selection also randomly choose some species members to have better inherent life qualities that would allow them to survive harsh environmental conditions.

Consequently, survivability is due to random natural selection based on two natural selection principles. The first natural selection principle is randomly-caused harsh environmental conditions. The second natural selection principle is random differentiation that causes some species and species members to have better inherent qualities that would give them increased survivability.

Because natural selection functions on a higher principle of fixed universal laws, it occurs differentially among species and individuals within the species. Randomly occurring mutations is the mechanism whereby this chance element of natural selection occurs. The organism does not specifically try to produce a characteristic or trait beneficial to the environment. It is by chance that natural selection endowed some organisms with the ability to evolve via random mutation (Holterhoff, 2014).

According to the tenets of pangenesis, altered pangenes due to mutation pass on to subsequent generations as heritable characteristics and traits (Holterhoff, 2014). Some random mutations might be beneficial for survival. If the random mutation is beneficial, then it can become heritable survivability or reproductively advantageous characteristics or traits. Although these beneficial heritable characteristics, traits, and behaviors might be passed on, even within species destined for evolution into higher and more complex forms, there are members of those species that will not manifest those beneficial heritable characteristics, traits, and behaviors (Sawyer et al., 2007). Variability, adaptation, and environment are factors of mutation (Santiago & de Visser, 2003; Sniegowski & Lenski, 1995).

Current research indicates that mutation can be beneficial, bad, or indifferent. Darwin purported that in the orthogenetic evolutionary process, accident or random mutation might occur that is beneficial for survival. However, current research shows that even if a beneficial accidental random mutation occurs, it is statistically unlikely that those beneficial random accidental mutations pass on to subsequent generations Moreover, accidental random mutation occurs at such a minuscule rate that it does not provide support that mutations can account for an evolutionary process (Sawyer et al., 2007; Sniegowski & Lenski, 1995).

THE PROCESS OF GENETIC DRIFT

Darwin also contended that species evolve very gradually over extended periods and that species go through transitional states. Natural laws of selection determine these transitional stages.

Each transitional stage brings the organism closer to its orthogenetic goals. At each transitional stage, the species has an improved gene pool. This improvement in the gene pool is genetic drift. Genetic drifts occur slowly, but accumulatively and serve the purpose of straight-line evolution (Darwin C., 1872).

> *Variations neither useful nor injurious would not be affected by natural selection, and would be left either a fluctuating element, as perhaps we see in certain polymorphic species, or would ultimately become fixed, owing to the nature of the organism and the nature of the conditions.*
> *(Darwin C., 1872, p. 63).*

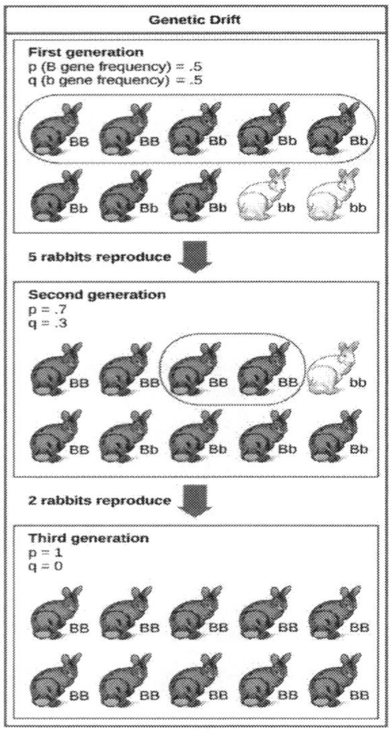

Figure 19-4
Genetic Drift

Genetic drift[28] is the process whereby a mutation or variation becomes fixed in a polymorphic species. A polymorphic species is one where the species exists in different forms. These differences in form do not appear to be induced by environmental conditions because the different forms of the species exist within the same habitat or environment.

Darwin contended that because different morphs or forms live in the same habitat, it establishes the case for genetic transmission as the mechanism that causes these differences. Even within species, there are differences among the members because of genetic differences. These genetic differences are due to pangenes. These within species differences also strengthened Darwin's argument that pangenes, a natural selection mechanism, cause these intraspecies differences, even though species members share the same habitat.

These differences occur randomly within the population. Because these differences occur randomly, it is an indication of orthogenetic directed mutation. The innate

---

[28] Figure 19-4 OpenStax, Rice University
(https://commons.wikimedia.org/wiki/File:Genetic_drift_in_a_population_Figure _19_02_02.png), https://creativecommons.org/licenses/by/4.0/legalcode

tendency for evolution to a speciation goal, such as a higher level of fitness or complexity is due to orthogenetic directed mutation. An interplay between innateness and directed random mutation is the internal mechanism or orthogenetic driving force (Ulett, 2014).

Genetic drift is a long process and indicative of the incremental stages of evolution through which a species passes. As random mutations that produced specific heritable characteristics and traits become more common in a population, mutation becomes fixed. This fixing of the mutation gives that species new distinguishing characteristics and traits.

Henceforth, these distinguishing characteristics and traits transmit to the entire species. The existence of these distinguishing characteristics or traits causes the species to drift forward into a higher and more complex form.

Orthogenesis was a unifying concept integrating natural selection and pangenesis. Efforts to support the tenets of orthogenesis with scientific data proved to be difficult; however, the conception of genetic drift is a thread that continues some aspects of orthogenesis (Star & Spencer, 2013).

Star and Spencer (2013) used simulated models and mathematical equations to assess the effects of genetic drift and gene flow on selectivity and genetic variations. The researchers concluded that genetic drift randomly changes allele frequencies from generation to generation. The researchers reasoned that while genetic drift mostly lowers the number of genetic variations found in their model. In larger populations, there will be increased variations for high levels of gene flow

Scientists argue that difficulties exist in determining whether an external force directs natural selection toward orthogenesis. However, the case of genetic drift suggests that internal genetic mechanisms lead to genetic drift. Evidence of genetic drift might provide support for orthogenetic drift.

PANGENESIS

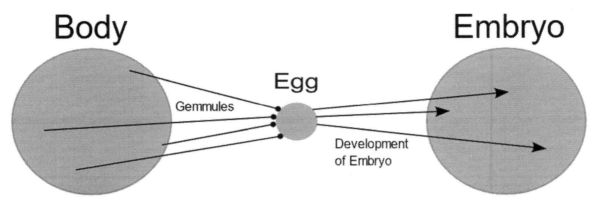

Figure 19-5 Darwin's Pangenesis

Darwin's concept of the transmission of random mutations formed the basis of pangenesis. Pangenesis is a hypothesis that arose from a conception of heredity held by early philosophers, such as Hippocrates.

Pan is a half-man and a half-goat Greek god. Pan distributed his seed to all living things. Pan engaged in sexual intercourse with humanoids and imparted his traits and characteristics to all humans descended from this lineage.

According to the pangenesis[29] theory, each parent gives equal amounts of all characteristics and traits to their offspring via pangenes. Pangenes exist in the sex-organs of both parents. By this means, pangenetic transmissions occur from parents to offspring (Holterhoff, 2014).

The chromosomal theory of inheritance emerged from pangenesis theory. According to modern theory, humans have germ cells and somatic cells. Sperms and ova are germ cells that carry equal amounts of heritable characteristics and traits from both parents (Liu & Li, 2012; 2014; Zou, 2014).

Although Darwin's theory of Pangenesis was refuted based on the results of earlier experiments, Liu and Li (2014) indicated that new research might be proving that Darwin's theory of pangenesis is valid. These authors argue that epigenetic inheritance, telegony, prion inheritance, ribonucleic acid (RNA) -mediated inheritance, and horizontal gene transfer are some of the new studies that support Darwin's pangenesis conceptualization.

---

[29] Figure 19-5 Ian Alexander
    (https://commons.wikimedia.org/wiki/File:Darwin's_Pangenesis.svg),
    https://creativecommons.org/licenses/by-sa/4.0/legalcode

GEMMULES

The existence of gemmules is another conceptualization that arose out of Darwin's pangenesis hypothesis. According to Darwin, gemmules are particles of inheritance. From this conception, a common belief persists that genes are materials or particles of characteristics and traits carried in cells (Darwin C., 1868).

CORRELATED GROWTH

This principle of the law of growth is an aspect of natural selection. Correlated growth is responsible for the confines of species. Variations will exist within species, but natural selection confines dogs to being dogs and varieties of dog. Likewise, natural selection determines the distinction between primates and humans (Darwin C., 1872).

Natural selection involves correlated growth. Darwin suggested correlated growth was due to "...other causes which lead to the many mysterious cases of correlation, which we do not in the least understand" (Darwin C., 1872, p. 171). Darwin referred to this principle as the law of growth.

NATURAL SELECTION AND SURVIVABILITY

Darwin's concept of natural selection was a speculative philosophical premise. In his conceptualization of natural selection, Darwin provides an explanation as to why some species are more populous than other species. He described survivability as the ability of an organism to remain alive and perpetuate itself and its species within the context of a harsh and hostile environment. Survivability explains differential survivability of species and subspecies (Darwin C., 1872).

Nature has various means to control populations. These are natural selection means such as epidemics, climate change, drought, famines, and harsh environmental conditions (Darwin C., 1872).

Natural selection[30], according to Darwin, is the process whereby a population declines because of the hostility of the environment. For example, a hostile environment would cause one subspecies of beetles with colors that made them easily spotted by predators to be killed off more quickly than a different subspecies of beetles with the ability to camouflage. Over time, the subspecies of beetles without the ability to camouflage will be killed off, and subspecies of beetles with the ability to camouflage will increase among the population of beetles. As such, according to Darwin, the environment is a significant aspect of the natural selection process (Darwin C., 1872).

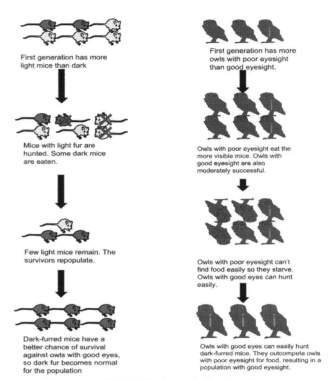

While the environment plays a role in eliminating unfit populations, Darwin proposed that humans must engage in actions to assist in the process of elimination of the unfit. Darwin contended that the favoured races were predetermined by means of natural selection to be the superior race. The favoured races must engage in actions that would assist in the process of natural selection. These actions should include strategies to cause undesirable populations to die off or decrease in number (Darwin C., 1872).

Figure 19-6 Natural Selection

NATURAL SELECTION AND DISPROPORTIONATE SURVIVABILITY

The conceptions of differential survivability and differential reproductive advantage have their origins in the theory of evolution by means of natural selection. The force that directs natural selection determined the "preservation of favourable individual differences and variations, and the destruction of those which are injurious" (Darwin C., 1872, p. 63). The specific purpose of natural selection is to produce fitness via orthogenetic processes. Fitness serves the purpose of long-term

---

[30] Figure 19-6 Ccaldwell19
(https://commons.wikimedia.org/wiki/File:Natural_selection_and_coevolution.sv
g), https://creativecommons.org/licenses/by-sa/4.0/legalcode

survivability. When unfit humans are eliminated, the human gene pool will become more superior (Darwin C., 1872).

According to the tenets of evolution by natural selection, races evolve unevenly. As such, some races become and will continue to become more highly evolved than others. The more highly evolved races have higher survivability than less evolved races. Hence there are differences in survivability among humans; the less evolved races are vulnerable. There is a disparate vulnerability in human subspecies. Vulnerability is at the core of differential survivability among human subspecies. Darwin attributed vulnerability to the overarching elements of natural selection, heredity, and environmental conditions (Darwin C., 1882).

Research indicates a higher rate of APR exists among minority races and populations (Minority Nurse Staff, 2013). This evolutionary tenet implies populations with higher rates of dysfunctionalities in child, intimate partner, and familial relationships are less evolved than those populations with a lowered risk for these dysfunctionalities (Darwin C., 1872; Darwin & Wallace, 1858).

According to the theory of evolution by natural selection, the individual's race is the result of natural selection. This argument suggests that higher occurrences of APR among specific populations might be due to predetermination and predestination according to natural selection principles.

Buss and Shackelford (1997) argued that aggression among humans might have been in response to the need for adaptation. Aggression could occur at the individual or group level. Co-opting the resources of others is one of the adaptive values of aggression (Buss & Shackelford, 1997).

Based on Buss and Shackelford (1997) arguments differences among human subspecies might be related to the adaptive value of co-opting the resources of others. Defending and attacking property, accumulation of resources, and restricting access to resources are a few strategies used to co-opt the resources of others. These strategies appear as sociocultural differences. Darwin, however, assigned these differences to genetics, hereditary transmissions, and orthogenesis (Buss & Shackelford, 1997).

REPRODUCTIVE ADVANTAGE

Darwin postulated reproductive advantage as a genetic survivability mechanism that renders favor to some species and vulnerability to others. The term reproductive advantage, like Darwin's concept of natural selection, can be misleading. One might think reproductive advantage means one individual or organism has an advantage that relates to their reproductive ability. Reproductive advantage does not mean that one organism has better reproductive rates because of superior biological reproduction capabilities. The term reproductive advantage means some organisms, individuals or group have a numerical advantage over another or have a larger population. The term reproductive advantage implies that a subspecies with a larger population is likely to have more members to engage in reproduction (Darwin C., 1872).

According to this tenet, some species or subspecies are more populous than other species or subspecies because of natural selection. Some species are endowed by natural selection with superior characteristics and traits, for example, the ability or inability of beetle subspecies to camouflage. Characteristics and traits, such as these, improve survivability because of the ability to adapt to harsh environments. The ability to adapt to harsh environments facilitates higher survivability and reproductive advantage for some subspecies when compared with other subspecies. A species has a reproductive advantage when members of that species have characteristics and traits that cause those species to be more populous than others (Darwin C., 1872).

According to this tenet, the reproductive advantage is due to heredity because some species possess characteristics or traits that will increase their survivability. Therefore, their survivability is due to heredity (Darwin C., 1872).

Through a process of deductive argument, Darwin presented that the numerical advantage one population has over another is due to heredity. A species has a numerical advantage because it can survive better in its environment. The species' ability to survive better caused their numbers to increase. There will be more members of that species reproducing because there are more of the species that survive. The numerical advantage of the species gives the species a reproductive advantage over those species with a smaller population. The species with a smaller population has a population vulnerability (Beutel, Friedrich, & Leschen, 2009).

The earlier example of the subspecies of beetles with the ability to camouflage provides an explanation of reproductive advantage. The inability to camouflage makes those beetles' subspecies more susceptible to the harsh environment. The hostile environment gave a reproductive advantage to beetles' subspecies with better camouflage ability. The ability of those beetles' subspecies to camouflage is due to their heredity. As such, the reproductive advantage is hereditary (Darwin C., 1868).

In the example with the beetles, those subspecies with more camouflage capability did not choose to mate with those species having better camouflage capabilities. The reduced ability to camouflage caused some subspecies to be easier targets for predator species. Those subspecies with reduced camouflage capabilities became less populous because they were killed, died off, or became extinct (Beutel et al., 2009).

On the other hand, those subspecies with the ability to camouflage did not make a conscious choice about their heredity; they naturally possessed those characteristics and traits because of natural selection. Those subspecies were able to camouflage because in the evolutionary process, there were mutations that caused those characteristics and traits to appear (Beutel et al., 2009).

According to Darwin's conceptualization, natural selection is not a neurophysiological process. For example, the ability of some subspecies of beetles to camouflage is not due to reproductive capabilities or abilities. A reproductive advantage does not mean members of the subspecies produce more offspring than members of species without a reproductive advantage. A reproductive advantage caused some subspecies to survive the hostility of the environment, such as predators. As such, there were more of those subspecies that survived; there is higher reproduction among them because they are more populous than those subspecies with lower survivability (Darwin C., 1868).

Consequently, a reproductive advantage is the result of heredity due to higher survivability. According to Darwin, this advantage was inherent in the subspecies' heredity. Due to this inherent advantage, those subspecies had greater perpetuity because they had a reproductive advantage. The converse to this argument is if there is a reproductive advantage that increases survivability, then population vulnerability is due to heredity (Darwin C., 1868).

Dawkins (1989) explained a reproductive advantage as an extended process. Phenotypic changes, genetic drift, and improvement in the gene pool are three elements of this extended process. Instinctive aggression is an inherent mechanism that facilitates this extended phenotypic process.

Phenotypic heritable mechanisms interact with aggression to accomplish reproductive advantage. Phenotypic mechanisms provide an explanation for male aggression, male aggression toward females, and the comparatively higher levels of aggression in men when compared to women (Dawkins, 1989).

When men engage in war, it increases their genetic survivability. Males' success in battle increases their reproductive value and their chances of mating with viable females, thereby increasing the likelihood of their continued genetic survival. As such, aggression is an integral aspect of reproductive advantage (Buss & Shackelford, 1997; Buss, 2009; Dawkins, 1989).

LOWERED SURVIVABILITY IS HEREDITARY

According to Darwin, some human subspecies have higher survivability and a reproductive advantage because of their heredity. Hence survivability is directly related to heredity. Heredity is due to pangenes, and pangenes are the products of natural selection.

The hypothesis of survivability and heredity implies vulnerable populations are not included among the favoured races. This hypothesis also suggests that vulnerable people do not have a reproductive advantage. Although vulnerable populations produce more offspring, this is not due to a reproductive advantage, but, rather, this is the product of debased moral habits. Nevertheless, these populations will readily succumb to natural disasters and harsh environmental conditions.

If APR is dysfunctional behavior, then it is a characteristic or trait that makes a population vulnerable. The concepts of reproductive advantage and heredity would then suggest APR occurs with higher frequency in vulnerable populations, and with lower frequency among the less vulnerable. Therefore, a higher prevalence of dysfunctional behaviors and disordered states, as evident in APR is an indication of inherited susceptibility to vulnerability.

RACE AND EVOLUTIONARY STAGES

Darwin applied his conceptualizations of speciation and natural selection to discuss differential rates of evolution, survivability, and vulnerability among different human subspecies.

> *man has been raised to his present state. But since he attained to the rank of manhood, he has diverged into distinct races, or as they may be more fitly called subspecies. Some of these, such as the Negro and European, are so distinct that, if specimens had been brought to a naturalist without any further information, they would undoubtedly have been considered by him as good and true species. Nevertheless, all the races agree in so many unimportant details of structure and in so many mental peculiarities, that these can be accounted for only by inheritance from a common progenitor; and a progenitor thus characterised would probably deserve to rank as man.*
> *(Darwin C., 1882, p. 608).*

A subspecies is a taxonomic classification below a species. Subspecies can crossbreed and interbreed. Subspecies can interbreed and produce fertile offspring. Subspecies can crossbreed and produce sterile offspring, such as the offspring of a horse and a donkey. Historically, offspring between European Whites and Enslaved Africans were called mulattoes, which was a derogatory epithet meaning human mules. The concept of a mulatto stemmed from the belief that certain superior traits could not transmit to these offspring.

Darwin proposed that all humans came from a common progenitor. However, human subspecies emerged because of interbreeding, crossbreeding, and environmental conditions. Interbreeding among the more fit individuals produced the higher ranks of humans or human species. Interbreeding occurred as a natural process because superior individuals occupied the same habitat. By a systematic rejecting of the inferior, a preferred species emerges.

> *It must not be supposed that the divergence of each race from the other races, and of all from a common stock, can be traced back to any one pair of progenitors. On the contrary, at every stage in the process of modification, all the individuals which were in any way better fitted for their conditions of life, though in different degrees, would have survived in greater numbers than the less well-fitted. The process would have been like that followed by man, when he does not intentionally select particular individuals, but breeds from all the superior individuals, and neglects the inferior. He thus slowly but surely modifies his stock, and unconsciously forms a new strain. So with respect to modifications acquired independently of selection, and due to variations arising from the nature of the organism and the action of the surrounding conditions, or from changed habits of life, no single pair will have been modified much more than the other pairs inhabiting the same country, for all will have been continually blended through free intercrossing.*
> *(Darwin C., 1882, p. 608).*

Figure 19-7 Evolution of Man

In his publication, "The Descent[31] of Man," Darwin reported that social, moral, and ethical behaviors were heritable characteristics and traits more common among highly developed civilized people and nations when compared with savages. These traits developed based on natural selection and adaptation and were elemental to survival. Differences in characteristics, traits, and behaviors distinguish the naturally selected favoured races from savages and barbarians (Darwin C., 1882).

Different races among humans were indications of different stages of evolution. Humans were at a higher stage of evolution than animals in the lower kingdom. Some races among humans were more highly evolved or at a higher stage of evolution than other races (Darwin C., 1882).

Savages, barbarians, indigenous peoples, the poor, and the degenerate were humans at a lower stage of evolution, and therefore, they were more susceptible to vulnerability than the favoured races. To support his argument of differential rates and stages of evolution, Darwin further argued that these characteristics, traits, and behaviors were different in humans when compared with animals not in their nature, but their degree. These differences were comparable to the differences among animals, such

---

[31] Figure 19-7 M. Garde
(https://commons.wikimedia.org/wiki/File:Human_evolution_scheme.svg),
„Human evolution scheme", https://creativecommons.org/licenses/by-sa/3.0/legalcode

as apes, monkeys, and dogs. Savages and barbarians were, therefore, closer to animals in the lower animal kingdom. Savages and barbarians possess characteristics, traits, and behaviors that Darwin referred to as weaknesses in body and mind. These differences were an indication of different stages of evolution. These differences presented as weaknesses in social and moral development (Darwin C., 1882).

In his thesis, Darwin contended that man evolved from an uncivilized state of savagery to highly complex, intelligent beings. Humans develop mental, intellectual, emotional, social, moral, and other psychological states as part of survivability. As such, humans in more highly civilized societies have higher moral and ethical behavior than savages. Savages being less civilized were lower in intelligence and moral-ethical behaviors. Darwin further contended that among savages, the weak in body and mind are eliminated (Darwin C., 1882).

SELECTIVE MATING

Darwin presented his argument of natural selection as a biological basis for selective mating. Selective mating is one of the means whereby natural selection occurs. Sexism is one of the elements in Darwin's tenets on selection. In selective mating, the superior male wins the affection of the favoured female.

Although the superior male does not kill the unsuccessful competitor, the unsuccessful inferior suitor is denied the opportunity to mate with the favoured female. The unsuccessful male can only mate with unfavourable females and produce inferior offspring.

By this means the superior male receives a reproductive advantage. Because the superior male mates with a preferred female, they produce more viable offspring that are superior, thereby increasing the number of superior males in society (Darwin C., 1872).

Darwin applied his concept of reproductive advantage to discuss measures to increase the favoured races' population. Darwin suggested efforts should be made to eliminate the weaknesses of body and mind. Darwin believed selective mating would provide an opportunity to increase the population of the favoured races and reduce the population of savages, poor, and degenerate. APR involves selective mating, infidelity, the battle among the sexes, and rivalry (Darwin C., 1882).

EXTERMINATION OF SAVAGES, AND BARBARIANS

Darwin described natural selection as social and environmental conditions, such as poverty, droughts, epidemics, and natural disasters that eliminated vulnerable races. Savages and barbarians are vulnerable and selected by nature and society for elimination.

Savages and barbarians are susceptible to elimination because of the natural selection process. As such, the favoured races should exterminate and replace the savage races. Darwin wrote: "At some future period, not very distant as measured by centuries, the civilized races of man will almost certainly exterminate and replace the savage races throughout the world" (Darwin C., 1882, p. 156).

According to this conception, vulnerability represents undesirable characteristics, traits, and behaviors. The process of natural selection, therefore, warrants elimination of vulnerable populations. When applied to victims as vulnerable populations, Darwinists, who contend APR is functional might contend that aggression is a valid strategy to eliminate vulnerability. An underlying assumption of this hypothesis is that perpetrators of APR are engaging in a natural selection process (Zukerman, 2011).

According to the concept of adaptation, those species with characteristics, traits, and behaviors better suited to the environment have higher survivability than those less well-adapted individuals (Darwin C., 1872). Populations less well-adapted to their environment have lower survivability and are more vulnerable than those populations that are better adapted to their environment (Darwin & Wallace, 1858).

Based on this rationale, individuals, families, and groups that are victims of APR are vulnerable. Vulnerable populations have lowered survivability when compared with other populations (Darwin & Wallace, 1858).

Heredity also involves the transmission of social-moral characteristics, traits, and behaviors. Darwin's conception of natural selection has implications for vulnerable populations. The conception of natural selection suggests vulnerable populations have heritable intellectual, social-moral, and cultural disabilities and impairments that negatively impinge on their survivability. Within this context, aggression against vulnerable populations is an acceptable strategy.

This combination of natural selection, variation, heredity, and environment determines survivability and vulnerability. As such, Darwin contended that "... the intemperate suffer from a high rate of mortality, and the extremely profligate leave few offspring" (Darwin C., 1882, p. 138), "... the intemperate, profligate, and criminal classes, whose duration of life is low" (Darwin C., 1882, p. 139).

Weaknesses in Darwin's Theory

Darwin identified several weaknesses in his theory. Darwin did not explain how the earliest life form came into existence. Some evolutionary scientists propose that the earliest life-form emerged from inorganic substances. However, scientists are still attempting to explain the process whereby inorganic changed its form to become living organisms (Darwin C., 1872; Oparin, 1957; Peretó et al., 2009).

The second weakness Darwin identified was finding evidence to support an unbroken chain of evolutionary development. Darwin contended his concept of evolution, occurring due to a gradual change, was a speculative hypothesis. However, Darwin confessed he was unable to find evidence to support his hypothesis that evolution was the result of an unbroken chain of events that resulted in the development of humans to become a higher life-form. Nevertheless, subsequent scientists have sought to provide evidence of this unbroken chain. So far, the evidence presented to support the concept of an unbroken chain of events has proven to be elusive, and there have been several retractions of evidence previously presented (Glansdorff, Xu, & Labedan, 2008).

Darwin contended that human species descended from a common progenitor:

> *We thus learn that man is descended from a hairy, tailed quadruped, probably arboreal in its habits, and an inhabitant of the Old World. This creature, if its whole structure had been examined by a naturalist, would have been classed amongst the Quadrumana, as surely as the still more ancient progenitor of the Old and New World monkeys. The Quadrumana and all the higher mammals are probably derived from an ancient marsupial animal, and this through a long series of diversified forms, from some amphibian-like creature, and this again from some fish-like animal. In the dim obscurity of the past we can see that the early progenitor of all the Vertebrata must have been an aquatic animal, provided with branchiæ, with the two sexes united in the same individual, and with the most important organs of the body (such as the brain and heart) imperfectly or not at all developed. This animal seems to have been more like the larvæ of the existing marine Ascidians than any other known form. (Darwin C., 1882, p. 609).*

While Darwin contended that human species descended from a common progenitor, he also alludes to the 'theory of preexistence.' In antiquity, the theory of preexistence is a theory that an Old World of prehistoric times existed. Darwin suggested that a closely-allied preexisting species in the Old World interbred with lower life-forms that would now be classed as quadrumana.

Evolutionists have also been able to provide evidence of an interspecies, but gaps in the fossil records persist. Despite these shortcomings, evolutionists contend that evolutionary theory is the only valid explanation for life, the origin of life, and the origin of species (Glansdorff et al., 2008).

Darwin contended, "...Natural selection acts only by taking advantage of slight successive variations; she can never take a great and sudden leap, but must advance by short and sure, though slow steps." (Darwin C., 1872, p. 156). Thus, Darwin concluded, "If it could be demonstrated that any complex organ existed, which could not possibly have been formed by numerous, successive, slight modifications, my theory would absolutely break down." (Darwin C., 1872, p. 146). Such a complex organ would be known as an "irreducibly complex system" (Meyer, 2013).

The contention that complex organs are composed of an irreducibly complex system has been the source of the severest criticism of his theory of evolution. An irreducibly complex system is one that comprises multiple parts, all of which are necessary for the system to function. Every individual part is integral. As such, such a system cannot have evolved slowly, piece by piece. Each component is integral to the entire system. If one part of the system is absent or improperly developed, it will cause the system to fail (Glansdorff et al., 2008; Meyer, 2013).

CONCLUSION

According to Darwin, species evolve based on selection and natural selection. Natural selection is a process of natural law that causes species to evolve in a straight line to become more complex. According to Darwin, fitness or survivability is elemental to evolution.

Instinct plays a role in this evolutionary process. Darwin contended that instinct originates from natural law. Some behaviors, such as polyandry, sexual promiscuity, and infanticide, are non-instinctive behaviors. Darwin concluded, "Our early semi-human progenitors would not have practiced infanticide or polyandry; for the instincts of the lower animals are never so perverted" (Darwin C., 1882, p. 46).

Although Charles Darwin has been credited as the father of the theory of evolution, the conception of evolution as an explanation of human origin spans several centuries before the time Darwin presented his theory. Charles Darwin used the theory of evolution to explain human behavior and survivability, reproductive advantage, and vulnerability differences among human subspecies. Despite its shortcomings, the evolutionary theory continues to inform and undergird theoretical development, research, and practice.

CHAPTER REVIEW

REVIEW QUESTIONS

1. Choose any two tenets of Darwin's evolution by natural selection.
   a. Explain each tenet.
   b. Assess their implications for APR.

CHAPTER TWENTY
SOCIAL DARWINISM AND EUGENICS

CHAPTER PREVIEW

Darwin's theory of evolution by natural selection and its tenet survival of the fittest was used to perpetuate the doctrines of social Darwinism and eugenics. The theory of eugenics inculcates that some races are selected by natural selection for decimation. Social Darwinism and eugenics are principles to promote the survivability of the superior race and the decimation of vulnerable populations.

In this chapter, there will be a discussion of the principles of social Darwinism and eugenics. There is a discussion of key proponents of eugenics, viz. Herbert Spencer and Gregor Mendel, beneficial random mutation, and the albino theory of race.

According to the World Health Organization (WHO), there is a disparity of aggression and victimization among minority populations. However, there is also a link among vulnerable populations, socioeconomic deprivation, and cultural differences. These may be the connection between race and vulnerability.

Eugenicists encouraged research in genetics as a means to substantiate innate superiority and vulnerability. Some geneticists also report a disproportionately higher risk of vulnerability among minority populations. Minority populations also have a racial component. Although geneticists continue to seek out a causal association between race and genetic predispositions to vulnerability, some researchers are indicating that the associative link is too small. Further, there may be flaws in the statistical methodology used to establish this association.

PURPOSE AND LEARNING OBJECTIVES

PURPOSE

Evolutionary theory undergirds the tenets of Social Darwinism, gene theories, and eugenics. The purpose of this chapter is to understand the basic principles of Social Darwinism, Eugenics, and Gene Theory that impinge on dysfunctionalities and disordered states as evident in APR.

LEARNING OBJECTIVES

After studying this chapter, the reader should

1. have an increased understanding of the basic tenets of Social Darwinism, Eugenics, and Gene Theory; and
2. understand the implications of Social Darwinism, eugenics, and Gene Theory for vulnerability, dysfunctional behaviors and disordered states, such as APR.

KEY TERMS AND DEFINITIONS

Eugenics

Eugenics is a targeted practice or policy aimed at reducing those persons and populations with genetic defects or those perceived to possess undesirable traits or negative eugenics. Eugenics emerged out of Darwinism, tenets of evolution, and neo-evolutionary theories. Eugenics is a belief system based on the tenets of survivability, the survival of the fittest, vulnerability, and reproductive advantage (Goering, 2014).

Social Darwinism

The concept of social Darwinism stemmed from the application of natural selection and reproductive advantage to the socioeconomic systems. Social Darwinists contend that within the context of society and the economy, the implementation of programs, measures, and policies should aim at eliminating the weak and the unfit by promoting the interest and well-being of the favoured races (Claeys, 2000; Spencer, 1852).

INTRODUCTION

Darwin's theory of evolution undergirds theories related to survivability. Social Darwinism, eugenics, and gene theory emerged from Darwin's theory of evolution. These foundational theories continue to inform research into behaviors that impinge on the dynamics of survivability, vulnerability, and APR.

Social Darwinism is a discriminatory ideology aimed at perpetuating and increasing the susceptibility of vulnerable populations. An examination of Social Darwinism will shed light on some of the genetic assumptions used overtly and covertly to validate and sanction policies that foster APR against vulnerable individuals and populations.

SURVIVAL OF THE FITTEST

Darwin concluded that natural selection is a process toward straight-line evolution. The natural selection process in straight-line evolution will eliminate the vulnerable and unfit. In his title, "On the Origin of Species" (or more completely, "On the Origin of Species by Means of Natural Selection, or the Preservation of the Favoured Races in the Struggle for Life"), published on 24 November 1859, Darwin contended that the favoured races should assist the natural selection process by engaging in selective mating, selective crossbreeding, and interbreeding.

Figure 20-1 Herbert Spencer

HERBERT SPENCER

The term survival of the fittest was coined by eugenicist Herbert Spencer seven years before Darwin used the term to explain natural selection. Herbert Spencer (1820 – 1903) was an English philosopher, who believed there was competition among humans for survival. Spencer wrote at a time when some officious members of the British elite were seeking legislation on social reforms.

Spencer[32] argued legislation that sought to help the poor by providing things such as, education, medical care, and religious instruction was detrimental to society. By providing such care, the governing body would cause the poor and degenerate to increase their survivability. The poor and degenerate would produce more children, thereby increasing the number of poor, inferior, and degenerate. Consequently, this would increase the burden on the government. Spencer believed the government should not implement social reforms and welfare programs. This way, the poor and degenerate would die out, and the wealthier people in society would survive. Darwin echoed these sentiments (Darwin C., 1872; 1882; Spencer, 1864).

Spencer was an avid supporter of Charles Darwin. Spencer believed Darwin's hypothesis that crossbreeding animals provided evidence that the wealthy should produce offspring with the wealthy. This way, the poor would die off. Darwin further expounded that the tendency of civilized men from the favoured races to provide medical care and social support, by building asylums for the imbecile, the maimed, and the sick was a detrimental incident of social and moral development. These actions might cause the number of savages to increase. On the one hand, savages tended to marry less and therefore might not bear as many offspring. On the other hand, when savages married less and bore a proliferation of bastardy children, whom they will not care for, by these means savages are fulfilling the mandate of natural selection by precipitating the early death and disability of their offspring (Darwin C., 1882).

The uneven occurrence of APR among vulnerable populations are reflections of Darwin's concept regarding the elimination of vulnerable populations and Spencer's advisory on policy development. The differential occurrences of APR among vulnerable populations are marked by ethnic, cultural, and geopolitical boundaries.

There are different conceptualizations of APR. These varying concepts determine the types of behaviors included in this phenomenon. The availability of programs and services to treat APR, criminal policies, enforcement measures, and other intervention measures to address APR also define the uneven occurrence of APR among vulnerable populations.

Social Darwinists and eugenicists correlated deprived sociocultural and economic environments with innate genetic defects. The socially deprived were genetically inept and were blamed for their sociocultural and economic environment.

Socioeconomic and Cultural Elements of APR

According to a WHO report, "Violence of all types is strongly associated with social determinants such as weak governance; the poor rule of law; cultural, social and gender norms; unemployment; income and gender inequality; rapid social change; and limited educational opportunities." (2014, p. 33). The WHO also reported concerning the disparity of services and service availability for those affected by APR:

> *Providing high-quality care and support services to victims of violence is important for reducing trauma, helping victims heal and preventing repeat victimization and perpetration. However, despite strong evidence linking experiences of violence to mental health problems, less than half of countries reported the availability of mental health services to address the needs of victims, ranging from two-thirds of countries in the Region of the Americas and the European Region, to only 15% in the African Region. (WHO, 2014, p. x).*

According to Darwin, social and moral development were also part of the evolutionary process, and the favoured races were far superior in body and mind when compared to savages and barbarians. As such, "with savages, the weak in body or mind are soon eliminated;" (Darwin C., 1882, p. 133).

The WHO recognized the correlation between socioeconomic and cultural elements with APR. The WHO (2014, p. 6), recommended the inclusion of social and educational policies relevant to multiple types of violence (e.g., incentives for youth at high-risk of violence to complete schooling, policies and strategies to reduce poverty in specific areas); to address the relationship between socio-moral development, poverty, and APR.

MAKING THE STRUGGLE SEVERE

Darwin proposed that the struggle for survival should be made severe for vulnerable populations by promoting those measures that would increase the chances of the success of the favoured races. These measures would cause the favoured races to rear the highest number of offspring. Measures that enhance the success of the favoured races would increase their numbers and give them a reproductive advantage. Making the struggle severe for unfit humans will reduce their survivability and increase their vulnerability (Darwin C., 1882).

Financial hardship and poverty are indicators of the severity of the struggle for vulnerable populations. Data reveal an association between poverty and APR. These correlations are consistent at the individual, group, and global levels.

Reporting at a Michigan seminar on family violence, Satyanathan and Pollack stated that:

> *Families who experience domestic violence are often also victims of poverty. Studies examining the association between domestic violence and poverty have found:*
>
> • *Of current welfare recipients in Michigan, 63% have experienced physical abuse and 51% have experienced severe physical abuse during their lifetimes [12].*
>
> • *Physical abuse/being afraid of someone was cited as the primary cause of homelessness (in a survey of homeless adults in Michigan) [7].*
>
> • *Half of homeless women and children report being victims of domestic violence [5,7].*
>
> *(Satyanathan & Pollack, 2001, p. 17).*

The WHO also established a link between socio-moral development, hardship, poverty, and APR.

> *Concentrated poverty is a visible aspect of disadvantage. Communities with high concentrations of poor and unemployed people also tend to have high levels of residential instability, making it difficult for people to establish common values and norms and to develop strong social ties and support networks. There is also a level of disorganization that compromises community participation and makes it difficult to exercise effective social control. These levels of economic and social disadvantage create the conditions for high rates of violence. They exacerbate social marginalization and also contribute to poor physical and mental health.*
> *(WHO, 2014, p. 34).*

Darwin also proposed that the favoured races should practice avid measures to reduce the population of savages and degenerate people. These endeavors should include rigorous promotional efforts to enhance the well-being of the favoured race, not promote the well-being of vulnerable populations, and engagement in rigorous strategies to decimate vulnerable and unfit populations. Social Darwinism and eugenics[33] arose from these tenets. Darwin's theory of evolution laid the foundation for the implementation of several measures, including compulsory sterilization, the Tuskegee Syphilis Experiment, genocide in Nazi Germany, population culling strategies, and other overt and covert strategies to curb the population growth of the unfavoured races (Levine, Williams, Kilbourne, & Juarez, 2012; West, 2011).

Figure 20-2 Eugenics Makes the World Go Round

---

[33] Figure 20-2 Glackens, L. M. (1913) Eugenics makes the world go 'round / L.M. Glackens., 1913. N.Y.: Published by Keppler & Schwarzmann, Puck Building. [Photograph] Retrieved from the Library of Congress,

THE LAW OF MENDEL

Gregor Mendel[34] (1822 – 1884) was a scientist and Augustinian friar

and abbot of St. Thomas' Abbey in Moravia. Unlike Darwin's proposition that both parents equally bequeath their characteristics, traits, and behaviors to their offspring, Mendel proposed that the transmission of traits depends on whether the genes are recessive or dominant. Although recessive genes can cause mutations, if both parents possess the recessive genes, the genes can become a dominant gene in offspring. Eugenicists and Social Darwinists apply Mendel's research on plant organisms to explain racial and ethnic differences (Mendel, 1996).

The favoured races were human subspecies that developed to higher ranks with greater survivability and reproductive advantage because of interbreeding

Figure 20-3 Gregor Mendel

among the fittest. Habitat facilitated successful selective interbreeding that increased survivability for the higher ranks of human species.

For example, in seeking to determine the evolutionary processes that caused a distinction between Caucasian and non-Caucasian races, some scientists fingered an interplay of random mutations, recessive genes, and habitat as the cause of albinism that produced Caucasians (Greaves, 2014; Manga, Kerr, Ramsay, & Kromberg, 2013).

Based on the notion that humans evolved from a common genus, some scholars identify Africa as the birthing ground for the ontogeny of the human genus. Proponents partisans to this line of reasoning suggest that random mutation and recessive genes produced albinism among African humans, hominins, hominids, or humanoids. According to this hypothesis, sexual intercourse, and interbreeding among humans with albinism produced a human subspecies with different hair, skin, and eye color (Genetics Society of America, 2015; Greaves, 2014).

---

[34] Figure 20-3 Hugo Iltis (https://commons.wikimedia.org/wiki/File:Gregor_Mendel_oval.jpg), https://creativecommons.org/licenses/by/4.0/legalcode

ALBINO THEORY OF RACES

An albino is a person or animal with a congenital absence of pigment in the skin, hair, and eye. Dysfunction in melanin production is symptomatic of albinism. According to Mendel's law of inheritance, albinism is a recessive gene that can transmit to subsequent generations. Albinism can become a dominant genetic characteristic if both parents have albinism or dominant albino genes. Albinism became a beneficial random mutation for those people that settled in colder climates. While the beneficence of the mutation was geographic, due to historical developments and processes, subspecies with a dominant number of persons affected with albinism manipulated social and economic laws and systems to establish hegemony over vulnerable populations (Greaves, 2014; Manga et al., 2013).

Some theorists dispute the proffer that the existence of the favoured races was the outcome of natural selection. These advocates altercated that the emergence of the favoured races was the offshoot of calculated historical processes that fostered poverty, racism, abuse, and dispossession at the expense of the poor (Dennis, 1995; Manga et al., 2013; Pocheville, 2015).

CRITICISMS OF SOCIAL DARWINISM AND EUGENICS

Evolutionists argue heritable characteristics and traits which transmit to subsequent generations occur as a neurobiological process. The idea that accidental beneficial random mutation is an essential element in this process is pivotal to evolutionary gene theory. One of the several criticisms of random mutation is that mutation does not specify environmental conditions to occur. The chances of a mutation being matched to an environmental condition are very unlikely, thereby reducing the role of random mutation as an evolutionary component. Also, random mutations tend to be deleterious rather than beneficial (Sniegowski & Lenski, 1995).

Despite these and other criticisms of the unlikelihood that random mutation was responsible for evolutionary speciation, scientists are continuing to seek out biological evidence to support the random mutation hypothesis of evolution by natural selection. Scientists are also researching whether neurobiological processes can cause some organisms to have a biological advantage over other organisms. The argument of reproductive advantage due to heredity makes an association between the random mutation and hostile environmental conditions (Pocheville, 2015).

Increasing evidence is emerging that race, as defined by Darwin and early evolutionists do not have a basis in genetics. Rather, race is a sociocultural concept that foster divisiveness and discrimination. Despite this, researchers continue to link genes and race.

The HapMap project is one such study being used to establish a link between race and genes. One of the objectives of the HapMap project researchers was to study the association of habitat, genetics, and geographic location in the human genome (Terwilliger & Hiekkalinna, 2006). As recent as 2015, Huang, Shu, and Cai (2015) reported a genetic basis of skin and eye color.

However, genome mappers recommend caution when attempting to make associations among race, genetics, and vulnerability. Genome mappers were only able to code 2.8% of the coding bases in the Human Genome Project. Human genome project researchers reported that the remaining 97.2% of genome bases that did not code was junk DNA. Further, researchers claim that only a small percent of the 2.8% of coding DNA, 99.9%, was similar among humans (National Research Council, Division on Earth and Life Studies, Commission on Life Sciences, Committee on Mapping and Sequencing the Human Genome, 1988).

MARGINALLY SMALL RACE – DNA ASSOCIATION

Huang et al. (2015) concurred that of the 2.8% coding genome bases, 99.9% was similar in all humans. The remaining 0.1% accounts for individual differences. Of that 0.1% of the coding bases, less than 15% correlates in any way with race. In addition to Huang et al. (2015), the National Institute of Mental Health (NIMH) further reported that research into the linkages among genes, susceptibility to vulnerability, psychiatric conditions, and APR was minuscule and weak (Huang et al., 2015; The Members of the Genetics Workgroup, 1997).

DISPROPORTIONATE RISK AMONG MINORITY POPULATIONS

Researchers indicate that minority populations, such as African-Americans, children, transgenders, and migrants, have a higher risk for dysfunctionalities and disordered states in their proximity relationships when compared with other populations. The concept that minority populations are vulnerable populations emerged from evolutionary theory (Wahowiak, 2015).

According to evolutionary tenets of reproductive advantage, susceptibility to a vulnerability in proximity relationships will occur with higher frequency among minority populations and with lower frequency among the favoured races. Further, these creeds associate conditions such as APR with genes as a mechanism of transmission (Huang et al., 2015; The Members of the Genetics Workgroup, 1997).

Nevertheless, NIMH (2013) acknowledged that "Although statistically significant, each of these genetic associations individually can account for only a small amount of risk for mental illness." The NIMH also indicated that these variations could not be "used to predict or diagnose specific conditions."

Terwilliger and Hiekkalinna (2006) fervently criticized studies seeking to determine a genetic basis for disorders, ethnicity, and gene-environmental interactions. Among their criticisms, Terwilliger and Hiekkalinna indicated that these studies "are based on theory, which assumes a multiplicative relationship among estimated correlation coefficients for different factors." (Terwilliger & Hiekkalinna, 2006, p. 429).

This erroneous statistical analytical process assumes a direct relationship between two factors, such as genes and violence. Based on this multiplicative relationship, statisticians convey that the higher component of one factor, such as genes, increases the likelihood of violence. Terwilliger and Hiekkalinna (2006) argued that even when both factors might be associative, the correlation does not necessarily mean causation. Presenting findings from studies based on assumptions of the multiplicative relationship among correlated factors conveys misleading conclusions (Terwilliger & Hiekkalinna, 2006).

Terwilliger and Hiekkalinna (2006) levied additional damming criticisms of statistical analysis using association-based mapping strategies to establish linkages between genes, ethnicity, and presentments such as medical conditions, psychiatric conditions, and aggression. Common-variant/common-disease hypothesis is the mainstay of these studies. However, Terwilliger and Hiekkalinna argue that these studies reinforce the impression of ethnic commonality of risk alleles. One such study that Terwilliger and Hiekkalinna stoutly criticized was the HapMap project.

Although Huang et al. (2015) supported the findings from the HapMap project, these authors reported that only 0.1% of bases in the entire genome makes a person unique. Huang et al. reiterated that 99.9% of the 0.1% bases in the entire human genome are similar. The human genome comprises merely 2.8% of coding DNA. Of this 2.8% only 0.1% is different. Less than 15% of this 0.1% or 0.00000378 or 000378% of humans have associative racial-alleles of skin and eye color, making such correlations difficult to establish (Huang et al., 2015).

Terwilliger and Hiekkalinna (2006) present a compelling refutation of correlation research involving such studies as genetics, ethnicity, and psychiatric conditions. The authors defended their position using statistical analysis and argued that "it is the exception, not the rule, for such conditional independence to hold in genetic studies of complex traits" (p. 434), and that "Conditional independence in genetics is rarely an appropriate assumption." (p. 434). Terwilliger and Hiekkalinna posited that geneticists have been avoiding using "classical statistical techniques in favor or complex likelihood-based models" (p. 434), which they use to make shaky inferences. Terwilliger and Hiekkalinna further stated:

> *The fact is that correlation coefficients are almost never multiplicative in practice, and in studies involving genetic risk factors for disease, we have known for decades that conditional independence of exposures never holds. In fact, this is the entire basis for the development of the complex likelihood methods we have relied upon for the past decades in understanding the genetic basis of simple diseases.*
> *(Terwilliger & Hiekkalinna, 2006, p. 434).*

CONCLUSION

Based on Darwin's conceptualization of survivability, reproductive advantage, and adaptation, there are specific populations at-risk for APR. These populations are likely to experience victimization. Survivability, reproductive advantage, and adaptation are the products of genes and heredity-environment interaction.

Proponents of Social Darwinism and eugenics endorsed Darwin's recommendation that the struggle should be made severe for vulnerable populations. A major question arising from this perspective is whether there are those that covertly endorse these tenets and to what extent, if any, these tenets are impacting policies related to vulnerable populations.

The force that directs natural selection is the driving element bolstering fitness and the struggle to survive. The struggle to survive reinforces disabilities such as poverty and social ills. The question arises whether those conditions that render a susceptible population vulnerable are due to the force that directs natural selection or whether they are the products of socioeconomic and cultural policies and practices. Although scientific evidence of accidental random mutation precludes the hypothesis that evolution occurs arbitrarily and by chance, by this means, it remains as a critical concept that guides research in molecular evolutionary biology and related disciplines (Sniegowski & Lenski, 1995).

Tenets fundamental to Social Darwinism and eugenics identify the socioeconomic and cultural environment as core elements in the evolutionary process (Goering, 2014; Spencer, 1852). Core doctrines of Social Darwinism and eugenics form the basis of research and studies that focus on dysfunctional behaviors and disordered states, such as APR. Theories influencing programs and services to address these dysfunctionalities and disordered states are reliant on evolutionary theory, Social Darwinism, eugenics, and gene theory to explain diathetic vulnerability or predispositional diathesis to APR (Gardner, 2016; Haig, 2012).

CHAPTER REVIEW

1. Identify a minority population and discuss the elements that constitute minority for this population.
2. Are some populations more susceptible to APR?
3. Conduct internet-based research that shows different APR prevalence among minority populations.
   a. Is there a disparity of APR among vulnerable populations?
   b. What might account for these differences?

CHAPTER TWENTY–ONE
PREDISPOSITIONAL VULNERABILITY

CHAPTER PREVIEW

Gene theory is an offspring of Darwin's theory of evolution by natural selection and its tenet of predispositional vulnerability. Due to natural selection, the favoured races have higher survivability. This tenet has been used to perpetuate racial disharmony under the auspices of Social Darwinism and eugenics.

In present-day genetics, the theory of predispositional vulnerability and ethnicity is considered as phenotypic expressions or risk alleles. One of the concepts of predispositional vulnerability emerged from Darwin's tenets of gemmules. This conception of gemmules resulted in the misconception that genes are particles of inheritance.

In this chapter, there will be a discussion of the misconceptions concerning genes as particles of inheritance. In this discussion, there will be a brief overview of the origin of genes as a concept emerging from pangenesis. In this overview, elements of philosophy such as realism and pragmaticism will be discussed.

These philosophical tenets were used to reframe mythical metaphysical constructs into physical concepts. The reframing of metaphysical constructs was elemental in the development of modern-day scientific research and study.

In this chapter, there will be a discussion of new disciplines and new research technologies such as technologies used in synthetic biological engineering. These new research technologies facilitate studies of metaphysical constructs as physical concepts and give impetus to modern-day genetic research.

Despite strides in genetic research, geneticists have not been able to establish an affirmative causal relationship between genes, ethnicity, and predispositional vulnerability. In addition to discussing genes as a mechanism of hereditary transmission, there will be a discussion of Darwin's tenets of race, evolutionary stages of development and species-to-species murder among humans.

PURPOSE AND LEARNING OBJECTIVES

PURPOSE

The purpose of this chapter is to examine findings from gene theory pertinent to APR.

LEARNING OBJECTIVES

After studying this chapter, the reader should

1. know the fundamental tenets of the gene and chromosomal theory of hereditary transmissions;
2. understand the methods and processes involved in genetic research;
3. be able to summarize the hypothetical assumptions of predispositional gene theory and common misconceptions about genes, genetic materials, and heredity;
4. be able to draw conclusions concerning the implications of predispositional gene theory, heredity, and DNA testing for APR;
5. understand the implications of these findings for APR; and
6. be able to critically appraise the applicability of gene theory and genetic research to APR.

KEY TERMS AND DEFINITIONS

Allele

Allele has two definitions, a traditional and a more loosely word usage.

Traditional definition: alternate forms of a gene, composed of one or more single nucleotide polymorphisms (SNPs).

More loosely: an SNP. For example, at a given position along a chromosome, most people might have the DNA base "A". A few might have an alternative sequence. Each defined type is an allele.

Genes

The word genes is a terminology used in the Genome Project to explain genetics. The stereochemistry or spatial relations of atoms and subatomic particles of conjoined deoxyribose and ribose that regulate protein synthesis and cell replication in a controlled cloned or asexual reproductive experiment. Stable, heritable characteristics, traits, and behaviors (Alberts et al., 2002).

Genetics

Genetics is a branch of study that uses a predictive model that establishes an association between DNA and RNA mechanisms and sequences (Alberts et al., 2002).

INTRODUCTION

Gene theory is an offspring of evolutionary theory (Ågren, 2016; Gardner, 2016). Darwin's conceptualization of pangenes and gemmules influence current research and practice related to genes and genetic materials (Darwin C., 1868). Gene theory and the chromosomal theory of inheritance provide explanations for sociocultural, medical, and psychiatric conditions. Genome mapping and research in genetics aim at finding genetic pathways responsible for predispositional vulnerability.

CLASSICAL AND MOLECULAR GENETICS

Molecular scientists conceive of genes differently than classical philosophers. Classical philosophers perceive that genes are underlying mechanisms that are responsible for the manifestation of characteristics, traits, and behaviors. These characteristics, traits, and behaviors are outward manifestations such as eye color, skin color, addiction, and drunkenness.

Whereas when molecular scientists refer to genes, they are making inferences based on mathematical calculations of abstract constructs. Molecular geneticists hypothesize that a gene is a stretch of DNA or RNA that determines a specific phenotypic trait.

Classical geneticists conceived of genes as a mythical, metaphysical non-tangible element governed by the force that directs natural selection. Based on this basic conceptualization, different human subspecies and subspecies are endowed with genes that are unique to the group. The endowment of genes made some human subspecies and species members superior and others inferior and led to orthogenesis. In classical genetics, the differences between the human subspecies and species members are to as the difference principle.

Classical philosophers applied their conceptualization of genes to make assumptions about different human subspecies and species members. These assumptions were fraught with discriminatory perception and racial superiority ideologies. These were identifiably eugenicists' ideologies.

Classical philosophers purported that genes were responsible for making some races superior and others inferior. The outward expressions of characteristics, traits, and behaviors, or phenotypic expressions were identified as being associated with genes. This conception of genes as an underlying mechanism that results in differences in phenotypic expressions is carried over into modern-day genetics at the molecular level.

THE DNA MOLECULE

Molecular genetics is founded on the conceptualization of the DNA molecule. The concept of the DNA molecule emerged from the theory of atoms. Atoms are concepts or ideas.

The concept of atoms and molecules is based on the idea that existences consist of both material and nonmaterial existences. Religious philosophies provide explanations of nonmaterial existences. Nonmaterial existences are explained as spiritual and metaphysical elements and entities. Atoms and molecules were conceptualized as spiritual and metaphysical entities and elements.

In ancient religion, there were philosophies concerning nontangible, metaphysical entities. The concept of atoms and molecules were taken out of ancient Greek and Hindu religion based on religious philosophies about metaphysics and nonmaterial existences.

Atoms and molecules were metaphysical elements and entities that are without tangible existences, but which were accepted as physical entities having a physical existence. Various rules of philosophy mandated that these metaphysical constructs and ideas be accepted as concrete, tangible existences. The philosophy of abstraction was developed to concretize metaphysical concepts and constructs from religious philosophies and integrate these into the scientific method (Russell, 2007).

Using theories of abstraction, religious philosophies concerning the characteristics and behaviors of metaphysical and spiritual existences were presented as mathematical formulae and equations. These philosophies concerning atoms and molecules were developed into theories of atoms and molecules and were applied to explain their behaviors. These philosophies were developed into scientific theory.

Mathematical and statistical calculations and experimentation using advanced technology substantiate atoms and molecules as a valid interpretation of life and existence. Abstract mathematical formulae and equations and their underlying philosophical tenets became undergirding assumptions in quantum physics and quantum mechanics. These calculations became integrated into the scientific method. Physicists apply the philosophy of abstraction to develop calculations that were used in physics (Russell, 2007; Swigon, 2009).

Until the 1980s, the concepts of atoms and molecules remained as hypothetical constructs. The modern-day conceptualizations of atoms and molecules were devised when scientists found a way to use imaging technology to identify representations of atoms and molecules.

In the 1980s technological developments allowed physicists to image and manipulate light particles on metal surfaces. Physicists applied previously developed mathematical formulae from quantum physics and quantum mechanics to calculate differences, movements, and other aspects of these minuscule particles. The ability to image, manipulate, and measure these particles were applied as validation for the theory of atoms and molecules. Molecular genetics is in large measure a combination of mathematical and statistical calculations and the imaging and manipulation of light particles (Palmer, 2009; Russell, 2007).

In 1953, James Watson, Francis Crick, Maurice Wilkins, and Rosalind Franklin figured out the calculations of the DNA molecule and conceptualized the molecule as a double helix mathematical structure. However, because the scientists conceptualizing the double helix structure of the DNA molecule were heavily influenced by eugenics beliefs and policies, there was a carry-over of the underlying assumptions from classical genetics into molecular genetics (BBC, 2019; Hubbard & Wald, 1999; Keller, 2013).

There are subtle differences in the conception of genes in molecular genetics and classical or traditional genetics. In classical or traditional genetics genes are conceptualized as a difference maker, whereas in molecular genetics, genes are hypothesized to be a chemical process.

The difference principle in classical genetics refers to the philosophy that genes are an underlying mechanism that is responsible for differences in phenotypic expressions. Classical geneticists apply the difference principle to make assumptions about superior and inferior human subspecies and species members. Genes were perceived as fixing the boundaries that differentiated between superior and inferior human subspecies and species members (Keller, 2013).

In molecular genetics, DNA is referred to as genes. The DNA molecule is a hypothetical construct that is linked to deoxyribonucleic acids in the nucleus of cells. Using imaging, microscopy technology, and calculations from molecular formulae and equations, scientists make inferences about chemical sequences and the way cell replication occurs during mitosis and meiosis (Keller, 2002).

There is some blurring of the lines between classical and molecular genetics. Some assumptions pertaining to genes and the difference principle rooted in eugenics were among these carryovers.

Some early molecular geneticists were avouched eugenicists. The aim of the early eugenicists was to find scientific support for racial superiority. Early eugenicists advocated that science, biology, and medicine should be employed in the movement to further eugenic mission and policies (Emerson, 1939; Ryle, 1938).

Early eugenicists employed calculations to assist in the establishment of mathematical and statistical formulations that could be used to prove their ideology. Among these were Francis Galton and Adolphe Quetelet that employed mathematical and statistical calculations to support their eugenics goals.

Quetelet gathered statistics that he determined to be normal characteristics, traits, and behaviors. Eugenicists used their ideas and standards to determine what they assessed to be normal characteristics, behaviors, and traits (Forth, 2005; Tylor, 1872).

Galton and Quetelet were eugenicists who did early work in mathematics and statistics to establish that population differences between human subspecies and species members were due to genetic variations. These conclusions were drawn based on mathematical computations (Forth, 2005; Johnson et al., 1985; Tylor, 1872).

Eugenicists continued to develop actuarial calculations concerning the atom and molecules. Actuarial calculations used in DNA analysis have their roots in the work of early eugenics and the mathematical and statistical formulae and equations used to explain the classical genetic difference principle.

James, Watson, and Crick developed an applied double-helix genetic mathematical model. A helix is a right circular cylinder. It is conceived of mathematically as a three-dimensional curve that lies on a cylinder or cone, so that its angle to a plane perpendicular to the axis is constant (Helix, n.d.).

Eugenicists that ascribe to the conception of orthogenesis and gene constancy contend that superior genes will persist during the adaptation process. This conception of gene constancy centers on the proposition that phenotypic traits are transmitted through biological mechanisms.

Due to the evolutionary processes involved in adaptation for the purpose of achieving orthogenesis, the best genes will persist in the species. This concept of gene constancy was an undergirding factor in James' Watson's, and Crick's mathematical model of DNA. The developers of the DNA mathematical model proposed a double helix mathematical structure.

The plane perpendicular to the axis in the helix is mathematically related to gene constancy. The double helix can relate to the inherited chromosomes from the two parents' cell in genetic equations (Bailey & Moore, 2012; Fisher, 1915; 1930; Hubbard & Wald, 1999; Pomiankowski & Iwasa, 1998; Swigon, 2009; Wahlsten, 2014).

Classical genetics has a strong root in discrimination, which manifests as racism and eugenics. Because early research into molecular genetics has a strong root in classical genetics, the thin line between classical and molecular genetics could become blurred.

While classical genetics is based on philosophical tenets with an integration of mathematical concepts, molecular genetics place greater emphasis on molecular processes and mechanisms. Molecular genetics apply principles from physics, mathematics, and statistics. Molecular geneticists explain genetics in terms of the behavior and characteristics of molecules.

GENES AND ALLELES

Classical geneticists posit that speciation occurred because of adaptation. According to some classical geneticists, genes are fixed, but with inbuilt variability to facilitate adaptation to environmental conditions.

Mutation is the process whereby adaptation occurs. When a mutation occurs, an alternative form or phenotypic expression of the gene, referred to as gene expression occurs.

Scientists infer that changes or differences in DNA calculations are indications that genes mutated and have taken on alternative forms; an allele is one of these forms. For example, the DNA combination for eye color has several variations (alleles) such as an allele for blue eye color or an allele for brown eye color. An allele is found at a fixed section of DNA.

Scientists identify DNA with each pair of chromosomes. In humans, chromosomes occur in pairs, so individuals have two alleles for each gene — one allele in each chromosome in the pair. According to the gene theory of inheritance, each chromosome in the pair comes from a different parent; individuals inherit one allele from each parent. The two alleles inherited from parents may be the same (homozygous) or different (heterozygous).

GENES, ALLELES, AND PREDISPOSITIONAL VULNERABILITY

The idea of predispositional vulnerability is premised on the notion that genes disposition organisms, individuals, species, subspecies, and species members to orthogenesis – a straight line of increased complexity and form or vulnerability. Classical geneticists contend that behaviors such as drunkenness, vagrancy, and violence are the products of genetic predispositions.

In the search to establish genetic predisposition for social and moral behaviors, molecular geneticists seek to examine such elements as DNA and alleles. However, genes, chromosomes, DNA, RNA, and alleles are all hypothetical constructs. Hypothetical constructs are ideas, and because ideas do not have tangible, corporeal existences, genes, chromosomes, DNA, RNA, and alleles cannot and have never been seen.

Genes, chromosomes, DNA, RNA, and alleles are mathematical models applied as substrates of biological features. Consequently, the interpretations of these hypothetical constructs are based on philosophical tenets and orientations. Conceptualization of genes, chromosomes, DNA, RNA, and alleles are founded on evolutionary premises of ontogeny, survivability, predispositional vulnerability, and orthogenesis. Conceptualization of predispositional vulnerability must be considered within these philosophical and theoretical boundaries.

PHILOSOPHICAL AND THEORETICAL BASES OF PREDISPOSITIONAL VULNERABILITY

Predispositional vulnerability is an apperception that some individuals, groups, and species have genetic weaknesses or diathesis that render them susceptible to vulnerability. Predispositional vulnerability theories hinge on the theory of evolution by natural selection. Researchers have made linkages between genetic predisposition and APR. These scholars identified the neurophysiological and psychiatric conditions associated with APR.

Predispositional vulnerability theories have natural selection, selection, variability, Social Darwinism, and eugenics embeddings. Scholars controvert that genes cause weaknesses or diatheses. Molecular biologists work to uncover the biochemical processes beneath diatheses. Genome mapping, genetics, and epigenetics studies focus on the pathways, the risk alleles, and the gene-interactions triggering diatheses.

RISK ALLELES

Allelic research is an attempt to fine-tune the specificity of the search for predispositional genes. These studies involve assumptions about genes, DNA, chromosomes, and mutation. Scientists believe that the presentment of a diathesis is traceable to a specific location within the chromosome called a risk allele. Allelic studies are an intricate and complex extension of gene theory and genetic research.

GENE THEORY

Two concerns relevant to APR are the beliefs that genes are particles of inheritance and that predispositional vulnerability exists in some species and species members. The conceptualization that genes are particles of inheritance emerged from a hypothesis of gemmules.

Darwin proposed that organisms possess genes and genes cast off gemmules. Due to gemmules, some species have a reproductive advantage, and others have a susceptibility to vulnerability (Dikmenli, Cardak, & Kiray, 2011; Lewis & Kattmann, 2004; Marbach-Ad, 2001).

According to Darwin, pangenes and gemmules are heritable particles of characteristics, traits, and behaviors that render some species, subspecies, and species members superior and others inferior or vulnerable. Social Darwinists and eugenicists use gene theory overtly and covertly to support their discriminatory policies and divisiveness.

Gene theory has been applied to explain racial differences. Based on this interpretation, social Darwinists and eugenicists attempt to establish a biological basis for explaining vulnerability. According to this tenet, vulnerability is natural selection causes predispositional genetic vulnerability (Dikmenli et al., 2011; Lewis & Kattmann, 2004; Marbach-Ad, 2001).

MISCONCEPTIONS OF THE CONCEPT OF GENES AND GEMMULES

Darwin contended that pangenes and gemmules existed in reproductive organs. Researchers found this notion of gemmules as particles, acts as an affirmation that genes are small particles of inheritance in reproductive cells. This perception is a common misconception of genes that persists (Dikmenli et al., 2011; Lewis & Kattmann, 2004; Marbach-Ad, 2001).

Gregor Mendel conducted experiments using pea plants. Specific characteristics of seeds and flowers were identified. When the plants were crossbred, the initial pair were called the parents, X and Y. Specific characteristics were assigned to parent X and other characteristics assigned to parent Y.

Based on the offspring or the crossbreed from parent X and Y, Mendel plotted a mathematical equation and graph that are commonly referred to as the X and Y chromosomes. The X and Y factors in the crossbreed were the grandparents of modern interpretation of the chromosomal theory of inheritance.

Two erroneous beliefs caused the misconception that genes, chromosomes, DNA, RNA, and alleles are tangible particles to perpetuate. The misconceptions relate to a lack of understanding of the metaphysical elements of gene theory and an incomplete understanding of the genetic testing process. These misconceptions have ramifications for the teaching, understanding, and application of genetics, specifically for the understanding of central hypothetical constructs such as genotype, phenotype, and phenotype expressions (Dikmenli et al., 2011).

This common fallacy that genes exist as corporeal particles within cells presents difficulties in conveying that genes are metaphysical constructs. As a hypothetical metaphysical construct, genes are the transmitter of heritable characteristics, traits, and behaviors. In disciplines concerned with the study of genes, these theoretical metaphysical constructs are physical concepts.

In the study of genetics, researchers employ hypothetical constructs of phenomena such as genes and atoms, which earlier theorists believed might exist and which they used to describe their perception of reality. Atoms and genes, for example, are concepts that represent hypothetical metaphysical constructs.

Hypothetical metaphysical constructs were assigned physical properties, characteristics, and behaviors. Philosophical tenets, such as realism and dualism, and research processes such as abstraction and modal abstraction, were used to gain acceptance of these metaphysical constructs and to permit their inclusion in scientific disciplines. The assigned properties, characteristics, and behaviors were tested to establish their validity and reliability in scientific study. Synthetic designs were used to represent these metaphysical creations and facilitate research into these metaphysical constructs. Once validated, these metaphysical constructs became accepted as reality (Dikmenli et al., 2011; Lewis & Kattmann, 2004; Marbach-Ad, 2001).

CLARIFYING MISCONCEPTIONS ABOUT GENES, GENETICS, AND DNA

Educators acknowledged that students have misconceptions about genes, genetic material, genetic code, and DNA. Students believe that genes, genetic material, and the genetic code are corporeal particles that exist inside of cells. Educators have presented suggestions to change these common misconceptions (Dikmenli et al., 2011; Lewis & Kattmann, 2004; Marbach-Ad, 2001)

A brief history of the term genes and its conceptualization might assist students in better understanding that genes are not corporeal particles of inheritance. More than 2,500 years ago, Greek philosophers held a religious belief that humans are the offspring of a god called Pan. Pan imparted his genes to humans to cause humans to become like the gods. These impartations were called pangenes.

The initial conception of pangenes was modified. In the current research, the concept of genes replaced pangenes. However, genes have metaphysical origins and are incorporeal (Dikmenli et al., 2011; Lewis & Kattmann, 2004; Marbach-Ad, 2001).

Several improvements and reconceptualization of pangenome were responsible for the changeover from pangenes to genes. Technological advances that facilitated new research in such disciplines as physics, chemistry, biology, and genetics were also instrumental in the changed perception and conceptualization of genes and genetics (Dikmenli et al., 2011; Lewis & Kattmann, 2004; Marbach-Ad, 2001).

Religion was also taken out of the theory of evolution by natural selection to make the theory more scientific. In antiquity, metaphysics theory was interwoven into the theory of evolution. Those elements of metaphysics that were intertwined in the theory of evolution belonged to the realm of the unseen and fell under the umbrella of religious philosophy.

When the religious philosophy of metaphysics was taken out of the theory of evolution, those elements of metaphysics that were intertwined in the theory of evolution became the study of physics leading to the emergence of new modern-day scientific disciplines. However, current disciplines have never extricated all of the source elements of pangenes, which we now call genes. The concept of heritability is an implied perpetuation of the source of pangenes. The ardent search to promote the validity of genetic predisposition might be a perpetuation of the belief in pangenesis, superiority, vulnerability, predetermination, and predestination, which are contributory elements of metaphysical ontogenetic philosophy (Dikmenli et al., 2011; Lewis & Kattmann, 2004; Marbach-Ad, 2001).

REALIST PHILOSOPHY AND CONCEPTS

In clarifying that elements and structures, such as genes, genetic material, and the genetic code are not physical, corporeal particles, students must first be able to understand the underlying philosophical principles of these concepts. Concepts such as genes, genetic material, and the genetic code are physical concepts of modern-day scientific disciplines. However, these are insentient.

Scientists hypothesize that genes, genetic material, and the genetic code reside in organisms. However, genes, genetic material, and genetic codes have never been sensorially observed. Scientists conceptually hypothesized the DNA molecule and infer that DNA calculations are indicative and representative of genes, genetic material, and genetic codes.

At the time of proposing the existence of pangenes, pangenes, which later was identified as genes, did not have a tangible, corporeal existence. The existence of genes presupposes that Pan imparted genes to organisms and gave credence to Darwin's theory of pangenesis.

Philosophers developed philosophies to facilitate and incorporate pangenesis and other theories of mythical religious origins into scientific study. Although at first empiricists rigidly criticized theories involving insentient, or impalpable phenomena, through philosophical tenets, these subject matters were slowly incorporated into scientific research.

Pragmatism or pragmaticism was one of the most critical developments in the philosophical movement to incorporate intangible, insentient, metaphysical concepts into modern-day scientific study. Pragmatism or pragmaticism is a philosophy concerned with changing the meaning and definition of words to incorporate metaphysical elements and constructs as a scientific discipline. The meaning and definition of the word physical were changed to facilitate the incorporation of metaphysical constructs into scientific study. Before the changing of the meaning and interpretation of the word physical, the word physical referred to sentient palpable things or objects. Impalpable phenomena were metaphysical sensations and concepts relegated to religion and spirituality.

Pragmatists argued that metaphysical elements and concepts could be defined as having a physical existence, even though they were insentient and impalpable. Several philosophies emerged to include impalpable metaphysical phenomena and concepts into the studies called the philosophical method. The philosophical method later became known as the scientific method.

Realism was one of those philosophies used to make the inclusion of metaphysical, insentient, impalpable phenomena, and concepts into scientific research. Realists of the metaphysical traditions argued that defining and assigning characteristics to any metaphysical constructs made them real and gave them a physical existence.

Redefining metaphysical constructs to give them a physical existence involved the application of metaphysical philosophies and principles. This redefinition of what is physical and what is not physical formed the basis of studies such as physics. Philosophers proposed that if a concept or an insentient element or structure could be defined and assigned properties from which abstraction could be made, then these metaphysical elements and structures can be defined as physical entities, elements, or structures.

Realism was among those philosophies applied to not only change these elements from metaphysical to physical but to make them real. Applied to science, theories of realism state that if a theorist creates a hypothetical construct of an element or structure that the theorist believes exists; by defining characteristics and qualities that identify and distinguish the construct, the construct is real. Genes, genetic material, and genetic codes are hypothetical constructs, but they are real because they have been defined and assigned qualities and characteristics that distinguish them from other things.

Philosophers ascribed characteristics to these hypothetical elements and structures. Synthetic biological engineers, computer animators, computer analysts, and statisticians devised and created artificial designs to represent these constructs. These creations along with new technologies in research, provide support and validate these concepts and constructs as mechanisms of heritability (Dikmenli et al., 2011; Lewis & Kattmann, 2004; Marbach-Ad, 2001).

SYNTHETIC CREATIONS

Understanding the work of synthetic biological engineers will further assist students in their understanding of fundamental hypothetical constructs used in genetics. A synthetic biological engineer is a person who creates artificial structures to represent elements and structures believed to exist. While genes, genetic material, and genetic codes are impalpable metaphysical phenomena, synthetic biological engineers designed and created artificial biological designs that facilitated their study.

Geneticists use hypothetical constructs for things they believe exist but which they cannot or have never seen. Synthetic biologists then create artificial structures to represent these hypothetical constructs. These hypothetical constructs and artificial creations are cornerstones of genetic research. The research and research process validate these hypothetical constructs as probabilistic elements in heritability (National Research Council, Division on Earth and Life Studies, Commission on Life Sciences, Committee on Mapping and Sequencing the Human Genome, 1988).

DISTINGUISHING BETWEEN DNA AND CHROMOSOMES

An explanation of the distinction between chromosomes[35] and DNA will assist students in their understanding of the conceptualization of such concepts as genes, genetic material, genetic code, and DNA used in genetic research. An understanding of the way that atoms became integrated into scientific disciplines will also assist the student in better understanding the way that genes, genetic material, and the genetic code were identified and conceptualized.

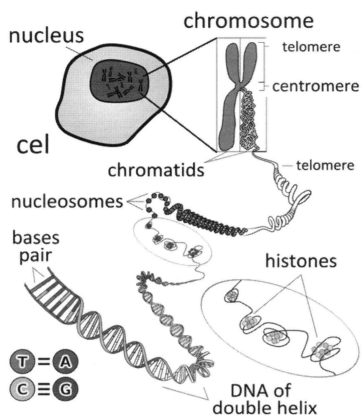

Figure 21-1 Chromosome Composition

HYPOTHETICAL CONSTRUCTION OF ATOMS

Around 400 BC, a Greek philosopher, Democritus, proposed the idea that all things are made up of atomos. Atomos is a Greek word meaning indivisible. Democritus proposed that if it were possible to cut any physical items, such as an apple, into the smallest possible pieces, then there is a point at which it is no longer possible to cut these infinitesimal pieces. He called these infinitesimal pieces, atomos, from which the modern-day word atom stemmed (Bailey, C., 1928).

A fundamental flaw in the initial proposition of the theory of atomos is differences in existence. For example, liquids and solids are two different forms of existences. If solids are segmented into infinitesimal parts, the division of the solid into infinitesimal parts will not change the nature of its existence from solid to liquid. Similarly, even if it were possible for a physical object to be divided into infinitesimal parts, the division of the

---

[35] Figure 21-1 File:Chromosome-es.svg: KES47derivative work: KES47 (https://commons.wikimedia.org/wiki/File:Chromosome_en.svg), „Chromosome en", https://creativecommons.org/licenses/by/3.0/legalcode

object into infinitesimal parts does not change the nature of existence from physical to metaphysical.

Nevertheless, philosophers accepted the conceptualization of atomos and the conceptualization that atoms comprise all things. Scientists and philosophers have never seen atoms, but they engage in thinking and provide their thoughts on the characteristics of things such as atoms and genes. Although impalpable, because of philosophical thoughts in pragmaticism and realism, scientists contend that atoms have a real existence. Being able to concretize atoms as a concept of physics changed the study of atoms from being metaphysical or beyond physical existence to having a physical structure.

Philosophers assigned qualities and characteristics to atoms and conceived subatomic particles, such as protons, neutrons, and electrons as constituents that make up atoms. This process is called abstraction (Ladyman et al., 2007; Lakadamyali & Cosma, 2015).

An understanding of light and the behavior of electricity were foundational in concretizing atoms and giving them a physical existence. Atoms are conceptualized as having particles. Measurements using light, light particles, or waves determine the composition, structure, and behavior of atoms. Based on these behaviors, atoms are grouped and classified as chemical symbols (National Research Council, Division on Earth and Life Studies, Commission on Life Sciences, Committee on Mapping and Sequencing the Human Genome, 1988).

Based on conceptualizations about light, electricity, and energy, all things are made up of atoms. In religion and metaphysical philosophies, light and energy are spiritual or metaphysical concepts.

METAPHYSICAL CONSTRUCTS AND PROPERTIES OF PHYSICS

Chemicals have properties and characteristics such as acidity, alkalinity, solubility, and hardness. Physicists assign different qualities and characteristics to different chemicals depending on the way they conceive atoms to behave. Physicists and chemists identify acids based on their atomic composition and atomic structures. The behavior of atoms determines the composition and structure of acids.

FROM METAPHYSICS TO PHYSICS

In physics, chemicals are structures comprising atoms with properties dependent upon the atoms in the chemical. In chemistry, chemicals have physical structures in various forms, such as liquids, solids, and gases. Acids are a group of chemicals that can exist in any of these forms. Based on an intermarrying of physics, chemistry, and biology, genetic research provides validation for the gene theory of heritability.

Conceptualization and behavior of light and electricity is the basis of the observation of atoms. In religion and spirituality, light is often used to refer to the gods, light, and metaphysical elements. Light in antiquity was the element that caused life and being. In antiquity, physical beings were a combination of matter and form. For Democritus, atomos is the unit or light that makes up the world (Bohacek & Mansuy, 2015; Caspi et al., 2003; Liu C., 2013).

Atomic theories provide explanations for the molecular structure of atoms and the behavior of DNA. Genes, genetic material, and genetic codes are extrapolations based on actuarial calculations ascribed to chemical reactions and the molecular structure of atoms within DNA (Dikmenli et al., 2011; Lewis & Kattmann, 2004; Marbach-Ad, 2001).

Figure 21-2 Walther Flemming

GENETICS AND THE CHROMOSOMAL THEORY OF INHERITANCE

Like Democritus, Darwin claimed that both parents transmit equally to their offspring. Thomas Hunt Morgan (1866-1945) furthered this theory. He proposed the chromosomal theory of inheritance. According to the chromosomal theory of inheritance, both the male's sperm and female's ovum contribute equally to the development of the organism. The word chromosome comes from a Greek word meaning colored body (Okasha, 2016).

Walther Flemming[36] (21 April 1843-4 August 1905) was a German biologist, who discovered that a chemical process could be applied to stainable fibers in replicating cells. Using aniline dyes, Flemming colored the fibers, which he named chromatin or colored bodies. Dyeing these fibers made them optically visible during the cell replication process (Okasha, 2016; Paweletz, 2001).

Flemming believed Democritus' proposal that all human cells contained pangenes, and these were passed on through the sex-organs to form new humans. Flemming proposed that the colorable thread-like fibers he observed when cells replicate were the carriers of pangenes. These

---

[36] Figure 21-2 Unknown author (https://commons.wikimedia.org/wiki/File:Walther_Flemming.jpg), „Walther Flemming ", marked as public domain, more details on Wikimedia Commons: https://commons.wikimedia.org/wiki/Template:PD-old

carriers of pangenes became known as chromosomes (Martins, 1999; Okasha, 2016).

With the use of microscopy imaging technology, the observation of the behavior of electricity using light imaging technology, and the application of chemicals different fibrous threadlike light particles become observable in replicating cells. These fibrous thread-light particles are called chromosomes.

At the time of the discovery of chromosomes, the theory of pangenes could not be aptly applied to identify chromosomes as genes, genetic material, genetic codes, or DNA. However, ardent eugenic geneticists proposed that these colorable fibers must represent genes. Advanced microscopic imaging technology allows magnification of the fibrous threadlike light particles. Complex mathematical calculations are then used to identify specific regions of the threadlike light particles, using these methods, the DNA molecule and chromosomes, invisible concepts become physical realities.

Chromosomes are hypothesized to be the carriers or indicators of genes. These carriers of pangenes form the zygote from which the entire organism develops. Skin, tissues, organs, and different body parts develop due to a process of cell division (Martins, 1999; Okasha, 2016).

Cells are microscopic, and most cells cannot be seen with the naked eye. Chromosomal theorists propose that chromosomes exist inside cells and that chromosomes contain genes, which are each associated with the development of specific regions, characteristics, tissue, organ, or bones in the embryo.

To establish a link between the colorable fibers as chromosomes that represent genes, another hypothetical construct and inference had to be devised. In 1953, eugenicists James Watson and Francis Crick solved this dilemma.

Crick and Watson hypothesized that because all things are made up of atoms, that all living cells must also possess invisible components of atoms. Crick and Watson developed the theory of DNA, an acid molecule that exists in cells. These researchers also theorized about the structure, chemical properties, and behaviors of the atom molecules. Based on their hypothetical model, mathematical, and actuarial calculations, the DNA molecule as a hypothetical model of the behavior of genes that could be linked to chromosomes became a reality.

Gene theorists propose that one set of 23 chromosomes, ranging from the largest with approximately 250 million base pairs to the smallest with approximately 50 million base pairs, and each of the female's haploid cell consists of approximately 3.2 billion base pairs[37]. Genes and base pairs are not tangible, visible particles. Genes, base pairs, and chromosomes are

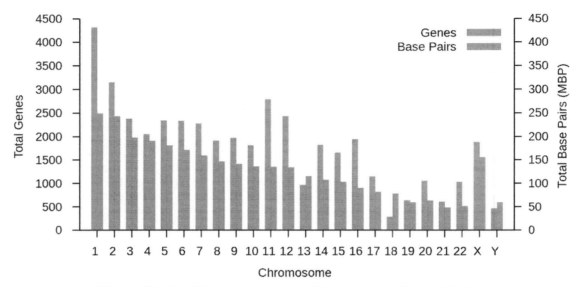

Chart 21-1   Chromosomes, Genes and Base Pairs

mathematical calculations. Similar to plotting XY coordinates on a graph, geneticists use actuarial calculations to map the genome. Geneticists create genome maps and genetic testing employing artificial creations, synthetic models, computerized models, computational analysis, biochemical engineering, and electron microscopic studies to substantiate their existence (National Research Council, Division on Earth and Life Studies, Commission on Life Sciences, Committee on Mapping and Sequencing the Human Genome, 1988).

GENES

Genes have never been viewed optically. They are not known to be corporeal particles within the nucleus of cells. However, scientists have been able to distinguish chemicals and chemical reactions within the cells of living organisms and have associated these with protein synthesis and cell replication.

These chemicals called DNA and RNA.[38] DNA and RNA are acidic. The concept of acidic molecules is a hypothetical idea based on beliefs about the invisible world. DNA and RNA molecules are hypothesized to be

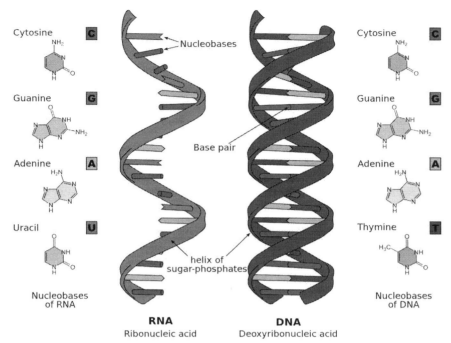

Figure 21-3 DNA RNA Differences

the mechanisms of genetic transmissions. Genes are structures in physics that support the underlying assumptions of substance and form in Greek religion concerning the source of life and heritability. Gene theory emerged from Hippocratic thought.

Hippocrates (c.460-c.375) proposed that pangenes were invisible seeds that existed in all the organs of a parent. These invisible seeds were miniaturized building blocks which the parents transmitted during intercourse. These building blocks reassemble themselves in the mother's womb to form a baby. Although some changes in the conceptualization of pangenes were made, this interpretation is the mainstay of modern-day gene theory. These invisible seeds exist in the nucleus of cells and are the mechanisms of hereditary transmissions (Winchester, 2018).

Most cells are microscopic. They are estimated to be about the size of 1/10 of the width of a single strand of hair. Inside this nanosized cell, there is an even smaller nucleus. Inside the nucleus there are chromosomes. Inside those chromosomes are tens of thousands of genes. Inside the genes, there are up to a million base pairs. An allele is a variant

---

[38] Figure 21-3 Difference_DNA_RNA-DE.svg: Sponk (talk) translation: Sponk (talk) (https://commons.wikimedia.org/wiki/File:Difference_DNA_RNA-EN.svg), „Difference DNA RNA-EN", https://creativecommons.org/licenses/by-sa/3.0/legalcode

of a gene and therefore has the same number of base pairs as gene. Each allele is responsible for the manifestation of very specific characteristics, traits, and behaviors (Kid et al., 2018).

Genes are not sentient, sensorial particles, but it is believed that they exist in cells. Light detection microscopes are used to make calculations and analysis of DNA and RNA during cell replication. Based on actuarial calculations, imaging technology, synthetic creations, and the behavior of electricity, statistical computations are applied to explain the hypothetical behavior of chemicals when cell replication is initiated. These calculations are used to estimate the behavior of the hypothetical mechanism defined as genes.

Genes, chromosomes, and the DNA molecule have their origins in metaphysic philosophies from antiquity concerning life, being, and atomos. Although insentient and impalpable, the concretization of these metaphysical constructs centers on the acceptance of philosophical tenets that inculcate that these concepts have a physical existence. Along with the philosophical tenets that inculcate that these have a physical existence, there must also be the acceptance of the assumptions that these mythical, metaphysical constructs are the originator and cause of life.

Scientific research into these phenomena is possible because of technology such as electron microscopy. The electron microscope is an imaging device that allows calculations based on hypotheses of the behavior of electrons and photons, which are hypothesized to be atomic particles, but light cannot be seen using the electron microscope (Dikmenli et al., 2011; Lewis & Kattmann, 2004; Marbach-Ad, 2001).

Integration of physics and chemistry allows scientists to create synthetic DNA in an interpretive model of the mechanisms and processes of hereditary transmissions. In addition to extremely complex laboratory experiments to prove the way these mechanisms and processes function, scientists also use extremely complex likelihood statistical computer analytical models to make an association between alleles and predispositional genetic vulnerability (Bohacek & Mansuy, 2015; Caspi et al., 2003; Liu et al., 2013).

GENOME MAPPING

The purpose of mapping the genome is to identify biological mechanisms and systems hypothesized as being responsible for the manifestation of the characteristics, traits, and behaviors of DNA, an atom molecule believed to be responsible for hereditary transmissions. Genome mapping aims at identifying areas in the chromosomes and specific chemical processes believed to play critical roles in cell replication and division (Phillips, 2019; Smith & Murphy, 2004).

ASSOCIATIVE MODEL

Molecular geneticists refer to DNA as genes. Molecular geneticists conduct allelic research to identify specific sections of the DNA molecule that serve specialized functions during mitosis and meiosis. However, there are still weaknesses to overcome in the gene theory model.

Genetic analysis is a computational predictive, associative analytical model. Geneticists find difficulties establishing causal relationships between genetic computations and predispositional vulnerability.

Although genome mappers have been able to use predictive computational models to draw conclusions about the statistical likelihood of vulnerabilities in people associated by close blood ties, in most studies, these are associative rather than causative correlations. Some researchers examine very specific alleles, but even in these studies, researchers make very cautious conclusions (Joober, Sengupta, & Boksa, 2005; Rees, O'Donovan, & Owen, 2015).

As such, epigeneticists continue to explore epigenomic generational transmissions. Epigeneticists argue that generational transmissions might occur outside of DNA mechanisms and seek to establish a biological basis to support the argument for epigenomic generational transmissions.

Geneticists have had the most success using knockout techniques in ethological studies. Using knockout techniques, geneticists confirm transmission through epigenetic mechanisms. Geneticists have been unable to identify genetic transmissions outside of epigenetic mechanisms (Cofre & Abdelhay, 2017; Manolio et al., 2010; Wyrobek et al., 2007).

PARTICLES OF INHERITANCE

The concept of particles of inheritance emerged from the theory of evolution by natural selection. No studies, so far, have substantiated that there are sentient sensorially-observed particles of inheritance called genes. Referring to genes, genetic materials, and genetic codes as particles rather than physical concepts with physical properties without a thorough understanding of metaphysics and pragmatic philosophy cause an erroneous belief that these are sentient, sensorially-observed particles of inheritance to persist (Yvert, 2014; Zou, 2014).

RANDOM MUTATION

Studies into mutagenesis also do not appear to support the hereditary transmission of behavioral traits via random mutation. Random mutations are chance occurrences. Random mutations occur on a minuscule scale and may not be a plausible explanation for evolutionary adaptation (Brücher & Jamall, 2016; Sniegowski & Lenski, 1995).

GENOTYPE AND AGGRESSION

Geneticists define genotype as the specific DNA sequencing of the individual or organism based on the genus, genome, genes, and genetic material. In classical genetics, genotypes distinguished superior human subspecies with good genes or eugenics from vulnerable human subspecies with undesirable genes.

In molecular genetics, broad regions responsible for critical molecular characteristics of the organism are believed to exist within each genotype. Underlying conceptions of race and genotype carried over from classical genetics into molecular genetic research. Classical geneticists posit that different human subspecies or races have different genotypes. Modern-day molecular genetic research also places focus on the relationship between race/ethnicity, DNA, and genes.

RACE AND ETHNICITY

The relationship between race, ethnicity, and genes is an offshoot of evolutionary theory. Darwin contended that each race belonged to a different human subspecies. Darwin believed an in-depth comparative analysis of specimens from different races would demonstrate that each belongs to a distinct species.

> *Some of these, such as the Negro and European, are so distinct that, if specimens had been brought to a naturalist without any further information, they would undoubtedly have been considered by him as good and true species. (Darwin C., 1882, p. 608).*

While Darwin's tenets of different human species might explain differential rates of aggression and victimization based on race and ethnicity, there is still the question relating to the high species-to-species murder among humans. When compared with other mammals, a higher rate of species-to-species murder occurs among primates. Primates are closest to humans genetically, hence the conclusion that phylogeny may account for the high rate of species-to-species murder among humans (Buss, 2005; Wrangham, 2018).

EVOLUTIONARY PHYLOGENESIS

Evolutionists contend that the high rate of species-to-species murder among humans is due to evolutionary phylogenesis. Scholars of phylogeny argue that species emerged from a common progenitor. Darwin concluded:

> *Nevertheless all the races agree in so many unimportant details of structure and in so many mental peculiarities, that these can be accounted for only by inheritance from a common progenitor; and a progenitor thus characterised would probably deserve to rank as man.*
> *(Darwin C., 1882, p. 608).*

EVOLUTIONARY STAGES

Like Darwin, evolutionary scientists claim that the differential rates of aggression and victimization among the different races are due to differences in the stage of evolution. Human species or subspecies at higher stages of evolution will have lower rates of species-to-species murder. Species-to-species murder will decline as evolutionary orthogenesis progresses.

Darwin's arguments in relation to different human species being at different stages of evolution, align with Darwin's hypothesis regarding the differences between the subspecies of savages and the favoured races. Darwin contended that advancement in civilization would cause an increase in positive moral traits which would widen the gap between humans and higher animals. Nevertheless, studies show that species-to-species murders among humans remain high and do not show a decline even with the advancement of civilization. Additional studies show that humans engage in more intentional aggression than other species, including primates (Buss, 2005; Wrangham, 2018).

CONCLUSION

Predispositional vulnerability theorists explain APR within the context of gene and chromosomal theory of inheritance. Systems and behavioral theories apply predispositional vulnerability to explain APR. Terwilliger and Hiekkalinna (2006) oppugned that researchers in genetics evoke credibility and faith in findings from associative genetic research.

However, genetic statisticians, Terwilliger, and Hiekkalinna (2006) cautioned that elements such as the bolstering assumptions, implied causative associations, and the application of likelihood statistical models represent serious flaws in good scientific methodology. Given their cautionary advice, Terwilliger and Hiekkalinna suggest that critical reappraisal should govern the applications of these findings.

Citing several severe limitations in genetic studies that link race and disorder, Terwilliger and Hiekkalinna (2006) cautioned:

> *We hope that as gene hunting approaches increase in cost and size, that rather than becoming more cavalier about theoretical assumptions, that we be much more careful about what we believe. Technological advances are wonderful, and make it possible to do science that we could not imagine a few decades ago, but excellent technology applied to poorly designed studies (driven by assumptions the investigators themselves probably would not really believe if consciously aware of them) are not particularly wise ways to do science – it would be far better to spend more time thinking and planning before jumping in to genotyping every sample we can get our hands on, lest no one listen to us when we cry fire and there actually is one, at some point in the future. (Terwilliger & Hiekkalinna, 2006, p. 435).*

CHAPTER REVIEW

REVIEW QUESTIONS

1. Distinguish between sentient and insentient objects.

2. How did philosophical development facilitate the inclusion of metaphysical phenomena into the scientific discipline of physics?

3. Does phylogeny theory provide evidence to support the high species-to-species murder among humans?

4. In addition to intentional aggression, in what ways do species-to-species murder in humans differ from other mammals?

CHAPTER TWENTY-TWO
DIFFERENTIAL SUSCEPTIBILITY TO VULNERABILITY

CHAPTER PREVIEW

The WHO reported differential susceptibility to vulnerability among minority populations. Darwin explained that these differential rates of susceptibility are due to evolutionary, orthogenetic processes. Although the manifestation of vulnerability is the product of an interplay between genes and the environment, Darwin contended that genes and natural selection have a more dominant impact on heredity than the environment.

In this chapter, there will be a discussion of differential susceptibility to vulnerability. The diathesis-stress/dual-risk and the differential susceptibility models are two theoretical approaches used to explain predispositional vulnerability.

Both models base their tenets on critical elements of Darwin's theory of evolution by natural selection. Proponents of the diathesis-stress/dual-risk model contend that biological traits are hereditary products. There is a discussion of several defining elements of this model, such as the selective manifestation of vulnerability, additivity of diathesis, and kindling phenomenon.

Proponents of the differential susceptibility model contend that natural selection processes are the higher principles in the manifestation of a diathesis. Differential susceptibility proponents argue that predispositional vulnerable populations demonstrate higher sensitivity to both positive and negative environmental stimuli.

The chapter ends with a discussion of the specific tenets of Darwin's theory of evolution by natural selection and vulnerability, and studies indicating a higher vulnerability among minority populations.

PURPOSE AND LEARNING OBJECTIVES

PURPOSE

The purpose of this chapter is to explore susceptibility to vulnerability theories and their applicability to APR.

LEARNING OBJECTIVES

After studying this chapter, the reader should

1. have a working knowledge of the key terms and concepts used in this chapter;
2. understand the tenets of susceptibility to vulnerability;
3. be able to make comparisons between the different susceptibility to vulnerability models; and
4. assess the applicability of susceptibility to vulnerability to APR.

KEY TERMS AND DEFINITIONS

Susceptibility

Susceptibility is the extent to which an individual or organism possesses the capacity or the tendency to be impressed.

Vulnerable Population

A vulnerable population is a population, individual, group, or organization with impaired capacity or ability to anticipate, cope with, resist, and recover from the impacts of disasters (World Health Organization, 2002).

INTRODUCTION

According to the WHO, vulnerability is the inability or absence of capacity of an individual, group, organization, or population to anticipate, cope with, resist, and recover from the impacts of disasters. By implication, an association exists between population vulnerability and survivability. The WHO defines vulnerability within the context of evolutionary models of genetic inheritance via natural selection (Darwin C., 1872; WHO, 2002).

APR poses a threat to survivability. Victims and perpetrators of APR represent special groups of a vulnerable population. Current research indicates disproportionate vulnerability among minority populations. Gender, race, and culture are said to influence the rate and nature of occurrences of APR.

Evolution by natural selection is a framework used to understand and interpret differential survivability and susceptibility to vulnerability. Understanding the assumptive premises of differential susceptibility models might be useful for increasing understanding of APR.

THEORETICAL FOUNDATIONS OF THE MODELS

The differential susceptibility and the diathesis-stress/dual risk are two models that are based on two divergent interpretation of evolutionary theory. The philosophical orientations of these two models are foundational elements in the approach to interpreting and applying theory in practice and research.

The differential susceptibility model is based on a traditional Darwinian concept of susceptibility. The second model, the diathesis-stress model, is based on a neo-Darwinian understanding of susceptibility.

Darwin conceived that Pan distributed genes differentially to species and subspecies. As such, different species and subspecies members have differential susceptibility because they possess different genes.

Darwin tied in the explanations of differential distribution of genes among species and species members with natural selection processes. Intertwining differential distribution of genes and natural selection was an explanation for differences between human subspecies such as the Europeans and the Negro.

According to this tenet, humans are a species and different races, according to Darwin, could best be described as subspecies. Based on this interpretation, different human subspecies were endowed with different genes. The force governing natural selection endowed some human subspecies with better genes than others.

Darwin further explained that habit differentiated superior human subspecies from vulnerable species. On the other hand, intelligence was the product of genetic endowment.

At the core of Darwin's proposition of differential susceptibility was the idea that humans should engage in eugenics. Darwin inculcated negative eugenics. According to Darwin's proposition, the state and the elite should not promote acts that would assist vulnerable people because in so doing, the state and the elite would only create a greater societal burden.

Social Darwinism involved deliberate policies to promote eugenics. Among academia, eugenics took several forms. Some eugenicists began experimenting to uncover a biological basis for heredity; others employed mathematical and statistical calculations to extrapolate a relationship between statistical variables and genes. Eugenicists employed two broad categories of calculations in their statistical models. These variables are genetic and environmental variables.

In their debates, eugenicists considered whether genetic qualities should be a fixed or variable calculation. By the 1900s, some eugenicists became convinced that genetic qualities should be a fixed calculation in mathematical and statistical genetic equations.

According to traditional Darwinian interpretation, genes are internal mechanisms that cause small incremental variations to facilitate evolutionary orthogenesis. Neo-Darwinists contended, however, that genes were fixed, but it was the natural selection process that produced variability.

These two divergent thoughts about whether genes should be a fixed or variable calculation were important for the development of eugenic policies. This Neo-Darwinian position formed the basis of statistical equations such as the Fishers statistical model. These statistical models were used to calculate predictions in population genetics within the context of environmental variables.

The differential susceptibility and the diathesis-stress/dual risk models are variants of the statistical models used to predict gene-environment interactions and behavior. These two models are reflective of traditional Darwinian and neo-Darwinian approaches to calculating gene-environment interactions and behaviors (Hubbard & Wald, 1999; Leibnitz, 1989; Roll-Hansen, 2014).

GENETIC PREDISPOSITION

Eugenicists conjecture a gene-environmental interplay in the manifestation of vulnerability. Although natural selection is the overarching element of straight-line evolution, Darwin contended, "great weight must be attributed to the inherited effects" (Darwin C., 1882, p. vi). Inherited effects, selections, and variability produce reproductive advantage or vulnerability. Although the interplay of habit and environmental conditions are the elements of behavioral transmissions, Darwin contended that genes play a more significant role (Chen, 2014; Darwin C., 1882).

The differential susceptibility and the diathesis-stress/dual risk models are based on statistical calculations that are plotted as XY coordinates on a graph. The straight-line also called orthogenesis, is a straight line drawn from the intersection of an XY quadrant. Darwin's suggestions of "great weight," refers to the weighted mean that should be given to genes as a variable in the mathematical-statistical equation.

The differential susceptibility and the diathesis-stress/dual risk models are reflective of the theoretical positions of the theorists that proposed the model. The theoretical positions and interpretations depend on the different statistical weightings given to inherited effects and habit in the mathematical-statistical equations.

In mathematical equations, the product is a multiplicative derivative, whereas a summation is an additive derivative. The differential susceptibility and the diathesis-stress/dual risk models are represented as two types of calculations. The differential susceptibility is an additive summation, and the diathesis-stress/dual risk model is a multiplicative derivative.

ADDITIVE AND MULTIPLICATIVE DERIVATIVES

The focus on genes as an element in behavioral transmissions is a central theme in neuroscience, cognitive psychology, and behavioral psychology. Classical gene theory is based on philosophical tenets from evolutionary theory. Molecular biology is based on mathematical and statistical derivatives and concretization of abstraction from research in physics and chemistry.

The gene concept is based on the idea that characteristics, traits, and behaviors could be passed on by a biological mechanism from one generation to another. This underlying assumption is integrated into molecular genetics and the conceptualization of DNA as genes and the storage unit of genetic materials and the genetic code.

The birthing of the DNA and RNA molecules as concretized physical entities, and the blurring of the lines between DNA and RNA as acids in cells were instrumental in the perpetuation of an erroneous, lay interpretation that genes are physical particles with a sentient existence. However, DNA and RNA molecular calculations are based on hypothetical constructs. Molecules are not tangible, physical particles. Like genes, DNA and RNA are also ideas, concepts, and notions, and therefore, like genes, do not exist in cells.

In molecular genetics, DNA is defined as genes and the storage unit of genetic material and the genetic code. The overlaps in terminology cause a carryover from classical genetics into the understanding of genes in molecular genetics.

Classical genetics is grounded in evolutionary philosophy where pangenes or genes are the hereditary carriers and transmitters. In classical genetics, genes have a causal relationship with characteristics, traits, and behaviors.

The DNA defined as genes in molecular genetics involves the hypothetical function of the DNA molecule and DNA as an acid as a process that could be calculably associated with specific molecular behavior and sequences. A thin line exists between functional processes and causality.

The redefinition of DNA as genes in molecular genetics infers a carryover of the conceptualization of genes as a causal mechanism from classical genetics. Hence, DNA processes interpreted as a causal element in molecular behaviors and sequences have an equivalence of genetic causation from classical genetics. However, in molecular genetics, DNA processes are associative calculations and not causative calculations.

Molecular biologists and geneticists apply theories from physics and chemistry and principles such as abstraction and modal abstraction to concretize impalpable, insentient concepts such as genes, DNA, and RNA. However, the concretization of abstract constructs does not render a corporeal existence these constructs. Using conceptual maps, microscopy imaging technology, and actuarial calculations, molecular biologists present scientific evidence of the study of chemical processes involved in DNA and RNA interactions, and use these calculations to hypothesize about genetic transmissions from one generation to another (Alberts et al., 2002; Noble, 2008).

To concretize these concepts, physiochemists begin with tissues from living organisms. These tissues are chemically treated and analyzed. Properties and characteristics from symbolic charts used in physics and chemistry are used to define and identify the tissues and chemicals to facilitate mathematical and statistical calculations.

Following up from Darwin's theory of evolution by means of natural selection, the concept that genes exist as an incorporeal phenomenon was accepted as a theory in science. Gregor Mendel, then developed a mathematical equation to calculate the way that this hypothetical construct might be accounted for in heredity.

These mathematical models continued to be developed. In 1953, James Watson and Francis Crick proposed that DNA consists of a specific chemical with a double-helix structure. They then build molecular models based on their idea. Based on their hypothesis of the chemical structure of DNA and its behavior, Crick and Watson construed that the DNA molecule is foundational in protein replication and is a physiological representation of genes.

Using microscopy imaging technology, mathematical, and statistical equations, chemical treatment and analysis of tissues and samples from living organisms, DNA and RNA are measured and extrapolated to reflect differences in tissues from living organisms. Nevertheless, because DNA, RNA, molecules, and genes do not have a corporeal tangible existence, their existence and behaviors are inferred assumptions that form the hypotheses of the genetic equation. Genetic equations are standardized mathematical and statistical formulae used in genetic calculations.

The foundational hypothetical assumptions are written as an inferential statement in mathematical-statistical equations. These mathematical-statistical equations become the premise of the theory that guides the research. The equations are used to calculate conclusions (Swigon, 2009).

> *From the very beginning, abstraction and modeling played a significant role in research on DNA, since the molecule could not be visualized by any available experimental methods. These models gave rise to mathematical concepts and techniques for study of DNA configurations at the macroscopic and mesoscopic levels (Swigon, 2009, p. 293).*

Mathematical-statistical equations in genetic studies are consistent calculations. Advances in key areas such as computer technology, advancement in computational software, and imaging technology have improved the consistency and the complexities of computational analyses in genetic studies. However, genes, DNA, and RNA are hypothetical constructs about acids in cells. DNA, RNA, and genes were developed and continue to be researched to support the evolutionary theory of genetic inheritance.

According to genetic predisposition proponents, common genes exist in both offspring and progenitors, causing a predispositional status in both the progenitor and the offspring. Genetic predispositional status is associated with reproductive advantage or susceptibility to vulnerability.

Susceptibility to vulnerability refers to the extent to which environmental conditions negatively impress or affect an organism, individual, group, or species. According to this hypothesis, genetic predisposition causes susceptibility to vulnerability (van Ijzendoorn & Bakermans-Kranenburg, 2015).

Genetic vulnerability theorists contend that increased susceptibility to vulnerability might be due to heredity. Like Darwin, some theorists suggest genetic factors are more significant determinants of susceptibility to vulnerability or predetermine vulnerability. Proponents who believe that genetic factors are more significant determinants of susceptibility to vulnerability give genetic variables a greater weighting that other variables in their statistical calculations.

These theorists use vulnerability assessment measures between twins and blood relatives to support their argument. Proponents of genetic vulnerability argue that there are similar levels of susceptibility to a vulnerability in twins, siblings, and near blood relatives. These theorists apperceive that proportionate susceptibility to vulnerability exists between twins even when the environmental conditions defining their upbringing or living conditions differ. Vulnerability genes, risk alleles, and biological reactivity to stress are the focus of a core body of genetic predisposition research (van Ijzendoorn & Bakermans-Kranenburg, 2015).

FUNDAMENTAL STATISTICAL MODELS

The diathesis-stress/dual-risk model and the differential susceptibility model are two theories developed to explain predispositional susceptibility to vulnerability. Each of these two theories presents different explanations for susceptibility to a vulnerability that reflect their gene-environment interaction theoretical position. Diathesis-stress/dual-risk theorists focus on environmental conditions to assess the diathesis. Differential susceptibility theorists emphasize individual differences (Ellis, Boyce, Belsky, Bakermans-Kranenburg, & van IJzendoorn, 2011; van Ijzendoorn & Bakermans-Kranenburg, 2015).

These two models of predispositional susceptibility to vulnerability are indicative of two fundamental Darwinist's hypotheses, selection, and natural selection. While natural selection might be more applicable to the differential susceptibility model, selection might apply to the diathesis-stress/dual-risk model of susceptibility to vulnerability.

According to Darwin's theory, although natural selection predetermines susceptibility or survivability, a predetermination, is responsible for differential susceptibility or survivability among species. Differential susceptibility or survivability will also explain why some organisms or individuals within the species have variations in susceptibility or survivability (Darwin C., 1868; 1872).

THE DIATHESIS-STRESS/DUAL-RISK MODEL

The diathesis-stress/dual-risk model is a psychological theory that attributes dysfunctional behaviors or disordered states to an interaction between stressful genetic predisposition and environmental conditions. Within the context of survivability, positive genetic predisposition presents a reproductive advantage; whereas a negative genetic predisposition presents as a diathetic vulnerability (Toft, 2014).

PREDISPOSITIONAL DIATHESIS

Although a gene is merely a concept, genes are believed to have a biological basis. This fundamental belief must be first accepted because it is the foundation of molecular genetic studies.

The second hypothesis in predispositional vulnerability is that phenotypic expressions are the products of genetic dispositions. Genes, as an underlying mechanism cause diathesis.

A diathesis is a predispositional constitution toward a particular state or condition. Proponents of the diathesis-stress/dual-risk model identify genetic predisposition as the diathesis. Psychological processes, cognition, emotions, and behaviors have a neurophysiological and neuroanatomical basis of which genes are the underlying mechanism. As such, diathesis has a neurophysiological and neuroanatomical genetic basis (Toft, 2014).

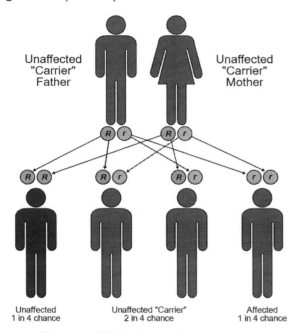

Unaffected "Carrier" Father

Unaffected "Carrier" Mother

Unaffected 1 in 4 chance

Unaffected "Carrier" 2 in 4 chance

Affected 1 in 4 chance

Figure 22-1 Auto Recessive Probabilities

SELECTIVE MANIFESTATION OF VULNERABILITY

According to the genetic predisposition hypothesis, although the gene is present in all family members, the gene expresses in some family members and not in others. Darwin attributed these within species and within-group variations to one of the processes of natural selection.

The natural selection processes involve a force outside of human control that selects some individuals and species members to encounter hardships and tragedies to cause them to succumb to destruction or develop mutations that would cause orthogenesis. According to the WHO definition of vulnerability[39], and the genetic predisposition hypotheses, those individuals and species members predestined for destruction have a susceptibility to vulnerability.

Geneticists and epigeneticists explain selective manifestations of vulnerability as the outcome of genotype and phenotype. Genotypes and phenotypes are hypothetical genomic constructs. The genome is the entire gene pool of a species. Each species has specific characteristics and traits that distinguish and identify that species. The genotype refers to the species-specific genes found in the individual. The phenotype refers to gene-environment interaction that is unique to the individual. Geneticists and epigeneticists use the differences in genotypic and phenotypic expressions to explain the existence of a diathesis among closely related individuals (Hamilton & Bowers, 2007).

---

[39] Figure 22-1 By en:User:Cburnett - Own work in Inkscape, CC BY-SA 3.0, https://commons.wikimedia.org/w/index.php?curid=1840082

According to geneticists and epigeneticists, predispositional vulnerabilities might exist as genotypes. Exposure to environmental conditions can cause phenotypic expressions resulting in dysfunctional behavior. A phenotypic expression refers to manifested characteristics, traits, and behaviors that are unique to the individual. Theorists contend that an individual's phenotypic expressions are the product of gene-environmental interactions (Hamilton & Bowers, 2007).

ENVIRONMENTAL CONDITIONS

Genetic and behavioral psychological models apply diathesis-vulnerability models in practice and research. According to the diathesis-stress/dual-risk model, a susceptible or vulnerable individual might never manifest a dysfunctionality or disordered state except under conditions that expose the individual to a specific type or degree of stress. According to this model, environmental conditions somehow trigger neurobiological processes that cause the dysfunctionality or disordered state to manifest (Choi & Kim, 2007; Hamilton & Bowers, 2007).

Diathesis-stress/dual-risk theorists posit that individuals without a diathesis will not manifest dysfunctionalities or disordered states, even when faced with stressful environmental conditions. According to this model, the presence of the genes is the underlying mechanism that causes diathesis. The manifestation of dysfunctionalities and disordered states are interactive products of the diathesis and the environment. The manifestation of the diathesis is dependent on the existence of genes or genetic structures that cause predispositional diathesis.

ADDITIVITY OF DIATHESIS

The diathesis-stress/dual-risk[40] model employs an additive component to the manifestation of disordered and dysfunctional states. The predisposition is present and might never manifest, except when there is an added element of stress. If the diathesis is not present, stress will have no effect on the individual (Belsky, 2013).

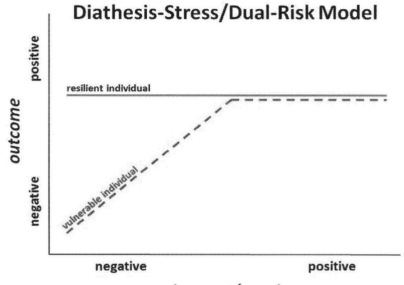

Chart 22-1   Diathesis/Dual-Risk Model

Even so, whether a dysfunctionality or disordered state manifests in a vulnerable individual is dependent on the severity of the environmental condition, the point at which exposure to the environmental condition occurs, and the level of susceptibility the individual possesses to the dysfunctionality or disorder (Belsky & Pluess, 2009).

KINDLING PHENOMENON

Alleles are calculations of specific points in the graphs and charts used in DNA calculations. Using environmental stress as a statistical variable, statisticians propose that the environment kindles the risk allele to produce a dysfunctional or disordered state. The kindling element can initiate or precipitate the diathesis. An initiating element is the first to trigger the diathesis. The precipitating event(s) cause(s) a symptomatic escalation of an already presenting diathesis (Belsky & Pluess, 2009).

The individual is hypothesized to have genes that cause a predispositional vulnerability that is causing a diathesis to manifest. If the diathesis is already manifesting due to some stress, additional stressors or increases in the level of stress might precipitate or accelerate the diathesis. The precipitating event represents the additive element of the diathesis. A precipitated or accelerated diathesis increases the severity of outcomes such as addictions, suicidality, or homicidality. Precipitating events could

---

[40] Chart 22-1 Mpluess
(https://commons.wikimedia.org/wiki/File:Diathesisstressdualriskmodel.JPG),
„Diathesisstressdualriskmodel", marked as public domain, more details on
Wikimedia Commons: https://commons.wikimedia.org/wiki/Template:PD-self

not only change the severity or outcomes but could also initiate a new or different diathesis (Belsky, 2013).

Proponents of the diathesis-stress/dual-risk model contend that although genetic factors present the vulnerability, other potentiating stress factors cause the dysfunctional behavior or disordered state to manifest. APR is an environmental condition that can initiate or precipitate a diathesis. For example, an individual might have a diathesis or a predisposition toward depression; APR can act as an initiator diathesis toward depression. Existing depression can also be accelerated because of exposure to APR (Belsky et al., 2009; Ellis et al., 2011).

Genetic Predispositional Variability and Diathesis

Proponents of the diathesis-stress/dual-risk model outline two approaches. Proponents of the first approach contend that a high genetic predisposition can cause dysfunctional behaviors and disorders to manifest even when relatively minor environmental stressors present. Proponents of the second model posit that both genetic predispositions and environmental stressors exist inan inverse relationship. These proponents argue that high levels of environmental stressors might trigger dysfunctional behaviors and disordered states, even when only a minor predisposition exists (Belsky et al., 2009).

Proponents of the second approach identify a positive correlation between genetics and environmental stimuli. According to this model, the higher presence of one component requires a smaller input from the other component for dysfunctional behaviors and disorders to manifest (Belsky, 2013).

Two broad conditions are involved in the manifestation of a diathesis. The genetic predisposition manifested as cognitive, psychological, and biological impairments and deficient social-moral habits and conditions. In the first instance, researchers using the diathesis-stress/dual-risk model contend that dysfunctionalities and disordered states have a biogenetic component. Further, proponents of the diathesis-stress/dual-risk model contend that cognitive, psychological, and social-moral conditions have physiological (chemical) and anatomical (structural) biogenetic compositions involved in the manifestations and transmissions of diatheses (Belsky et al., 2009; van Ijzendoorn & Bakermans-Kranenburg, 2015)

Both biogenetic components, biochemical and anatomical biogenetic compositions, are involved in the manifestation of dysfunctional behaviors and disordered states. However, the environment is a critical element in the manifestation of disordered states and conditions.

According to the diathesis theoretical model, genetic predisposition increases susceptibility to diseases. Practitioners apply the diathesis theoretical model as the diathesis-stress/dual-risk model in psychology to explain behavior. Proponents of the diathesis-stress/dual-risk model contend that in addition to genetic predispositions; cognitive, psychological, and social-moral conditions also create a predispositional diathesis (Belsky & Pluess, 2009).

DUAL-RISK ELEMENT

The dual-risk element in the diathesis-stress/dual-risk model is derived from two elements, the predispositional vulnerability and the risk in the environment. An underlying theme of the diathesis-stress/dual-risk model is the specificity of vulnerability. An individual might have a specific genetic predispositional susceptibility due to impaired neuroanatomical and neurochemical functioning associated with risk alleles or vulnerability genes. These impairments cause heightened biological reactivity to stress. In the classical genetics model, the specificity of vulnerability or reproductive advantage was associated with superior and inferior genetic compositions (Belsky & Pluess, 2009).

Proponents of the diathesis-stress/dual-risk model conceive that resilience is a factor in susceptibility to vulnerability. This model suggests that developmental experiences play a role in susceptibility to vulnerability or resilience. A positive environment and developmental experiences increased resilience. Although the individual might have a specific diathesis, the same individual is resilient when exposed to positive environmental conditions specifically linked to the diathesis (Belsky & Pluess, 2009).

DIFFERENTIAL SUSCEPTIBILITY THEORY

Both the diathesis-stress/dual-risk model and differential susceptibility model have a common element of biogenetic predispositional diathesis or susceptibility to vulnerability. The theoretical position that genetics play a more dominant role in susceptibility to vulnerability hinges on the hypothesis that some individuals are predispositionally more susceptible to both negative and positive environmental conditions. Based on the principle of natural selection, susceptibility, or reproductive advantage is due to the selective and predetermined principles of selection and natural selection (Belsky & Pluess, 2009).

According to the differential susceptibility[41] hypothesis, individuals with more susceptibility experience a proportionately higher negative impact when exposed to negative environmental experiences. Individuals

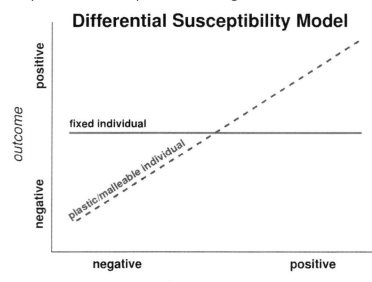

Differential Susceptibility Model

outcome — positive / negative

fixed individual

plastic/malleable individual

negative   positive

environment/experience

Chart 22-2   Differential Susceptibility Model

with more susceptibility experience a proportionately higher positive response when exposed to positive development-enhancing environmental conditions (Ellis et al., 2011).

According to the differential susceptibility theory, the higher principle of natural selection governs susceptibility to vulnerability. As such, the effectiveness of adaptive strategies, which are dependent on selection and natural selection drive the outcome of exposure to adverse conditions. Even though the immediate strategy might be harmful, it redounds to the ultimate benefit of society. Individuals who engage in negative behaviors because of adverse environmental conditions are merely working out the orthogenetic goals of the destruction of the unfit and preservation of the fittest (Belsky & Pluess, 2009).

Population vulnerability might be a product of an orthogenetic natural selection process via biogenetic transmissions. As such, population vulnerability might be hereditary. According to Darwin, some populations are predetermined via natural selection to have increased vulnerability (Brisson, 2003; Loewe & Hill, 2010).

Differential susceptibility theorists postulate that individuals and groups are sensitive to both negative and positive environments. These theorists conclude that human experiences are always an admixture of negative and positive elements. As such, although APR presents adverse environmental experiences that can adversely impact neurodevelopment, there might also be positive developmental experiences that increase individual resilience (Belsky & Pluess, 2009).

---

[41] Chart 22-2 Differentialsusceptibilitymodel.JPG: Mpluess derivative work: Snubcube (talk) (https://commons.wikimedia.org/wiki/File:Differentialsusceptibilitymodel.svg), „Differentialsusceptibilitymodel", marked as public domain, more details on Wikimedia Commons: https://commons.wikimedia.org/wiki/Template:PD-self

Differential susceptibility theorists also posit that the heightened sensitivity to both adverse and favorable environmental conditions means the individual will also have heightened benefit from the positive experiences. Both the positive and negative experiences will have a short and long-term neurobiological impact (Belsky & Pluess, 2009; Ellis et al., 2011).

Short-term and long-term neurobiological impact due to the negative experiences, as well as the exposure to physical risks, might endanger victims of APR. However, the long-term positive neurological impact can be transmitted biogenetically. This biogenetic transmission will have long-term adaptive survivability benefits (Ellis et al., 2011).

The long-term benefits to society are putative. In the short-term, strategies that individuals adopt to address negative and adverse conditions might be harmful to the self, family, and society. However, biological adaptation to positive environmental conditions might be transmitted biogenetically over the long-term. This biogenetic adaptation is beneficial to orthogenetic drift (Belsky & Pluess, 2009).

Differential susceptibility to environmental conditions is a phenomenon that is common to individuals of all ages. Differential susceptibility theorists contend that the neurobiological susceptibility to environmental conditions varies from one individual to another. Individuals might also have differential susceptibility across their lifespan. Differential susceptibility manifests as a heightened sensitivity to environmental conditions (Ellis et al., 2011).

Individuals with differential predispositional susceptibility have heightened sensitivity to both negative and positive environments. These individuals have a heightened sensitivity if exposed to adverse environments but will also demonstrate increased sensitivity to positive environments. Consequently, developmental experiences are critical to individuals with heightened susceptibility (Ellis et al., 2011).

Individuals with heightened sensitivity will demonstrate a sustained developmental change in response to environmental conditions. Developmental changes in response to both adverse and favorable environmental conditions are more likely to be prolonged (Belsky & Pluess, 2009).

Due to biological sensitivity to environmental conditions, developmental changes occurring because of environmental exposures are more likely to increase genetic susceptibility. Consequently, genetic susceptibility appears to be more likely for individuals with heightened sensitivity to environmental conditions (Ellis et al., 2011).

DIFFERENCES IN ADAPTABILITY

The genetic impact of heightened sensitivity is a purposeful element in the orthogenetic natural selection process. Due to orthogenesis, individual differences in neurobiological susceptibility are adaptive elements (Ellis et al., 2011).

Different individuals will manifest different adaptive neurobiological variations depending on the blend of their sensitivity and the blend of positive and negative environmental conditions to which they are exposed. As such, individuals might be exposed to the same environmental conditions but demonstrate different behaviors. These variations can be seen between twins and blood relatives, even when they share very similar neurobiological systems and traits (Belsky & Pluess, 2009; van Ijzendoorn & Bakermans-Kranenburg, 2015).

Two strands of evolutionary theory influenced tenets related to predispositional susceptibility to vulnerability. The diathesis-stress/dual-risk model theorists posit that neurobiological diathesis can be triggered or precipitated by environmental stressors. These theorists contend that if there are no environmental stressors, the diathesis would never manifest.

On the other hand, proponents of the differential susceptibility theory contend that neurobiological sensitivities are dynamic interactors with both adverse and favorable environmental conditions. Differential susceptibility is subject to adaptive laws of natural selection.

EVOLUTIONARY THEORY AND VULNERABILITY

Darwin, in the theory of evolution by natural selection, purported that disproportionate survivability occurs among some populations because of natural selection. Darwin contended that life is a struggle, and the environment is hostile. However, the favoured races have higher survivability than savages and barbarians because the favoured races possess unique characteristics and traits that allow them to overcome hostile and harsh environments. These characteristics and traits are due to innate qualities the favoured races inherit and pass on to their descendants. As such, survivability is due to heredity.

Implied in Darwin's conception of survivability and heredity, victims of APR are vulnerable because they have lowered survivability. Moreover, this reduced survivability is due to heredity (Darwin C., 1872).

Findings from a plethora of studies indicate disproportionate survivability that presents as a higher prevalence of dysfunctionalities and disordered states among socioeconomically disadvantaged populations. Disproportionate survivability results in a disproportionate vulnerability. Populations with reduced survivability have increased susceptibility to vulnerability.

DISADVANTAGED POPULATIONS AND SURVIVABILITY

Age, gender, ethnicity, culture, race, and socioeconomic status identifiers delimit boundaries of susceptibility to vulnerability. Age subsets, which include children and the elderly are more susceptible to APR when compared with young-to-middle-age adults. Gender and sexual orientation define another set of boundaries associated with susceptibility to vulnerability. Other vulnerable populations, including minority groups such as African-American, Hispanics, transgenders, children, lower-income persons, and groups, are disadvantaged populations with increased susceptibility to vulnerability (American Psychological Association, 2017; Georgia State University, 2016; Schäfer et al., 2012).

The Women of Color Network reported that African-American females experience IPV at a rate 17.5% higher than White females, and more than 65% higher than other non-mixed races (Truman & Morgan, 2014, p. 11). Homicide is one of the leading causes of death for women under the age of 44. In 2015, 3,519 females under 46 years of age were homicide victims, and nearly half of those homicides were victims of IPV (Petrosky et al., 2017, p. 741).

Data from the National Violent Death Reporting System (NVDRS) for the years 2003 – 2014, shows that for women aged 18 and older, non-Hispanic Black and American Indian/Alaskan Native women experienced the highest rates of homicide (4.4 and 4.3 per 100,000 population respectively). More than half of all murders (55.3%) were intimate partner-related (Petrosky et al., 2017, p. 741).

A national survey reported by Georgia State University (2016) indicated that non-Hispanic Blacks are almost twice as likely as non-Hispanic Whites to be diagnosed with schizophrenia (Coleman et al., 2016, p. 752), but they are significantly less likely to receive medication for treatment (Coleman et al., 2016, p. 753). The disparity in prevalence among these two groups in both mental and physical impairment is similar (Schwartz & Blankenship, 2014).

There is a link between the disproportional representation of African-Americans or non-Hispanic Blacks with mental and physical ill-health and historical racial discrimination and stigmatization. An exploration of Darwin's hypotheses of disproportionate survivability might shed light on the increased susceptibility to vulnerability among minority populations (Georgia State University, 2016; Petrosky et al., 2017).

DISPROPORTIONATE VULNERABILITY

If there is a biological basis for dysfunctionalities and disordered states, then, does genetics explain the disproportionate vulnerability among disenfranchised groups, minorities, and individuals?

Early geneticists purport that favoured races possess favourable gemmules savages and barbarians do not possess. As such, the favoured races had a reproductive advantage. This reproductive advantage was hereditary. Further, savages and barbarians are vulnerable because of natural selection. These contentions were foundational elements in later theoretical developments associated with a genetic predisposition. Although modern-day geneticists disavow the concept of favoured races and vulnerable populations, these assumptions might unintentionally underlie modern theories and research (Rothstein, Harrell, & Marchant, 2017).

In seeking to establish a biological basis for dysfunctionalities and disordered states, geneticists argue that certain individuals are vulnerable or more susceptible to dysfunctionalities and disordered states (Rothstein et al., 2017). Several genetic studies provide calculations that show a higher susceptibility for dysfunctionalities and disordered states among close relatives and siblings. On the other hand, several studies show no correlation between heredity and vulnerability. This variance in susceptibility seems to be present even when siblings and blood relatives are raised in different environments (Frisell, Lichtenstein, & Långström, 2010).

Moreover, geneticists posit that calculations of DNA sequencing can account for the manifestations of similar characteristics, traits, and behaviors in closely related people. By extension, this argument suggests that biological predispositions to vulnerability might be higher in some families and groups (Nilsson & Skinner, 2015). Geneticists posit that these transmissions are merely a genetic predispositional vulnerability. Epigeneticists argue that epigenome and environmental conditions might trigger this predispositional vulnerability (Bohacek & Mansuy, 2015).

CONCLUSION

While some researchers believe that heredity causes susceptibility to vulnerability, current research also fingered race, ethnicity, and culture as elements causing susceptibility to vulnerability. However, these vulnerable populations, such as minorities and underprivileged groups, have a strong link with historical and sociocultural patterns of disadvantage and discrimination, suggesting that these conditions might play a role in susceptibility to vulnerability.

CHAPTER REVIEW

REVIEW QUESTIONS

1. Compare the two major predispositional vulnerability models.
2. Compare their strengths and weaknesses.
3. Is vulnerability due to genetic or environmental conditions?

CHAPTER TWENTY–THREE
GENETICS AND EPIGENETICS

CHAPTER PREVIEW

Epigeneticists distinguish between DNA and epigenomic markers to assess whether changes in molecular behaviors and sequences could occur between progenitors and progenies via epigenomic mechanisms. In this chapter, there is a discussion of epigenesis. Epigenesis refers to intergenerational and transgenerational transmissions due to the epigenome and environmental conditions.

There is a discussion of the impact of exposure, nonexposure, direct, and indirect in utero exposures to environmental conditions and their implications for intergenerational and transgenerational transmissions. There is a discussion of transgenerational transferences to a third and fourth cloned generations in ethological studies that did not have direct exposure to environmental conditions that triggered changes in the individual's genome. Using similarities or changes in DNA sequencing, epigeneticists make their assessment whether a transmission is epigenetic, epigeneticists make comparisons between biogenetic markers and the epigenome in relations to exposure to environmental conditions.

Behavioral psychologists in the field of genetics seek out answers whether there is a biological basis for behavior and whether biogenetic markers are involved in the manifestation of these behaviors. Studies in genetics and epigenetics make use of ethological studies to assess the involvement of genetics or epigenetics in the transmission of characteristics, traits, and behaviors.

PURPOSE AND LEARNING OBJECTIVES

PURPOSE

The purpose of this chapter is to explore the hypothesis that dysfunctionalities and disordered states such as APR are transmittable via nonbiogenetic mechanisms and processes.

LEARNING OBJECTIVES

After studying this chapter, the reader should

1. be able to distinguish between genetics and epigenetics;
2. be able to distinguish between intergeneration and transgenerational transmissions; and
3. understand the mechanisms of epigenesis and challenges in scientific research into this phenomenon.

KEY TERMS AND DEFINITIONS

Bio-Epigenetic or Nongenetic Transmissions

Bio-epigenetic or nongenetic transmissions are the transmissions of heritable characteristics, traits, and behaviors from progenitors to offspring that occurs outside genetic mechanisms.

Intragenerational

Intragenerational phenomena are the existences or occurrences of characteristics, traits, and behaviors among members of the same generation (Intragenerational, n.d.).

Transgenerational Epigenetic Inheritance

Transgenerational epigenetic inheritance is evident by changes in the calculations of the molecular structure and sequence in DNA in third and fourth generation progenies occurring without alterations in ancestral DNA structures.

Transgenerational Transference

Transgenerational transference refers to changes in manifested characteristics, traits, and behaviors that occur because of environmental conditions that resulted in changes in biogenetic or epigenomic mechanisms.

INTRODUCTION

Based on the findings from several studies, the prevalence of APR in one generation is a predictor of APR in subsequent generations. Either one of two types of generational transmissions, intergenerational and transgenerational, determines whether the transmissions are biogenetic or non-biogenetic. Nonbiogenetic transmissions are called epigenetic transmissions (Dall et al., 2012; Kulminski et al., 2013).

Epigeneticists suggest that epigenomic mechanisms might be responsible for hereditary transmissions. Epigeneticists hypothesized that epigenomic transmissions occur outside DNA mechanisms and might be due to environmental influences and stimuli (Bohacek & Mansuy, 2015; Caspi et al., 2003).

UNDERSTANDING CHARACTERISTICS, TRAITS, AND BEHAVIORS

Traditionally defined, characteristics, traits, and behaviors are understood as manifested, expressed phenotypes such as height, weight, or other physical appearances. Using characteristics, traits, and behaviors or ideas such as genes, DNA, and RNA also helps to promote that these are tangible, corporeal particles. Nevertheless, references to characteristics, traits, and behaviors in genetics, epigenetics, and molecular biology often do not refer to physically, manifested sentient observable elements.

In genetics, epigenetics, and molecular biology, characteristics, traits, and behaviors often refer to analytical calculations based on hypothetical or synthetic representations of atoms and molecules. When interpreting findings and reviewing studies, these differences must first be clarified so as to gain insight into genetic and epigenetic research.

EPIGENOMIC TRANSMISSIONS

A nongenetic transmission is a hereditary transmission that occurs via epigenetic mechanisms and presents as phenotypic expressions for which there are no associated genetic, biological markers. In genetic and epigenetic research, hereditary transmissions are calculations, and hereditary mechanisms are the conceptualization of ideas such as genes, DNA, and RNA. Biological markers are calculation points that are representative of a physiological trait.

Both geneticists and epigeneticists use conceptual ideas and actuarial calculations of biological markers to calculate whether transmission occurs via genetic or epigenetic mechanisms. Geneticists contend that these calculations and biological markers occur due to DNA.

Epigeneticists contend that these calculations and biological markers are not due to DNA but, might be due to RNA and the epigenome. RNA and epigenomic transmissions are heredity transmissions for which DNA calculations cannot account.

Systems theoreticians postulate social-learning and behavior modeling theories to explain hereditary transmissions. Geneticists and epigeneticists remain locked in the nature-nurture debate. Heritability and genetic transmissions are the foundations of evolutionary theory.

Citing behavioral changes without changes in genetic biomarkers, epigeneticists premise that nongenetic mechanisms might be media for generational transmissions. Further, research is also indicating changes in genomic and epigenetic biomarkers occurring during the lifespan, which might be due to environmental experiences and effects (Black, Sussman, & Unger, 2009; Dias & Ressler, 2014; Frisell et al., 2011).

INTERGENERATIONAL TRANSMISSION

Epigeneticists define intergenerational transmissions as phenotypic changes or changes in characteristics, traits, and behaviors that occur between progenitor and progeny resulting from direct exposure to environmental conditions and for which heredity and genetics do not explain. These changes occur in parents, embryos, and offspring exposed to the same environmental conditions. There is a link between direct exposure and changes in characteristics, traits, and behaviors (Klengel, Dias, & Ressler, 2015).

Epigeneticists typically use mice models to conduct their analysis. Mice are treated to environmental conditions under laboratory conditions. Tissue samples are then taken from the different strains of mice with and without exposure to environmental conditions. These tissue samples are then chemically treated.

Imaging microscopy technology is used to examine the chemical reactions. Atomic and molecular reactions due to the chemical analyses are calculated. Characteristics, traits, and behaviors refer to the different calculations derived from the differences in chemical reactions from the different sample tissues. Epigeneticists study whether exposure to environmental conditions produces changes in molecular characteristics, traits, and behaviors, in the DNA, RNA, and epigenome of progenitor and progeny .

To assess the impact of an environmental stressor as a trigger for intergenerational transmissions, exposure to the stressor must have occurred before conception. This implies that either one or both parents experienced the environmental stressors producing the phenomenon and the impact of their experiences changed the parents' phenotype. Epigeneticists using mice models examine tissue samples of progenitor and progeny cells with and without exposure to environmental stressors under laboratory conditions (Klengel et al., 2015).

Epigeneticists also premise that in-utero or postnatal exposure of offspring may produce epigenomic changes in their germline. To calculate for epigenomic changes, epigeneticists factor in a large subset of undefined statistical variables, other than a DNA variable. Epigeneticists calculate that exposure to environmental conditions will result in differences in calculations for germline and somatic cells.

These calculations translate as direct exposure that would affect the germline of the fetus and offspring. Epigeneticists propose that changes in the epigenome of fetus and offspring could be passed on to their generations, thereby resulting in an intergenerational transmission (Klengel et al., 2015).

Epigeneticists examine changes in nonbiogenetically marked neurophysiological processes and mechanisms to establish that changes in molecular sequences and behaviors ensue after direct exposure to environmental stimuli. Epigeneticists observed that these nonbiogenetically marked neurophysiological processes and mechanisms or phenotypes did not exist before exposure to the environmental conditions. Epigeneticists conclude that the existence of changes in nonbiogenetic markers following direct exposure to environmental conditions in both progenitor and offspring is an indication of epigenetic transmission (Bierer et al., 2014; Klengel et al., 2015).

EXPOSURE, NONEXPOSURE, DIRECT AND INDIRECT IN UTERO EXPOSURES

Geneticists define the individual's genome as the complete set of DNA, genes, genetic codes, and genetic materials specific to the organism. Epigeneticists posit that direct exposure to environmental conditions can cause changes in the individual's phenotype without seeming to affect the individual's genome. The epigeneticists conjecture that changes in heredity occurring without changes in biogenetic markers is an epigenetic transmission. Epigenomic changes occur when phenotypic changes occur outside the genome. The epigeneticists reason that epigenomic changes might exist in the parents, their germs seed or germline cells, embryos, and offspring because of direct or indirect exposure to environmental stimuli.

Acquired phenotypic expressions might be due to direct exposure to environmental conditions and might not be hereditary. For example, a pregnant person might experience direct exposure to radiation, which produces cancer in somatic cells.

DIRECT MATERNAL AND FETAL EXPOSURE

This exposure to radiation might affect the mother, but not the fetus. However, under some conditions, both the pregnant mother and the fetus can experience radiation due to direct exposure. The fetus might experience the environmental condition indirectly because of neurochemical transfers from the mother to the embryo. Maternal exposure can also result in indirect fetal exposure.

DIRECT MATERNAL EXPOSURE AND INDIRECT FETAL EXPOSURE

Direct maternal exposure to environmental conditions can cause neurophysiological and neuroanatomical changes to occur in the mother. Although the fetus might not have direct exposure to the environmental conditions, changes in maternal neurophysiology could affect the fetus. Under these conditions, the fetus can have indirect exposure to the environment caused by changes in maternal neurophysiology and neuroanatomy. Maternal neurophysiological and neuroanatomical changes can appear in future offspring who did not have either direct or indirect embryonic exposure.

TRANSGENERATIONAL TRANSMISSION

Exposure to environmental conditions and epigenomic changes distinguish intergenerational and transgenerational transference. Epigeneticists posit that direct exposure to environmental conditions is responsible for intergenerational transference via epigenomic mechanisms and processes.

For example, hands and feet in humans developed because of a need to adapt to environmental conditions. Humans continue to develop hands and feet, even though they might not have direct exposure to the initial environmental conditions that caused hands and feet to develop the way they did in humans. Genomic manifestations are the existence of characteristics, traits, and behaviors that manifest without direct exposure to environmental conditions.

Transgenerational transference occurs when behaviors, traits, and characteristics exist in several generations, but actuarial calculations cannot account for these changes as being due to the genome. Epigenomic mechanisms and processes can cause phenotypic expressions of characteristics, traits, and behaviors that are passed on to epigenomes of the third and fourth generational germs and embryos that did not have direct exposure to the environmental stimuli that caused the acquired epigenomic mechanisms.

Epigeneticists contend that exposure to environmental conditions, including social behaviors, could trigger epigenomic changes. Biogenetic and epigenetic theories emerged from evolutionary conceptualizations of adaptation, survivability, survival of the fittest, reproductive advantage, natural selection, mutation, random mutation, beneficial mutation, and directed mutagenesis.

THE EPIGENOME AND EPIGENESIS

Epigeneticists engage in similar research as geneticists. Geneticists seek to establish whether phenotypic expressions manifested in progenitors and cloned offspring is related to DNA processes. They aim to determine

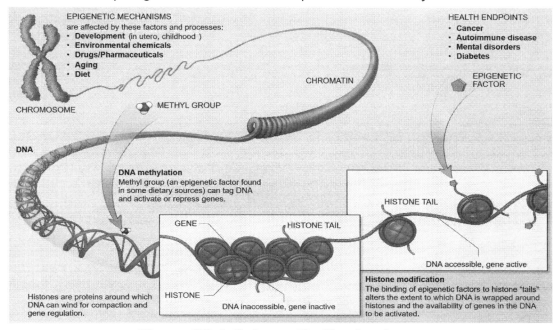

Figure 23-1 Epigenetic Mechanisms

whether calculable biological mechanisms[42] could explain hereditary transmissions. Biogenesis is the theory that calculable biological mechanisms are the process whereby hereditary transmissions occur (de Almeida et al., 2015).

Epigeneticists, on the other hand, seek to determine whether exposure to environmental stimuli and epigenomic mechanisms are the pathway for phenotypic expressions that are common between ancestor cells and cloned progenitors. Both geneticists and epigeneticists engage in research involving the use of DNA and cloned progenies. Synthetic biological engineers create synthetic DNA models that are used as biogenetic markers in genetic studies (Bohacek & Mansuy, 2015; Caspi et al., 2003).

EPIGENETIC AND BIO-EPIGENETIC TRANSMISSION

The National Research Council (US) Committee on Mapping and Sequencing the Human Genome. Mapping and Sequencing the Human Genome. Washington (DC): National Academies Press (US), (1988)

---

[42] Figure 23-1 National Institutes of Health
(https://commons.wikimedia.org/wiki/File:Epigenetic_mechanisms.jpg),
„Epigenetic mechanisms ", marked as public domain, more details on Wikimedia Commons: https://commons.wikimedia.org/wiki/Template:PD-US

conceded that genome mappers were only able to map a very tiny portion of the human genome. The committee further acknowledged that even with the achievement of the mapping of this minuscule portion, the error rate is high, and "the accuracy of DNA sequencing has not yet been firmly established." (p. 66) The committee reported: "Errors in DNA sequence determination occur at several levels" (p. 65), and, "unless the human genome sequence is determined accurately, it will be of little use" (p. 65) (National Research Council, Division on Earth and Life Studies, Commission on Life Sciences, Committee on Mapping and Sequencing the Human Genome, 1988).

Epigeneticists identified these shortcomings of the very small number of coding genes and the limited accuracy of genetic testing as support for their claim that environmental conditions and not heritability might be responsible for transmissions of vulnerability. In addition to the limitations of the genome projects, epigeneticists observed that there were differences in molecular behavior and sequences in parent and clone cells, but these differences were not due to DNA mathematical functional analysis.

Based on comparisons of DNA and epigenomic calculations, epigeneticists proffer that hereditary transmission might be occurring outside those biological markers that geneticists claim are responsible for hereditary transmissions. Because there are calculable differences between the parent and clone cells that are unrelated to DNA functional analysis, epigeneticists hypothesized that hereditary transmissions might be occurring outside those biological markers that geneticists identify. Epigeneticists purport these transmissions might be due to epigenomic and environmental stimuli (Bohacek & Mansuy, 2015; Caspi et al., 2003).

According to epigeneticists, changes in biological processes might be due to exposure to environmental stimuli. However, changes in biological processes might be occurring outside of what geneticists identify as genetic mechanisms. Epigenesis occurs when there are changes in biological process in both ancestors and progenies with exposure to initiating environmental stimuli when calculations show that these changes occur outside genomic mechanisms.

Both geneticists and epigeneticists use DNA calculations from progenitor transgenes and clones to determine whether DNA could account for differences or similarities in the parent's and clone's cells. Notwithstanding, these studies have been fraught with challenges and limitations.

Epigeneticists study transgenes, germ cells, and clone progenies to identify changes in chemical reactions and processes such as histone modification, DNA methylation-related chemical processes, and non-coding RNA to assess whether there are acquired sequences and changes in DNA markers that were not present in progenitor or ancestral germ cells prior to exposure to initiating environmental stimuli. The changes in the clones are then linked to a biological process or function. Geneticists and epigeneticists then analyze the results using a likelihood statistical model to determine whether there are correlations. In behavioral genetics, DNA and RNA calculations are then associated with a neurochemical or neuroanatomical process, or function believed to influence behavior.

APPLYING GENETICS TO BEHAVIOR

To apply genetics to behavior, behavior psychologists in the field of genetics seek to first establish the biological basis for the manifestation of dysfunctionality or disordered states. After determining a biological basis for the dysfunctionality or disordered state, behavioral psychologists then assess whether these biological processes occur in both ancestors and offspring. The third consideration in genetic psychology is whether these biological processes and mechanisms can be calculated as DNA markers or due to epigenesis. The evaluation of molecular markers associated with histone proteins is one of the processes used to analyze whether a genomic or epigenomic transmission occurred.

One of the biological processes that influence behavior relates to the production or activation of neurochemicals. Serotonin is an example of a neurochemical that is believed to influence behavior, and serotonin production is an example of a biological process that has an influence on behavior.

There is an association between serotonin production processes and functions and mood. Extensive studies have been done using mice models to assess the effect of serotonin dysfunctions and behaviors in mice. These studies indicated that environmental stress could alter biological processes of serotonin metabolism in mice.

Studies assessing gestating mice with exposure to environmental conditions showed that both the adult mice and their offspring showed serotonin dysfunction. Serotonin dysfunction also appeared in third and fourth generation samples of gestating mice that were exposed to stressful environmental conditions (Klengel et al., 2015; Milholland et al., 2017).

Findings from these studies have been extrapolated to explain human behavior. Based on these studies, the conclusion was made that the serotonin production and functioning processes might also be responsible for mood disorders in humans. Findings from other studies also indicated a biological basis for mood disorders as well as for other psychiatric conditions (Kendler, Kuhn, Vittum, Prescott, & Riley, 2005; Le-Niculescu et al., 2009; Nordquist & Oreland, 2010).

DNA calculations are used in studies that link psychiatric conditions to genetics. According to conclusions from genomic studies, there is a higher correlational risk among blood relatives for developing mood disorders. Findings from these studies suggest that mood disorders involve genes and have a hereditary component (Kendler et al., 2005; Le-Niculescu et al., 2009; Nordquist & Oreland, 2010).

Findings from studies linking mood disorders and heredity have established a biological basis for these disorders. Some studies have also calculated genomic biomarkers associated with these disorders. As with other genomic studies, some genomic researchers have identified multi-genomic pathways in the presentment of mood disorders. Epigenomic studies have also implicated environmental stressors in the presentment of mood disorders. While studies show similar patterns of psychiatric disorders in blood relations among humans; studies have not been able to establish an affirmative causal link between psychiatric disorders and genetic material (Kendler et al., 2005; Le-Niculescu et al., 2009; Milholland et al., 2017; Nordquist & Oreland, 2010).

CONCLUSION

DNA, RNA, genes, genetic, material, genetic codes, histones, and transcriptional regulation are terms used in describing the mechanisms of heredity in gene theory. Epigeneticists identify intergenerational and transgenerational transmissions based on exposure. Direct exposure facilitates intergenerational transference, and indirect exposure facilitates transgenerational transference. Epigeneticists contend environmental conditions can increase susceptibility or vulnerability to dysfunctional behaviors and disordered states, such as APR.

While genome mapping is being used as a means to determine either a genetic or epigenetic transmission of dysfunctionalities and disordered states, the approach has significant flaws and limitations. The National Research Council (US) Committee on Mapping and Sequencing the Human Genome. Mapping and Sequencing the Human Genome. Washington (DC): National Academies Press (US) (1988), cited the severe limitations of the approach. Terwilliger and Hiekkalinna (2006) argued that:

> *Genome-wide association studies have been very successful at identifying loci involved in rare Mendelian traits in population isolates, and as such have been suggested in recent years to be potentially useful for dissection of the etiology of complex traits as well.*
> *(Terwilliger & Hiekkalinna, 2006).*

However, Terwilliger and Hiekkalinna (2006), further contended that in addition to the assumptive flaws that common-variants equate common-disease, GWAS also have serious statistical analytical assumptive and practical application flaws. As such, findings from GWAS and new research GWAS should be approached with extreme caution.

CHAPTER REVIEW

REVIEW QUESTIONS

1. What is epigenesis?
2. Give examples of epigenetic transmissions.
3. Explain the differences between the concepts of biogenesis and bio-epigenesis.
4. What is the difference between transgenerational and intergenerational epigenetic transmissions?

CHAPTER TWENTY–FOUR
BIOGENETIC TRANSMISSIONS

CHAPTER PREVIEW

In this chapter, there is a brief discussion of the mechanisms and processes used to determine genetic transmissions. Genetic researchers use DNA and RNA calculations and associate these with protein synthesis mechanisms and processes as indicators of gene behavior. Genetic researchers use transgenes and clones to examine whether there are changes or similarities in parent and progeny cells. Similarities in DNA calculations are determined to be indications of genetic transmissions. Differences in DNA and RNA calculations are analyzed as indications of nongenetic transmissions.

Neurochemistry and neuroanatomy are implicated in psychiatric conditions linked to APR. In this chapter, there is a discussion of the processes involved in assessing whether there are biogenetic mechanisms that explain psychiatric conditions in ancestors and progenies. Thus far, researchers have not been able to identify a single gene variant that might explain the existence of psychiatric conditions and predispositions to these conditions in ancestors and offspring. Psychiatric conditions predisposing individuals to APR seem to implicate several brain regions and functions.

PURPOSE AND LEARNING OBJECTIVES

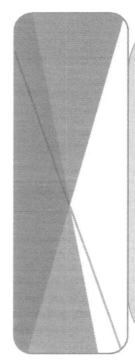

PURPOSE

The purpose of this chapter is to explore the hypothesis that biogenetic social and moral generational transmission occurs via biogenetic mechanisms and processes and the relevance of this hypothesis to APR.

LEARNING OBJECTIVES

After studying this chapter, the reader should

1. understand the conceptualization of biogenetic social and generational transmissions;
2. critically assess its tenets and the implications of these tenets; and
3. understand the applicability of its tenets to APR.

KEY TERMS AND DEFINITIONS

Biogenetic Transmissions

Biogenetic transmission is defined as the occurrence of similarities in DNA sequencing among progenitors and offspring accompanied by similarities in characteristics, traits, and behaviors (de Almeida et al., 2015).

INTRODUCTION

Geneticists theorize that a biogenetic transmission occurs when a characteristic, trait, or behavior passes from one generation to another through mechanisms involving genes, genetic codes, or genetic materials. Geneticists claim that genetic transmissions reflect biological processes. Geneticists contend that a biological transmission occurs when the same protein synthesis mechanisms and processes exist in both progenitor and progeny cells (Banaszak, 2000; Dias & Ressler, 2014).

PROTEIN SYNTHESIS AND GENETICS

Geneticists argue that cell replication, a process which is integral to reproduction, involves protein synthesis and that protein synthesis in organisms occurs because of biochemical processes. Using a cloning method, genome mappers use chemical processes to initiate cell replication. Genome mappers then examine the parent cells and the cloned offspring to assess whether there are similarities or differences.

Genome mappers hypothesize that similarities in the behavior and structure of DNA in both the parent cells and the cloned cells are indications of genetic transmission. Genome mappers attribute changes or similarities between parent cells and cloned offspring to metabolic actions involving protein synthesis. Geneticists use mathematical calculations, statistical likelihood, and theoretical applications from physics and chemistry to create an analytical map. Based on this analytical map and likelihood statistical equation, geneticists assess whether a genetic transmission has occurred (Banaszak, 2000; Kulminski et al., 2013).

Scientists hypothesize that DNA is an acid molecule that is involved in the cell replication process. However, the science of DNA and genetics leaves many unanswered questions that might possibly be answered as DNA technology and calculations become more advanced.

Cell replication occurs in a very complex environment. Therefore, hypothesizing about the existence of DNA and isolating it as a mechanism of hereditary transmission is based primarily on an academic, cultural framework of evolutionary eugenics (Dodd, Belbin, Frank, & Webb, 2015; Zhu et al., 2017).

When cells replicate, colorable fibers called chromosomes also replicate in the new cells. Using a mathematical calculation of factor analysis, researchers predict the likelihood that chromosomal replication will be the same in the parent cell and the duplicated cells.

DNA and genetic analyses are based on the application of a set of mathematical equations that are then correlated with a very long chain of calculations. Based on current conceptualization and technology, no one has ever seen or will ever see atoms, molecules, DNA, or genes.

Because no has ever seen or will ever see atoms, molecules, DNA or genes as conceptually defined, the science of DNA and genetic analyses are the ideas of scientists about what they believe would happen and exist if atoms, molecules, and subatomic particles existed at a nanoscale. Because imaging and other microscopic technologies consistently produced the same measurable results, assumptions made about invisible, impalpable concepts, such as DNA, RNA, genes, genetic materials, and genetic codes were validated.

However, based on these validations, early evolutionary eugenicists employed the science of genetics to promote their agenda. Many of the scientists involved in the development of early genetics were avowed eugenicists. Further, these eugenicists openly confessed that genetics as an academic discipline along with other disciplines such as molecular biology, chemistry, and physics should be employed in extending eugenics,

It was easy to employ racial differences as a foundation in the eugenics program. Racial differences were most obviously identified with outward phenotypic characteristics such as hair, skin, and eye color and type. These outward characteristics were attributed to proteins and protein synthesis mechanisms.

Additionally, racial categorizations were also identified with vulnerability and low moral character. APR, criminality, and drunkenness were among the vices and debased moral characteristics associated with vulnerable races. Genetics was employed as a scientific approach to integrating eugenics policies.

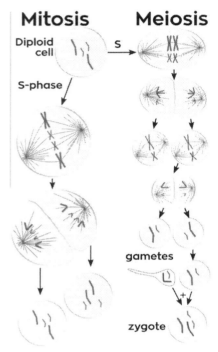

Figure 24-1 Mitosis - Meiosis

Hence, DNA a hypothesized concept validated by consistent measurements and techniques could be applied to support a genetic basis for susceptibility to vulnerability. Early genetic research focused on a disease model of diseases and disabilities that could be attributed to vulnerable classes. Vulnerable classes were not confined to the racially inferior, but the poor and deprived members of superior races and species fit the mold of susceptibility to vulnerability.

DNA analysis would be the tool to scientifically prove a genetic reproductive advantage and predispositional genetically-programmed vulnerability. It is within this logic that DNA, as genes could be applied in behavioral genetics to substantiate APR and those conditions that render an individual susceptible to APR.

In genetic analysis, geneticists observe artifacts representative of a DNA molecule. Using microscopy imaging technology, geneticists engage in careful observation of photons, for example, which are believed to be particles of light. However, no one has ever seen photons, but the behavior of images is mathematically calculated to describe their behaviors in relations to other invisible but hypothesized particles such as electrons[43].

Using these technologies along with colorable fibers in replicating cells, scientists assigned the DNA molecules and their hypothesized behaviors during cell replication. Based on these considerations, associations, and calculations, the hypothesized invisible world of atoms

---

[43] Figure 24-1 domdomegg
(https://commons.wikimedia.org/wiki/File:Three_cell_growth_types.svg),
Cropped to show only Mitosis and Meiosis by BritFix,
https://creativecommons.org/licenses/by-sa/4.0/legalcode

and molecules are applied to metabolic functions in living cells. The outcomes from these analyses are presented in terms of DNA molecular structure and sequences. These behaviors are then correlated with specific regions of colorable fibers in replicating cells to draw conclusions about the behavior of genes.

Geneticists use extremely complex calculations to make correlations about similarities or differences in chemical compositions and processes between parent and progeny cells as the mechanisms of genetic transmission. Geneticists identified three mechanisms, histone protein modifications, DNA methylation and related chemicals, and non-coding RNA as being associated with hereditary transfers (Kulminski et al., 2013; Lakadamyali & Cosma, 2015).

Genetic research fueled further research and theoretical applications of the biological basis for psychiatric dysfunctionalities and disordered states. Predispositional vulnerability to psychiatric conditions suggests there might be a biochemical biogenetic element in the presentment of APR. Based on these theoretical applications of genetic analysis, some theorists conclude that behavioral genes exist in some individuals that predisposition those individuals to aggression (de Almeida et al., 2015; Kulminski et al., 2013).

NEUROCHEMICAL BASIS OF SOCIAL–BEHAVIORAL TRANSMISSIONS

There must be evidence that the neurobiological processes and mechanisms exist in both the offspring and the ancestral generations to establish a biogenetic explanation for the existence of neuropsychiatric disorders. To ascertain the neurobiological basis for neuropsychiatric disorders, researchers must also identify specific neural pathways, anatomies, mechanisms, and processes directly related to a particular disorder. After identification of the neural pathways, anatomies, mechanisms, and processes, researchers should show that biogenetic processes produced these disorders and that these biogenetic processes are similar or identical in both offspring and progenitors. Moreover, statistical calculations and observations that directly establishes linkages in both the offspring and progenitor must also correlate (Lohoff, 2010).

Alleles are postulates of the existence of invisible particles. Alleles and allelic positions are based on ideas of atoms, molecules, and subatomic particles.

Identification of risk alleles is also based on mathematical computations, statistical correlations, and observations of events using microscopy imaging technology. Allelic research is based on even more minute positioning and correlations between chromosomes on DNA chains.

Risk alleles are associated with the presentment of several psychiatric conditions. Researchers have made a connection between stress and depression. Based on mathematical calculations and statistical equations, researchers contend that mutation exists in the serotonin transporter region; a brain region associated with depression. Arising from these calculations, geneticists propose a genetic basis of depression that is calculated to correlate to allelic risk at serotonin transporter sites.

Some studies indicate that depression coupled with social stressors, such as abuse, physical or sexual abuse increases the likelihood of APR. Other studies indicate co-morbid conditions of depression and social stressors, such as abuse. Behavioral geneticists correlate these studies with actuarial calculations of allelic risk to present a case for the genetic basis of social behaviors (Negele, Kaufhold, Kallenbach, & Leuzinger-Bohleber, 2015; Rehan, Antfolk, Johansson, Jern, & Santtila, 2017).

The presentment of depression involves several brain regions. Thus far, researchers using actuarial calculations have not been able to identify any single genetic variant that would increase the risk of depression. Findings from current research seem to suggest that the risk of depression involves interaction between multiple metabolic functions and environmental factors (Lohoff, 2010).

NEUROPHYSIOLOGICAL TRANSMISSIONS

Neurochemical and neuroanatomical mechanisms initiate a neurophysiological transmission. Neurochemical and neuroanatomical processes and mechanisms are biological. Geneticists argue that similarities in neurochemical and neuroanatomical mechanisms among blood relatives might be associated with dysfunctionalities and disordered states. However, despite similarities in neurophysiological processes between offspring and ancestors, current studies have not been able to establish that the existence of dysfunctionalities and disordered states are the products of biogenetic mechanisms and processes.

ESTIMATING THE RELIABILITY AND VALIDITY OF GENETIC TRANSMISSIONS

The science of DNA is estimated as a reliable, measurable calculation of invisible, impalpable concepts and ideas. Technological advancement has further increased the accuracy and reliability of DNA analysis.

However, there are still flaws in the measurements, specific types of analysis, and the purposes for which DNA analysis are applied. Intertwined in these inherent weaknesses due to technological limitations are the conceptualization of DNA as an indicator of genes, the storage unit of genetic materials, and the template for the genetic code.

The flawed conception is linked to the integration of philosophical constructs in classical genetics and their integration into molecular or current-day genetics. Based on classical philosophical constructs genes caused reproductive advantage or vulnerability.

This philosophical construct of genes as a causal element, is transferred into the perception that DNA, defined as genes, causes reproductive advantage or vulnerability. DNA, however, is a measurable calculation of a process and not a causal element of reproductive advantage or vulnerability. As such, there is a need to clarify the distinction between philosophical conceptualizations of genes derived from classical genetics and the functional element of DNA as genes in molecular genetics.

To establish a relationship between DNA, genetics, and behaviors, several steps of correlations must occur. Because the disease model is a focus in genetics, the dysfunction or disordered state must first be identified. The dysfunction or disordered state must then be linked with some neuroanatomical, or neurochemical process. These processes must then be converted into chemical terms and linkages before engaging in DNA assessment. Other calculations linking the dysfunctionality or the disordered state to a vulnerable group also have to be established.

After these complex associations, statistical likelihood, and correlation studies are conducted, research into generational transferences could then be undertaken to calculate the statistic likelihood relationship between DNA, environmental stimuli, and variations in molecular behavior and sequences. Further, intergenerational and intragenerational DNA assessment most commonly uses mice models from which extrapolations about human behaviors are made. Given the complexities of these calculations, correlations, and extrapolations caution is employed when making conclusions about DNA, intergenerational, and intragenerational transmissions.

CONCLUSION

Social learning theorists attribute behavior to conditioning and learning. This conceptualization suggests that APR is a learned behavior. Applying findings from genetic and epigenetic studies, behaviorists conjecture that behavior has a biological basis. While geneticists argue that these behaviors might be the products of hereditary transmissions, epigeneticists posit that there might be elements of social learning implicated in generational transmissions.

Although geneticists and epigeneticists engage in research and use DNA and RNA calculations to try to understand their implications in intergenerational and transgenerational social and behavioral transmissions, there are weaknesses in conclusively applying these findings as being causal elements in these transmissions. As such, caution should be used when applying findings from biogenetic and epi-biogenetic research in understanding social and moral behaviors.

CHAPTER REVIEW

REVIEW QUESTIONS

1. Examine the applicability of social learning theory to epigenesis.

2. Can social learning theory explain neurophysiological intergenerational and transgenerational epigenetic transmissions?

CHAPTER TWENTY-FIVE
SOCIAL-BEHAVIORAL TRANSMISSIONS

CHAPTER PREVIEW

Geneticists and epigeneticists explore whether hereditary transmissions occur via genetic or epigenomic transfers. Some studies suggest that social and behavioral cues might be involved in the transference of dysfunctional behaviors.

In this chapter, there will be a discussion of the theoretical basis of epigenetic transmissions. Epigeneticists contend that social-moral behaviors and environmental cues could trigger generational transmissions. These generational transmissions occur via epigenesis and not via genetic mechanisms. There will also be a discussion of the differences between intergenerational and transgenerational transmissions, and a discussion of generational epigenetic transmissions.

. The epigenome refers to molecular elements and processes that occur outside DNA and the genome. Epigeneticists study the epigenome to assess whether epigenetic generational transmissions have occurred. In this chapter, there will be a discussion of acquired DNA mechanisms in third and fourth generations that did not have direct exposure to environmental stimuli and social-behavioral cues.

Epigeneticists contend that social-behavioral cues and environmental conditions can trigger neurophysiological changes in offspring and subsequent generations. Epigeneticists use extrapolations of social-behavioral transmissions from ethological models — epigeneticists study inherited and acquired DNA mechanisms in progenitor and progeny to make their assessments.

This chapter also includes a discussion of the limitations and challenges of genetic and epigenetic research. Some studies are directed at fetal exposure and the impact of these exposures in future generations.

PURPOSE AND LEARNING OBJECTIVES

PURPOSE

The purpose of this chapter is to explain the difference between genetic and epigenetic transmissions and explore their implications for APR.

LEARNING OBJECTIVES

After studying this chapter, the reader should understand

1. the differences between biogenetic and bio-epigenetic transmissions; and
2. the implications of bio-epigenetic transmissions for APR.

KEY TERMS AND DEFINITIONS

Correlation

Correlation is the mutual relation between two or more things.

INTRODUCTION

Scholars engage in gene-environment interaction studies to explain its implications in the transmission of social behavior and the presentment of psychiatric conditions. However, researchers could only make conclusions from these studies that are associative. Researchers have not been able to establish a causal relationship between hereditary, social behavior, and psychiatric conditions.

Increasingly, findings from a number of studies also identify an associative correlation between neurobiological functions and processes and psychiatric conditions. However, results from these studies also have not affirmatively established a causal neurobiological-hereditary relationship (Joober et al., 2005; Lohoff, 2010).

RESEARCH INTO BIOGENESIS AND SOCIAL-BEHAVIORAL TRANSMISSIONS

Seeking to establish whether intergenerational and transgenerational transmissions occur via biogenetic or epigenomic mechanisms is the main contention between geneticists and epigeneticists. Scientists from both disciplines use complex hypotheses and extrapolate postulates from several disciplines including chemistry, physics, and molecular biology, to establish whether there is a biogenetics basis for behavior. Researchers from both disciplines present varying research outcomes (Joober et al., 2005; Lohoff, 2010).

PSYCHIATRIC PRESENTMENT AND NEUROBIOLOGY

Psychiatric presentments are the basis for diagnosing dysfunctional behaviors and disordered states. Psychiatric presentments, dysfunctionalities, and disordered states have neurobiological bases. The neurobiological bases of psychiatric or psychological presentments might be impairments and dysfunctions associated with neuroanatomy, neurochemistry, and brain electricity.

Although APR represents dysfunctionalities and disordered states, these presentments might or might not be diagnosed within the context of

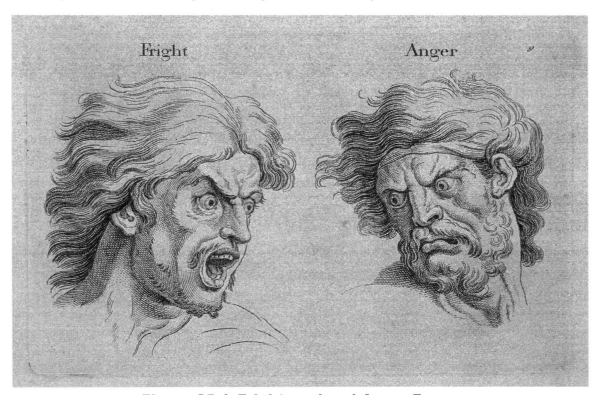

Figure 25-1 Frightened and Angry Faces

psychiatric disorders and neurobiological impairments and dysfunctionality, but might be perceived within the context of social-moral and behavioral learning theories. As such, although APR presents, its presentment[44] might not be associated with the neurobiological bases for its presentment (Carnes & Winer, 2017; Tasca, Rapetti, Carta, & Fadda, 2012).

---

[44] Figure 25-1 Wellcome Library, London
(https://commons.wikimedia.org/wiki/File:A_frightened_and_an_angry_face,_left_and_right_respectively._Wellcome_V0009326.jpg),
https://creativecommons.org/licenses/by/4.0/legalcode

Because APR is not diagnosed within its neurobiological contexts, APR is diagnosed based on social learning theories. Social learning theories focus on social-behavioral cues.

Findings from some studies suggest that social and behavioral cues might be involved in the generational transference of dysfunctional behaviors in intimate and familial relationships. Some genetic studies apply likelihood statistical equations to provide estimates and probability of generational transmissions by extrapolating historical data for specific populations and specific presentments. Geneticists that use historical data in their research base their findings on probabilistic calculations.

Because genetic and epigenetic studies apply calculations of DNA and allelic molecular behaviors and sequences, some researchers focus on the neurobiological bases for the presentment of dysfunctional behaviors and disordered states. These researchers tend to use mice models from which to make extrapolations.

In mice models, knockout techniques might be employed. Using knockout techniques, researchers could take tissue samples that are used to make correlational extrapolations. Geneticists and epigeneticists engage in ethological studies to calculate correlations of DNA and allelic variations.

Ethologists using mice models, make extrapolations for various variables, and arrive at their conclusions after several steps in research and calculations are conducted. For example, epigeneticists may make assumptions and correlations from previous allelic research into neurobiology and DNA and apply these previous findings into their current research using mice models. As such, the final calculations are derived from findings of previously-conducted research that are transferred as assumptions into their current research.

Genetic and epigenetic research include many confounders, such as chemical reactions not directly related to mitosis or meiosis. Due to these elements, findings from studies in genetics and genome mapping attempting to establish a biological basis for social-moral and behavioral generational transmissions often cannot be used as broad generalization, and must be applied with caution (Bohacek & Mansuy, 2015; Kulminski et al., 2013; Sittig & Redei, 2010).

Epigeneticists and geneticists often engage in ethological studies to assess the implications of biological mechanisms and processes in social-behavioral transmissions. These studies tend to conclude associative relationships between specific alleles using controlled methodologies, such as knockout techniques. Findings from these studies are very specific. As such, it is difficult to make generalization using these findings (Bohacek & Mansuy, 2015; Kulminski et al., 2013; Sittig & Redei, 2010).

EPIGENETIC THEORETICAL BASIS

Epigenetic research is a product of genetics and genome mapping studies. Epigeneticists agree with geneticists regarding the use of molecular behavior and sequences and the disease model to make calculations about dysfunctional behaviors. However, epigeneticists contend that the manifestation of dysfunctionalities and disordered states might be due to epigenomic and environmental conditions not involving DNA behavior and sequences. Epigeneticists explore the epigenomic elements implicated in the transmission of social-behavioral cues (Bohacek & Mansuy, 2015).

GENERATIONAL TRANSMISSIONS

A generation usually refers to an age subset of individuals in familial relationships. Several generations or age subsets may exist within one family. For example, mother, daughter, and grandmother represent three generations or age subsets within one family. Epigeneticists make a distinction between intergenerational and transgenerational transmissions (Black et al., 2010; Bohacek & Mansuy, 2015; Klengel et al., 2015).

INTERGENERATIONAL TRANSMISSIONS

An intergenerational transmission is a behavioral change that occurs among ancestral generations, such as grandparents and parents; to children and grandchildren. when they have all experienced direct exposure to environmental stimuli believed to be responsible for the behavioral change. Because there is a neurobiological basis for all behavior, behavioral changes will also elicit a neurobiological change. An epigenetic intergenerational transmission occurs when behavioral changes and biological changes co-occur that cannot be accounted for by DNA calculations.

An individual's genome and DNA structure change throughout their lifespan based on the individual's experiences. Consequently, behavioral changes and biological changes co-occur when exposure to environmental conditions elicit behavioral changes that result in changes in the individual's biological structures and processes.

TRANSGENERATIONAL TRANSMISSIONS

Transgenerational transmissions occur when biological and behavioral changes occur in both ancestral and progeny generations when the progenies did not have direct exposure to the environmental conditions that caused the behavioral and biological change. For example, a gestating female might have exposure to environmental stimuli or conditions resulting in biological changes in the fetus. The grandchildren of the female that experienced exposure to the conditions initiating biological and behavioral changes during gestation did not have exposure to the environmental conditions or stimuli, yet they show biological and behavioral changes associated with the environmental conditions to which their grandparents and great grandparents were exposed. In this case, the impact of the environmental conditions or stimuli shows up in progenies that did not have direct exposure to the environmental conditions or stimuli. Behavioral and biological changes in the third and the fourth generations that did not experience direct exposure to the environmental conditions that initiated the changes in biological and behavioral changes are referred to as transgenerational transmissions (Klengel et al., 2015).

INTERGENERATIONAL EPIGENETIC INHERITANCE

An intergenerational vulnerability exists in the transmission of APR. This vulnerability appears to occur as an epigenetic transfer that results in changes in molecular behavior and sequences that cannot be accounted for by DNA calculations. Although biological and behavioral changes occurred, calculations of DNA molecular behavior, structures, and sequences remain unchanged. Findings from epigenetic studies suggest that changes in manifested characteristics, traits, and behaviors due to adaptation occur more frequently and much faster than inferred under the theory of evolution (Black et al., 2010; Bohacek & Mansuy, 2015; Klengel et al., 2015).

Intergenerational transmission is believed to entail a biological component referred to as the epigenome. Epigenetic inheritance includes both intragenerational and intergenerational transmissions. Intergenerational epigenetic inheritance occurs when all three generations have direct exposure to the environmental stimuli that impacted the epigenome. Direct exposure to environmental conditions that produce phenotypic changes emerges in ancestors, parents, their germs, and eggs.

The embryos of these parents will also experience direct exposure during their in-utero experience. Intergenerational transmissions are only applicable to the fetal experiences if parental exposures affect the fetal epigenome causing the impact of the exposure to show up in the third generation.

Under experimental conditions, epigenetic inheritance occurs when research animals experience direct exposure to changed or specific environmental conditions. For example, exposure of adult rodents to stressful or aversive conditions caused neural changes in adult rodents' epigenomes, their offspring, germs, and embryos that also experienced directly in utero exposure to the stressful or aversive conditions. Epigeneticists refer to the shared neural changes in sequential molecular patterns and mechanisms between parents and their offspring, germs, and embryos with direct in utero exposure to the stressful or aversive conditions as an intergenerational transference. An intergenerational transmission or transference is determined to be epigenetic when these changes in sequential molecular patterns and mechanisms cannot be accounted for by changes in the calculations of molecular sequences, behaviors, patterns, and composition of DNA (Black et al., 2010; Bohacek & Mansuy, 2015; Klengel et al., 2015).

TRANSGENERATIONAL EPIGENETIC INHERITANCE

Transgenerational epigenetic inheritance refers to a transmission that affects several generations of the same family. However, transgenerational epigenetic inheritance differs from intergenerational epigenetic inheritance in that changes occur in the third generation and beyond, even when there is no direct exposure to the environmental conditions. Transgenerational epigenetic inheritance refers to the transmission of the epigenome as an inherited change in molecular structure, patterns, sequences, behaviors, and compositions that occur from one generation to another, but which cannot be accounted for by DNA mechanisms.

When epigeneticists observe epigenetic inheritance in the offspring, germs, and in utero embryos in the third and fourth generations based on their ancestors' epigenomes; epigeneticists associate the epigenetic inheritance with the ancestral generations' direct exposure to environmental conditions. The epigenetic inheritance that occurs in the third and fourth generations because their ancestral generations experienced direct exposure to environmental conditions that produced the epigenome, even though third and fourth generation offspring and embryos had no direct exposure to the environmental conditions responsible for the epigenomic change in their ancestral generations. In those instances where both parents experienced exposure to the environmental conditions before conception, the changes in behavioral expressions might also occur in the second generation although the embryo did not experience direct exposure to the environmental conditions.

Epigeneticists refer to epigenetic inheritance in the third generations and beyond as transgenerational transferences because epigenetic inheritance occurred in the third generations and beyond without direct exposure to environmental conditions. The absence of direct exposure to the environmental conditions and the transfer of the epigenome to the third generation and beyond distinguish transgenerational from intergenerational transference.

Intergenerational transmissions of manifested characteristics, traits, and behaviors occur when a parent with direct environmental exposure transmits the effects of the exposure to subsequent generations by means of developing germline cells or fetuses. When exposure occurs before conception, both male and female parents that experienced the exposure can trigger the epigenetic transfer. Intergenerational transmissions occur when both the parents and the embryo have direct exposure to the environmental stimuli.

Transgenerational transfers occur when offspring of the third generation manifest acquired molecular patterns, sequences, behaviors, compositions, and mechanisms, even when the embryo or offspring experienced no direct exposure to the environmental stimuli. Transgenerational transfers occur when offspring and fetus manifest acquired molecular patterns, sequences, compositions, behaviors, and mechanism without direct exposure to the environmental stimuli (Black et al., 2010; Bohacek & Mansuy, 2015; Klengel et al., 2015).

BEHAVIORAL AND SOCIAL TRANSMISSIONS

Behavioral or social transmissions imply the conscious or unconscious transfer of information from progenitors to progenies causing behavioral adjustments to occur. Information that causes behavioral modifications in entrainment and conditioning can occur during behavioral and social interactions between parents and offspring. Social learning theorists interpret APR as behavioral and social transmissions due to entrainment and conditioning (Black et al., 2010).

Behaviorists define social and moral behaviors[45] as learned transmissions that can occur between and across generations. Nevertheless, all behaviors have a neurological component. Social and moral behaviors are environmental stimuli and responses that trigger neurobiological changes. As such, social and moral behaviors can result in changes in biological processes and mechanisms (Carnes & Winer, 2017; Rosenfeld, Lieberman, & Jarskog, 2011).

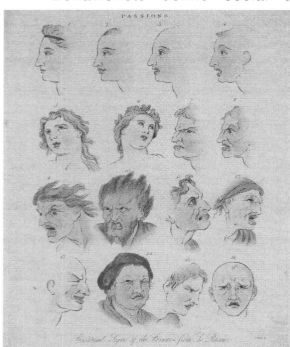

Figure 25-2 Emotions

Current technological and ethical limitations preclude research into the role of DNA and behavioral and social generational transmissions in humans. As such, researchers engage in ethological studies to assess whether changes in biological and behavioral

---

[45] Figure 25-2 Wellcome Library, London
(https://commons.wikimedia.org/wiki/File:Sixteen_faces_expressing_the_human _passions._Wellcome_L0068375_(cropped).jpg), https://creativecommons.org/licenses/by/4.0/legalcode

processes are due to aversive social and behavioral environments (Bohacek & Mansuy, 2015; Klengel et al., 2015).

Epigeneticists contend behavioral and social cues are environmental stimuli that might be transmittable through nongenetic intergenerational and transgenerational mechanisms. According to the theory of epigenesis, exposure to the environmental stimuli is the variable that determines whether the transmission is intergenerational or intragenerational. Epigeneticists assess that the transfer is biogenetic if exposure to environmental stimuli produces changes in mechanisms and processes identified as genetic materials; and if these changes occur similarly in parents, ancestors, and progenies. However, changes in characteristics, traits, and behaviors are deemed to be non-biogenetic, if these changes occur without affecting genomic mechanisms and processes (Bohacek & Mansuy, 2015; Klengel et al., 2015).

INHERITED AND ACQUIRED DNA SEQUENCES

In the study of epigenesis, researchers observe hypothetical particles inferred from complex calculations using imaging technology. Under laboratory conditions, epigeneticists use concepts and theories of physics and chemistry to create physiochemical models to simulate exposure to environmental stimuli. Like geneticists, epigeneticists also apply actuarial calculations and predictive statistical equations to make inferences about DNA and RNA molecules. Comparing calculations from before and after, or using controlled samples, epigeneticists infer whether the molecular structures of DNA and RNA are impacted by exposure to environmental stimuli. Epigeneticists refer to those changes in molecular sequences, behavior, patterns, compositions, structures, and mechanisms that occur, but which did not exist in progenitors prior to exposure are acquired.

DIRECT AND INDIRECT EXPOSURE

Direct exposure to environmental stimuli can occur in humans and their embryos. Embryos can also experience indirect exposure due to parental exposure transmitted as embryonic experiences. Progeny generations can have indirect exposure because ancestral exposure impacted their epigenome.

In a few epigenetic studies, laboratory animals received exposure to specific environmental stimuli. Epigeneticists make observations and calculations to assess the likelihood that new molecular structures, patterns, sequences, and compositions are acquired. Ethological researchers use biological samples from laboratory animals that had first-hand exposure and animals that had direct and indirect in-utero exposure as evidence of direct exposure to the stimuli.

Researchers study before and after exposure biological samples or compare biological samples between laboratory animals with exposure to environmental stimuli and with biological samples from animals with no exposure to calculate whether exposure to environmental stimuli affected molecular structures. Calculations showing the same molecular structures in the adult laboratory animals with direct exposure, direct exposure of in-utero animals, and indirect exposure of in-utero animals are defined as intergenerational transmissions.

Research into whether the descendants of progeny clones or the emergence of changes in the third and fourth generations are critical elements used in determining whether epigenesis occurs. Epigeneticists refer to the existence of changes in molecular structures, patterns, sequences, composition, and behavior in the third and fourth generation laboratory animals without either direct or indirect in utero exposure to the environmental stimuli as intragenerational transmissions (Bohacek & Mansuy, 2015; Klengel et al., 2015).

CHALLENGES RESEARCHING BIOGENETIC BEHAVIORAL TRANSMISSIONS

Behavioral and social transmissions can occur between parents and offspring. However, to determine whether these transfers occur as a biogenetic transmission process presents several ethical and practical challenges. The most effective ways to research whether there is a biogenetic transmission of social behavior is by engaging in cross-fostering, in vitro fertilization, or by conducting experiments over several generations. These methods of research pose ethical and practical considerations.

One plausible means of exploring whether there is a biogenetic transmission of social behavior involves the study of epigenesis. Studies in genetics aim at determining whether information transmissions take place via chemical processes through germ cells from ancestral generations to offspring. Transmissions that occur without changes in DNA calculations are referred to as epigenetic transmissions. Recent studies seem to implicate the epigenome as being involved in the transmission of social behavior (Bohacek & Mansuy, 2015; Klengel et al., 2015).

Geneticists identified three types of cells in humans, germ cells, somatic cells, and stem cells. Germ cells are haploid cells formed in the gonads and testes. Germ cells are transmitted from parents to offspring. Germ cells are believed to possess DNA and chromosomes responsible for genetic transmissions from parents to offspring.

Somatic cells and stem cells replicate to form tissues, organs, and plasma. Somatic cells are diploid cells and have been shown to be sensitive to environmental stimuli and conditions.

Environmental conditions and stimuli can cause changes to somatic and stem cells. Ancestral exposure to environmental conditions and stimuli causing changes in somatic and stem cells, but not in germ cells, and which are transmitted to progenies are determined to be epigenetic transmissions (Bohacek & Mansuy, 2015; Klengel et al., 2015; Solana, 2013).

CHALLENGES RESEARCHING EPIGENETIC BEHAVIORAL TRANSMISSIONS

Epigeneticists assess epigenomic transmissions by evaluating and comparing calculations of the molecular structure, behavior, composition, and sequences of RNA from the germline, somatic, and stem cells in ancestors and progeny clones. Epigeneticists retrieve their biological samples from progeny clones of transgenes and the organisms' or parents' cells.

However, like conclusions from genetic studies, epigeneticists encounter difficulties making generalizations from epigenetic studies. Three foundational elements preclude the establishment of generalizations regarding biological epigenetic transmissions; these include the associative nature of genetic and epigenetic studies, variability and volatility of phenotypes and RNA, and ethical concerns regarding the use of human subjects and embryos in scientific studies.

Thus far, findings from genetic and epigenetic research are largely associative. Research findings remain tenable because DNA analysis and genome mapping are based on hypothetical assumptions that cannot be conclusively attested also because these concepts are ideas and not real entities. Findings are limited to studies involving vector mapping and transgene cloning. These findings have very specific applications.

Genome mappers aim to identify allelic areas responsible for hereditary transmissions. Allelic research has several setbacks associated with the use of transgenes in the mapping process. DNA evaluation is a physiochemical analysis process. However, DNA testing involves the use of additional chemicals to biological samples, such as the addition of a methyl group, which is an alkyl derived from methane. These chemicals, when added to the samples, might cause additional chemical modifications that are not associated with DNA. The addition of these chemicals might act as confounders (Marini et al., 2015).

Moreover, chemical interactions with only a limited number of proteins are analyzed in DNA evaluation. Research indicates that several protein modifications besides these four nitrogenous bases might occur and present a combination of modifications that are not included in the analysis.

Genetic testing and epigenetic research focus on DNA instead of RNA. RNA believed to be the interactor with DNA is believed to be highly variable and volatile (Bohacek & Mansuy, 2015; Klengel et al., 2015).

EPIGENESIS, IN UTERO EXPERIENCES, AND FUTURE GENERATIONS

Neuropsychiatric disorders often accompany dysfunctional relational behaviors. Several studies indicate that embryonic exposure to stressful environmental stimuli causes predispositional vulnerability to neuropsychiatric disorders, such as depression, anxiety, and post-traumatic stress disorder (PTSD). Maternal exposure to stressful environmental conditions suggests that the embryo might also experience direct exposure while in-utero.

While several studies cite maternal exposure to environmental stimuli as the pathway to epigenetic intergenerational transmissions, other studies indicate that the embryo could have direct exposure to environmental stimuli as an in-utero experience. Neuropsychiatric disorders have a neurobiological basis. Nevertheless, a neurobiological basis for a disorder does not indicate a biogenetic association (Serón-Ferré, Richter, Valenzuela, & Torres-Farfan, 2016; Sittig & Redei, 2010).

Currently, ethical, legal, and practical considerations curtail research assessing exposure to aversive environmental conditions involving human subjects. Current levels of technology cannot be used to ascertain even limited findings or to make generalizations. Most studies that attempt to establish a gene-environmental interaction due to exposure to aversive and stressful environmental conditions have these limitations and have been unable to present conclusive evidence for this phenomenon (Bohacek & Mansuy, 2015; Klengel et al., 2015).

CONCLUSION

The diathesis-stress vulnerability model purports environmental stimuli can ignite biogenetic predispositional vulnerability. According to the tenets of this model, APR represents a biogenetic predisposition that might be ignited by environmental stimuli. This model is premised on evolutionary theory, which purports that genes are responsible for the hereditary transmission of vulnerability. Although hypothetical assumptions concerning genes, genome, and genetics purport the existence of genetic transfers, research, thus far, has not uncovered the existence of genes as a physical component.

The hypothetical assumptions concerning DNA, genes, and genetic materials, have thus far, only yielded an associative relationship between manifested characteristics, traits, and behaviors and the hypothetical constructs of genes and genetic materials. As such, although the diathesis-stress vulnerability model has been applied as an explanation for APR, current research does not support the diathesis-stress as an unequivocal causative element in this phenomenon.

Despite these shortcomings in the research, APR represents dysfunctionalities that appear to stem from epigenetic vulnerability. Two aspects of environmental conditions are critical to the manifestations of these dysfunctionalities, contributing environmental conditions, and exposure to abuse and violence. An array of socioeconomic, moral, ethical, cultural, nutrition, and emotional elements can be environmental triggers that predispose victims and perpetrators to engage in dysfunctional behaviors in their intimate and familial relationships. Direct exposure to these dysfunctional behaviors can also be elemental in epigenetic inheritance.

CHAPTER REVIEW

REVIEW QUESTIONS

1. Distinguish between genetic and epigenetic transmissions.
2. How can direct and indirect influences affect epigenetic transmissions?

CHAPTER TWENTY-SIX
PANSPERMIA

CHAPTER PREVIEW

Some theorists use the panspermia theory to explain the origin of life on earth. According to this theory, an interplanetary interception is responsible for the origin of life on earth.

Panspermia theorists propose that an interplanetary interception involving reptile-like creatures produced life on earth. The reptilian brain theory was used to substantiate aspects of this theory. Interplanetary interception caused hostile beings from other planets to produce life on earth. Hostility and aggression are the products of interplanetary interception.

In this chapter, there will be a discussion of the main elements of the panspermia theory. Panspermia theory is considered pseudoscience and has a basis in religious myths and legends. Theories of panspermia have religious influences that might suggest a common literary source.

The emergence of organic from inorganic substances is among the early proposals concerning the origin of life. Currently, researchers using protocell technology are seeking to validate the concept that organic life might have emerged from inorganic substances. This proposal that organic might have emerged out of inorganic is discussed against the background of current studies and philosophies from antiquity.

Several tenets are associated with interplanetary interception including interplanetary seeding, and the exploded planet hypothesis. Interplanetary interception is believed to be the answer to the missing intra-species link between prehistoric progenitors and modern-day humans.

A review of myths, legends, and cultural explanations concerning the origin of life on earth is also provided in this chapter. Current research into the hybridization and genetic chimerism seem supportive of legends of interspecies hybridization found in myths, legends, and cultural explanations. There is also a discussion of the link between science and religion in explaining the origin of life on earth in this chapter.

PURPOSE AND LEARNING OBJECTIVES

PURPOSE

The purpose of this chapter is to explore the assumptions of alternative explanations regarding relational dysfunctionalities among humans.

LEARNING OBJECTIVES

After completing this chapter, the reader should understand the applicability of alternative assumptions regarding relational dysfunctionalities.

KEY TERMS AND DEFINITIONS

Chimerism

Chimerism stemmed from the Greek mythological god known as Chimaera, a fire-breathing Greek god with a lion's head, goat's body, and a serpent's tail.

Demyelination

Demyelination is the loss of myelin from the nerve sheaths.

Genetic Hybridization

Genetic hybridization is a scientific creation of an intraspecies from which a new species is created.

Panspermia

Panspermia is the theory that life exists and is distributed throughout the universe in forms that permit development based on the planetary atmosphere.

INTRODUCTION

A theoretical premise that the brains of mammals evolved, possibly over millions of years, is the basis of the reptilian brain theory. Some theorists contend that an interplanetary interception might explain the existence of the reptilian brain in humans. The interplanetary interception explanation has emerged from panspermia and related theories. Myths, legends, and religions also have similar propositions. Theorists present these propositions as explanations for the origin of life and the ontogeny of species (Boulay, 2003; Burke, 1986).

REPTILIAN BRAIN THEORY

Some theorists contend the reptilian brain evolved from a form of mammal-like reptile that once ranged widely over the world but disappeared during the Triassic period. These theorists believe that all modern-day mammals, including humans, have this reptilian brain also called the R-complex. These theorists believe the reptilian brain in humans, and modern-day mammals developed from reptilian creatures who invaded the earth (Boulay, 2003).

Interplanetary interception theorists use archaeological and anthropological literature to support their theories. Scientists have also been engaging in outer space research to search for answers that might explain the origin of life and the ontogeny of species. Theorists argue that hybridization between hominids and hominin is a likely explanation to bridge the gap of the missing link in theories of evolution (Burke, 1986; Choi C. Q., 2018).

There is a disproportionate level of violence among humans when compared with other primates, mammals, and reptiles. Evolutionary theorists explain human aggression within the context of survivability. However, survivability might not provide an adequate explanation concerning the disproportionate level of violence among humans when compared with other species (Natarajan & Caramaschi, 2010; Wrangham, 2018).

Alternative theorists, such as those positing interplanetary interception suppositions, suggest that malevolence against humans might be due to hostility from inhabitants from another planet. These theorists contend that interbreeding between interplanetary beings and humans caused genetic expressions of violence and aggression in humans (Boulay, 2003; Wallis, 2014).

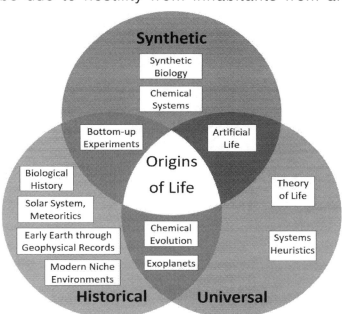

Figure 26-1 Origin of Life Determination

ALTERNATIVE THEORETICAL PROPOSITIONS OF ONTOGENY OF SPECIES

Some proponents of the origin of life[46] suggest life emerged from a process called abiogenesis. Proponents of abiogenesis suggest the original life-form or forms emerged from inorganic materials from which species evolved. Abiogenesis is integrated into evolutionary studies that include paleontology, fossil records, biochemistry, and molecular

---

[46] Figure 26-1 (Scharf et al., 2015)

biology. Some abiogenesis and neo-abiogenesis theorists suggest that original life-forms emerged from oceanic inorganic material (Peretó, 2005; Scharf et al., 2015).

Other theorists suggest that the origin of life might be the result of panspermia, processes of astrobiology, creationism, or extraterrestrial organic molecular processes. These theorists emphasize elements and processes that originated from outside the organism. Three fundamental perspectives, internal, internal-external, or external influences are elemental in all these seemingly diverse theories concerning life and the origin of life (Peretó, 2005; Scharf et al., 2015).

PANSPERMIA THEORIES

Panspermia theorists hypothesize that life did not originate on earth. According to this theory, life was transported to earth from some other planet or place in the universe. The common thread of panspermia is found in several world religions and cultures. As such, religious and cultural theories, myths, and legends provide a large body of literature in support of panspermia (Oparin, 1957; Wallis, 2014; Yunis, Zuniga, Romero, & Yunis, 2007).

The Greek god Pan, depicted as half-god and half-man, is one of the legends handed down through Greek mythology. Darwin coined the term pangenes based on the connection with the Greek god Pan and genetic transmission. Modern-day genetic theories consider genes as the method through which hereditary transmissions occur. The concept of panspermia[47], germination of seeds through the god Pan is also at the root of theory and research into panspermia (Peretó, 2005; Peretó et al., 2009).

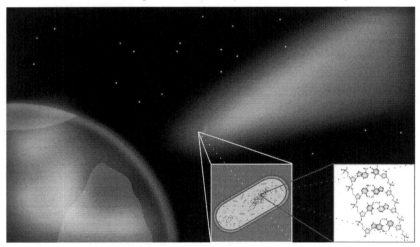

Figure 26-2 Panspermia

Two additional principles, the nature of matter and the nature of life are associated with the conceptions of living creatures and the eternity of

---

[47] Figure 26-2 Silver Spoon Sokpop (https://commons.wikimedia.org/wiki/File:Panspermie.svg), „Panspermie", https://creativecommons.org/licenses/by-sa/3.0/legalcode

life. These conceptualizations were foundational to the theory of panspermia (Oparin, 1957).

COMMON LITERARY SOURCES

Based on extrapolating from the work of several early philosophers and scientists, it can be concluded that both religious and scientific theories concerning the origin of life emerged from similar literary sources. These were primarily religious and cultural literary sources. These sources tended to ascribe spiritual, ethereal, and incorporeal explanations for the origin of life (Alexandria, 1981; Burke, 1986; Oparin, 1957).

LIVING CREATURES AND THE THEORY OF ETERNITY

Research into the emergence of living creatures developing from out of the water also has a basis in the Biblical book of Genesis. "Let the waters bring forth abundantly, the moving creatures that hath life" [Genesis 1: 10, KJV]. The principle that living creatures emerged from the water fueled research into microbes. This belief remains fundamental to evolutionists, who contended that early life-forms emerged from the water. Evolutionary research into microbes and sea creatures continue based on this early belief found in religious scripts.

According to Oparin, idealists believe that

Living creatures are born and die, but life itself, being a non-material principle, the essence of life, is spiritual and hence eternal. Life is never destroyed, nor does it arise afresh, it only changes its external material envelope, as it transforms inert material into living organisms. (Oparin, 1957, p. 43).

Darwin argued that modern-day man might have emerged from preexisting life-form. In antiquity, the theory of preexistence was based on the belief that the earth or planet existed possibly in another form prior to modern-day earth. The hypothesis that modern-day man emerged from the combined elements of living creatures and eternal, invisible life is foundational to the theory of panspermia.

THIS IS THE ACCOUNT OF HOW ALL WAS in suspense, all calm, in silence; all motionless, still, and the expanse of the sky was empty.

This is the first account, the first narrative. There was neither man, nor animal, birds, fishes, crabs, trees, stones, caves, ravines, grasses, nor forests; there was only the sky.

The surface of the earth had not appeared. There was only the calm sea and the great expanse of the sky.

There was nothing brought together, nothing which could make a noise, nor anything which might move, or tremble, or could make noise in the sky.

> *There was nothing standing; only the calm water, the placid sea, alone and tranquil. Nothing existed.*
>
> *There was only immobility and silence in the darkness, in the night.*
> *(The book of the people: POPUL VUH, 1954, p. 1:1).*

> *Thus let it be done! Let the emptiness be filled! Let the water recede and make a void, let the earth appear and become solid; let it be done. Thus they spoke. Let there be light, let there be dawn in the sky and on the earth! There shall be neither glory nor grandeur in our creation and formation until the human being is made, man is formed. So they spoke.*
>
> *Then the earth was created by them. Then the earth was created by them. So it was, in truth, that they created the earth. Earth! they said, and instantly it was made.*
>
> *Like the mist, like a cloud, and like a cloud of dust was the creation, when the mountains appeared from the water; and instantly the mountains grew.*
> *(The book of the people: POPUL VUH, 1954, p. 1:1).*

PRINCIPLES OF INORGANIC AND ORGANIC

In their 2010 study, Schrum et al. (2010) apperceived that life on earth might have emerged from prior chemical and geophysical processes. The initial building block of organic life might have come from a combination of organic and inorganic substances that facilitated "spontaneous and catalyzed assembly processes that might have led to the formation of primitive membranes and early genetic polymers, their coassembly into membrane-encapsulated nucleic acids and the chemical and physical processes that allowed for their replication" (Schrum et al., 2010, p. 1).

According to the principle of the nature of matter, matter cannot produce life without some infusion of elements that contain life. As such, organic matter cannot spontaneously emerge from inorganic matter. Matter, in this case, the slimy earth and the atmospheric conditions were ideal for fertilization. Some source caused the infusion of spermata or germ cells. This source might be external to the earth (Oparin, 1957).

Scientists concluded that carbon changed form from inorganic to organic states to produce life. Nevertheless, some philosophers concluded "summing up all the evidence at our disposal, we may conclude that, under natural conditions, the conversion of carbon from its inorganic to its organic compounds is only effected by the agency of living beings" (Oparin, 1957, p. 111).

Schrum et al. (2010) contend:

> The hollow channels within the rocks of the alkaline off-axis hydrothermal vents provide a protected compartmentalized environment where it has been suggested that primitive metabolic activities might have originated. Recent theoretical studies suggested that the strong thermal gradients present in hydrothermal vents, together with the thin channels produced by mineral precipitation, could greatly concentrate small organic molecules such as nucleotides as well as larger nucleic acids from a very dilute external reservoir (Baaske et al. 2007).
> (Schrum et al., p. 11).

INCORPOREAL MEANS AND PANSPERMIA

The conception of the earth by incorporeal means was also elemental in the theory of panspermia. Philo[48] contended incorporeal elements, such as light and heavenly bodies, were created and that this creation occurred before the corporeal, tangible elements of the earth. Using the Mosaic account, Philo argued that the Genesis account is one of chronicity and not necessarily an account of time. As such, incorporeal elements, such as light that are essential for the emergence of life were created before the emergence of tangible and corporeal elements (Alexandria, 1981).

Figure 26-3 Philo of Alexandria

According to Philo, the creation of incorporeal heavenly bodies happened before the emergence of a firmament. The firmament represents the physical elements of heaven or Uranus. The firmament emerged due to the physical existence of the earth. Philo further argued that the combined elements of the incorporeal heavenly bodies and the corporeal firmament were integral in the origin of life on the earth (Alexandria, 1981; Kaspin-Powell, 2018).

---

[48] Figure 26-3 André Thévet creator QS:P170,Q523054 (https://commons.wikimedia.org/wiki/File:PhiloThevet.jpg), „PhiloThevet", marked as public domain, more details on Wikimedia Commons: https://commons.wikimedia.org/wiki/Template:PD-old

INTERPLANETARY SEEDING

Researchers continue to assess the validity of early theories used to explain the emergence of life on the planet (Oparin, 1957). Supporters of the interplanetary seeding hypothesis draw information from several disciplines, including anthropology, archaeology, chemistry, physics, genetics, and biology (Wallis, 2014).

Research in interplanetary seeding explores life and conditions that facilitate the emergence of life through interplanetary media (Choi C. Q., 2018). Some research centers on the earliest fossil records used to establish the timetable for the existence of life on earth. Some geneticists suggest many genes were available at the very beginning of life on earth and many more genes apparently preceded the earthly advent of the features these genes encode (Wallis, 2014; Wickramasinghe, 2018).

WAR IN THE HEAVENS: THE EXPLODED PLANET HYPOTHESIS

A belief exists in several world cultures that there was a war in the heavens that caused upheavals of some sort on the earth. Myths and legends held by some people in some of these cultures uphold an affiliation between the ruling class and interplanetary beings. This idea of war in the heavens has been passed into modern-day literature as myths, fiction, cultural, and religious beliefs. However, increasingly, scientific evidence seems to be pointing to the occurrence of massive meteoroid activities that occurred somewhere around 4.6-billion-years ago in the history of the planet (Van Flandern, 2007).

Research indicates that two major explosions occurred somewhere during the 4.6-billion-year history of the planets. These explosions might account for the origin of life on earth, the current atmosphere surrounding the earth, the current state and existence of the planet Mars, and possibly the destruction of a hypothetical planet referred to as Phaeton in Greek mythology (The Editors of Encyclopædia Britannica, 2007; Van Flandern, 2007).

Melott et al. (2004) suggested that a catastrophic gamma-ray burst might have caused the extinction of ancient life on the earth. The authors also contend that this catastrophic event might have initiated changes in the earth's environmental conditions caused the new life to emerge on the earth. The authors further contended that this devastating event might also be responsible for hydrothermal conditions responsible for the emergence of life. These conclusions have striking similarities to other scientific postulates, as well as anthropological, historical, biblical, and other accounts of the origin of life on earth (Melott et al., 2004; Peretó, Controversies on the origin of life, 2005).

INTERPLANETARY INTERCEPTION: MISSING LINK THEORY

Myths, legends, cultural, historical, anthropological, archaeological and religious documents assert that aliens referred variously as the reptilians and gods came to the earth at the time that planetary explosions of some sort occurred. In these documents, the planetary explosions described as a war in heaven or war among the gods (Alexandria, 1981).

Interplanetary interception of the earth occurred when a nonhuman interplanetary race merged with humans, hominids, hominins, or humanoids that lived on the earth. Historical and anthropological records also reported cataclysmic climatic changes that might account for adaptation among humans, hominids, or humanoids. Some of the existing literature suggests the interplanetary interception was hostile. Malevolent, interplanetary gods manipulated hominins, hominids, and humanoids into subjugation and slavery (Boulay, 2003).

Theorists use the interplanetary interception hypothesis to explain the missing intra-species progenitors that link reptiles and humans. These theorists propose that adaptation, environmental, and climatic changes required for the evolution of modern-day man came about because of war among these interplanetary beings called gods. Interplanetary interception theorists use the reptilian brain theory to support their theory as an explanation for the existence of modern-day man (Alexandria, 1981).

Darwin recognized the missing link as a fundamental flaw in the theory of evolution. Although the missing link and the absence of fossil support continue to exist, the interplanetary interception hypothesis has reemerged. In the historical and anthropological literature, these gods were both malevolent and benevolent (Boulay, 2003).

These legends of hybridization inform current research into evolution. The missing genetic link in current evolution theories refers to the absence of a common ancestor between modern-day man and an anthropoid progenitor. Hybridization with a reptilian race might bridge the gap related to a missing genetic link. Researchers in biogenetics, genetic chimerism, and hybridization seek to establish the validity of interplanetary interception hypothesis and provide elucidation on interbreeding or intermingling between two distinct genetic forms (Boulay, 2003; Chen, 2014; Laurent et al., 2016; Melott et al., 2004).

Malevolence toward humans and combat among these gods caused malicious manipulation of the human brain to cause a statistically higher rate of species-to-species violence among humans. As the gods engaged in war among themselves for planetary control, humans became pawns in the conflicts among the gods (Boulay, 2003).

Interplanetary interception theory provides an explanation for neural changes and brain development among hominins, hominids, or humanoids.

Changes and development occurred in the three broad brain regions found in modern-day human due to this interplanetary interception. Interplanetary interception theorists contend that the first brain or the reptilian brain has similarities with the brains of nonhuman interplanetary beings who hybridized with hominins, hominids, or humanoids on the earth in ancient times (Boulay, 2003; Chen, 2014; Laurent et al., 2016).

MYTHS, LEGENDS, AND CULTURES

Depictions from cuneiform tablets, petroglyphs and hieroglyphs provide clues to modern-day human origins as being due to interplanetary interception. Several ancient cultures share a common legend that a nonhuman or reptilian race, descended to the earth and intermingled with hominins, hominids, or humanoids resulting in the evolution of a superior species or modern-day man. Some researchers are now stating that these were not legends but actual occurrences (Boulay, 2003; Chen, 2014; Laurent et al., 2016).

These legends of hybridization inform current research into evolution. The missing genetic link in current evolution theories refers to the absence of a common ancestor between modern-day man and an anthropoid progenitor. Hybridization with a reptilian race might bridge the gap related to a missing genetic link. Researchers in biogenetics, genetic chimerism, and hybridization seek to establish the validity of interplanetary interception hypothesis and provide elucidation on interbreeding or intermingling between two distinct genetic forms (Boulay, 2003; Chen, 2014; Laurent et al., 2016; Melott et al., 2004).

GENETIC CHIMERISM

Genetic chimerism is scientific research into the merging of two zygotes to form a single organism. Hybridization occurs when two zygotes are fused at a very early stage. Hybridization and enzyme manipulation to cause fusion that results in the production of one unit or entity with distinct

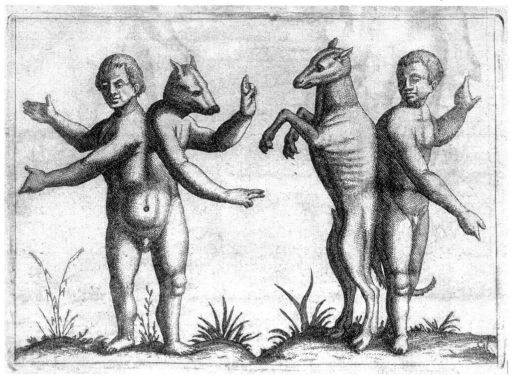

Figure 26-4 Liceti, De monstris, 1668 Wellcome

characteristics representative of the fused organisms. Chimerism[49] has its origin in myths and legends related to the genetic mixing of spiritual beings or gods with humans. Genetic chimerism stemmed from the Greek mythological god known as Chimaera, a fire-breathing Greek god with a lion's head, goat's body, and a serpent's tail (Boulay, 2003).

Enzyme manipulation and demyelination are used in hybridization to produce the chemicals or characteristics the scientist wishes to produce in the new crossbred organism. Findings from biogenetic, genetic chimerism and hybridization might provide support for an interplanetary interception theory. Hybridization and chimerism theories suggest a lower life-form can be hybridized with a superior form to create a distinct life-form. The new life-form or hybrid is of higher intelligence than the lower life-form (Boulay, 2003; Gaidos & Selsis, 2007; Robson, 2017; Yunis et al., 2007).

---

[49] Figure 26-4 anonymous
(https://commons.wikimedia.org/wiki/File:Liceti,_De_monstris,_1668_Wellcome_
L0027463.jpg), https://creativecommons.org/licenses/by/4.0/legalcode

Since 2011, scientists in the United Kingdom created more than 150 human-animal embryos involving various animals, such as pigs, dogs, rabbits, cows, and sheep under the 2008 Human Fertilization and Embryology Act. Reptilian brain theorists suggest that hybridization between the reptilian race and humans affects the way modern humans' brain functions, especially the unconscious processes. Moreover, DNA imprinting for adaptation and survival, primarily located in the reptilian brain region, might be due to chimerism between hominins, hominids, or humanoids and the reptilian races (Boulay, 2003; Gaidos & Selsis, 2007; Robson, 2017; Yunis et al., 2007).

HYBRIDIZATION AND THE REPTILIAN RACE

Interplanetary interception hybridization between hominins, hominids or humanoids and the reptilian race might have occurred during the Triassic period. The Triassic period is called the Saurian dynasty or reign of the Saurus or dinosaurs (Ezcurra, Scheyer, & Butler, 2014; Pu et al., 2013).

An etymological study links the dinosaurs with an interplanetary reptilian race. Deinós is a Greek word meaning fearful, mighty, or terrifying. Deity comes from the word deinós. Deinós or dino is the root word for dinosaur. Saurus is a scientific term meaning reptile. The word Saurus forms the root word for thesaurus. Thesaurus is a book where a body of similar words is grouped. Theo, which means god, is the affix in the word thesaurus. The ancient Greeks, words conceived as spirit or energy. Word is energy that intertwines with the electromagnetic field. Etymologically, dinosaur means the rule or reign of the terrible or the rule of the word (Liddell & Scott, 2007).

Some theorists believe the Saurians was an interplanetary reptilian race from Uranus. The first reptiles were the reptoids, who formed the initial building block for human DNA. The scientists who developed DNA theory calculate that DNA replicates when cells divide. Because of this, DNA is presented as a self-replicating material present in all living organisms. Because DNA is presented as a self-replicating material, scientists hypothesizing about the behavior of DNA believe that DNA are the carriers of genetic information, which defines the fundamental and distinctive characteristics of species and the individuals (Boulay, 2003; Choi C. Q., 2018; Ezcurra et al., 2014; Liu C., 2013).

Reptilian brain theorists state that the reptilian brain in mammals shares fundamental characteristics with reptiles. They believe a species referred to as the reptilian race imparted their traits to humans and mammals. Reptilian theorists argue that the reptilian brain is the powerhouse and driving force of aggressive behaviors (Ezcurra et al., 2014; Pu et al., 2013).

According to the triune brain model, the neocortex was the last region to be developed in the human brain. This region is primarily responsible for cognition, verbal, and nonverbal communication. Some theorists contend the Saurian race was an intelligent, more advanced race than the hominins, humanoids, and hominids, the intermingling of these species with Saurians initiated the development of the neocortex in humans (Ezcurra et al., 2014; Laurent et al., 2016).

Interbreeding between these interplanetary gods with hominins, hominids, and humanoids produced a superior race that now had greater sophisticated cognitive abilities, such as the ability to speak and process speech. As such, central to several theories of evolution is the conception that the human brain evolved from being primarily the reptilian brain, then the formation of the mammalian or middle brain, and last the neocortex, which is the center of cognition and intelligence. The neocortex is foundational in verbal communication. The development of the mammalian brain and the neocortex serve as modulators of the impulsive and aggressive elements in the reptilian brain (Choi C. Q., 2018; Gaidos & Selsis, 2007; Laurent et al., 2016).

These theorists rationalize that the Saurian era or dynasty of Saurus, etymologically, relates to a period in earth's history when a unique combination of waveforms or electric energy pervaded the earth. Evolutionists and ontogenetic theorists allude to this energy as the catalyst that initiated life on earth. Several theories, including interplanetary seeding and panspermia, emerged that suggest life was a distinct form transplanted to earth from somewhere outside the earth (Burke, 1986; The Editors of Encyclopædia Britannica, 2007; Ezcurra et al., 2014; Melott et al., 2004).

Extrapolating from these theorists, some of the information alluded to in ancient myths, legends, lore, religious documents, and glyphs might contain elements that pointed to interplanetary interception and seeding. Interplanetary beings might have been intangible or metaphysical substances, structures, or elements. In deciphering several historical, anthropological, and archaeological accounts, it appears that ancient people referred to these beings as gods (Boulay, 2003; The Editors of Encyclopædia Britannica, 2007).

Some theorists purport that the reptilian race had a physical form, while others suggest that the reptilian race might merely have been a different form of energy that caused the mutations resulting in modern-day humans. Reptiles move in a twirling and twisting manner like electric waves or a double helix. The double helix model of DNA is a hypothetical description and calculation of a molecule called DNA. According to DNA theory, DNA could be used and might explain the interbreeding between two different life-forms (Choi C. Q., 2018; Joshi, 2008; Melott et al., 2004).

Theorists contend that the vestigial tail in humans is evidence that the reptilian race had a physical presence on the earth. All humans begin fetal development in amniotic fluids and have a tail during embryological development, suggesting an affinity to reptiles. This tail usually pulls back into the body during the first trimester and forms the coccyx or tailbone. If the tail does not disappear at this time, the child is born with a tail. On average, every five years, a human is born with a tail. The vestigial tail lacks vertebrae and is harmless. If it not removed at birth, a vestigial tail in an adult human can grow as long as 18 inches (Solt, 2011).

RELIGION AND SCIENCE

Several theories and thoughts exist regarding the fusing of hominids and Saurian DNA. One school of thought distinguishes between Saurians and Dinoids as two distinct groups of Reptoids. Some researchers reported that dinosaurs existed in Asia. However, a common school of thought links Saurus to the Annunaki in ancient Mesopotamia (Boulay, 2003; Pu et al., 2013).

The ancient Greek, Egyptian, Far East, African, and Mayan civilizations, depicted the Saurians as gods that dwelt on the earth alongside humans. Archons, dragons, serpents, Chimaeras, Quetzalcoatl, Kukulcan, Jhins, demons, Nephilim or giants were some of the names used for the reptilian gods among Judeo-Christians. Nephilim means to breathe or pertaining to the atmosphere, elements, or the electromagnetic field among Judeo based and Christian religions. The same element of gods intertwining with humans exists in Hinduism. These belief systems are cogent in understanding the worldviews of both perpetrators and victims and are significant contributors to understanding aggression and victimization (Boulay, 2003; Lewis P. J., 2016).

The conflict between science, religion, and myths is whether the reptilian race(s) existed and if they did, whether they were spiritual or metaphysical entities, physical beings, or a combination of both physical and spiritual. Research into genetics and genetic chimerism appear to accept that the reptilian race might have been a physical entity, represented as reptiles, such as dinosaurs. Consequently, evolution might have occurred as a fusion of Saurians and humans, hominids or humanoids (Chen, 2014; Gaidos & Selsis, 2007; Laurent et al., 2016).

On the other hand, in myths, legends, and religions, supported by hieroglyphs, artifacts, evidence in history and anthropology, the Serpentine race(s) were gods with superior intelligence that fused with hominins, hominids, or humanoids to produce a race of superior intelligence. Concerning the intelligence level of dinosaurs, paleontologists differ in their conclusions. Intelligence level in organisms is typically measured based on brain size and body mass. Using measures of brain size and body mass, paleontologists conclude dinosaurs were less intelligent than humans, although more intelligent than other mammals (Larsson, 2001; Lü et al., 2010).

Although the debate continues concerning Saurian's intelligence, reptilian brain theorists contend that the reptilian brain in humans has key characteristics similar to the brain of reptiles. These characteristics have a bearing on territoriality, aggression, obsessive-compulsive behaviors, oppression, suppression, and survival instinct. Theorists contend that the reptilian brain in humans exerts influence on unconscious thoughts that are constantly being processed in emotional regulation and behaviors. These thought processes continue without conscious recognition but influence behavioral outcomes in key areas of interpersonal relationships.

CONCLUSION

Panspermia theory, the exploded planet hypothesis and other recent theories emerging from research in astrobiology suggest life might have originated from outside of earth. Findings from these studies also indicate there might be some validity to the documentation from mythology, historical, anthropological, archaeological, cultural, and religious literature.

According to these documents, the war in the heavens suggests malevolence among other intelligent life-forms that existed beyond earth's planet at a time prior to the origin of life on earth. Current calculations DNA are suggesting that there is evidence that human genetic encodings might be influenced by encodings found prior to the existence of life-forms on the earth. The purported malevolence among these intelligent beings purported to exist outside the planet earth might have been transported genetically into human gene pools and might account for aggression that is contrary to survival instinct that seems to exist within the gene structure.

Alternative theories, including an interplanetary interception hypothesis, have been purported to support the reptilian brain hypothesis. Thus far, research into cloning methods, genetic modifications, genetic chimerism, and hybridization have been explored to further the understanding of the origin of humans. These alternative theories present different etiology of aggression, violence, abuse, as dysfunctional behaviors and disordered states in child, intimate partner, and family relationships.

CHAPTER REVIEW

REVIEW QUESTIONS

1. What are the major tenets of the panspermia theory?

2. How do panspermia theorists explain species-to-species murder among humans?

CHAPTER TWENTY-SEVEN
INTELLIGENT DESIGN

CHAPTER PREVIEW

Knowledge of the origin of life might provide answers regarding life, the nature of being, and being. These answers might help solve challenges related to APR. ID is a scientific approach to questions concerning the origin of life.

ID scientists criticize evolutionary theory for its inadequate explanations concerning the first cause. The absolute principle is a premise of the first cause in the scientific methods.

In this chapter, there will be a discussion of the teleological deductive inferential argument of cause and functionality that are implicated in ID theory. There will be a discussion of aspects of ID theory such as irreducible complexities.

ID scientists present several refutations of Darwin's theory by means of natural selection. A discussion of research findings on nucleotide convergence and divergence and its centrality in Darwin's hypothesis of common descent. There will be a revision of other research findings such as aberrations in the theory of phylogenesis, genetic distance, beneficial mutations, and junk DNA. In their refutations of Darwin's theory by natural selection, ID scientists demonstrate flaws in the fitness model.

ID scientists present findings that support their arguments. These include complexities of embryonic brain development in primates, hominids, and humans. ID researchers present compelling evidence to support their hypothesis concerning the complexities of embryonic brain development in primates, hominids, and humans. ID scientists argue that common explanations related to evolutionary development time elements, and beneficial random mutations cannot account for the development of these complexities.

ID scientists contend that beneficial random mutation cannot be used to explain independent ontogenetic and epigenetic information guiding hereditary transmissions. In this chapter, there are further discussions of structuralism, the genetic code, and invariance in a diverse lineage.

PURPOSE AND LEARNING OBJECTIVES

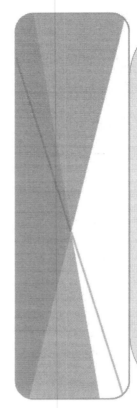

PURPOSE

The purpose of this chapter is to explore the scientific evidence of the ID theory on the origin of life.

LEARNING OBJECTIVES

After studying this chapter, the reader should

1. understand the hypothetical assumptions concerning the origin of life;
2. comprehend the philosophical tenets undergirding ID theory;
3. recognize the scientific support for ID theory; and
4. realize the implications for understanding worldview, being, and diversity intervention.

KEY TERMS AND DEFINITIONS

Absolute Principle

The first absolute principle or the Ultimate Reality refers to the thing, being, entity, power, force, reality, presence, law or principle that possesses the maximal ontological status that infers effect (Adamson, 2017).

First Cause

The first cause is the first absolute principle. The first cause is the cause of the existence of the first thing or being (Adamson, 2017).

Homology

Homology is the state of having the same or similar relation, relative position, or structure.

Intelligent Design

The theory of ID is a scientific theory that certain features of the universe and living things are best explained by an intelligent cause, not an undirected process.

INTRODUCTION

> *There is grandeur in this view of life, with its several powers, having been originally breathed by the Creator into a few forms or into one; and that, whilst this planet has gone cycling on according to the fixed law of gravity, from so simple a beginning endless forms most beautiful and most wonderful have been, and are being, evolved.*
> *(Darwin C., 1872, p. 429).*

Darwin contended that the Creator breathed life into a few forms or one and that natural selection, like the fixed laws of gravity, propelled straight-line evolution into greater complexities of forms and beings. Darwin distinguished between the origin of life and the origin of species (Darwin C., 1872; Peretó et al., 2009).

Several theorists, including Darwin, purported speculative hypotheses concerning the origin of life (Oparin, 1957). These speculative hypothesizers applied various philosophical tenets to facilitate the incorporation of these theories into objective scientific studies. In addition to several philosophies of metaphysics, these philosophers integrated tenets of the first cause and the absolute principle into theory (Andersen & Hepburn, 2016; Beebee et al., 2012; Hofweber, 2018).

THE FIRST CAUSE

Hypotheses are central to the origin of life focus on the first cause. The theory of evolution is probably the foremost theory positing hypotheses to explain the nature of being in relation to life. Although evolutionary theories and theories of adaptation begin with some form of explanation concerning the early appearance of life on the earth, the answer as to the first cause, or what caused the things or conditions that caused life to appear remains elusive (Beebee et al., 2012).

To arrive at objective scientific hypotheses concerning the first cause, philosophers made a distinction between truth as an existing literal fact, and truth based on a plausible, logical explanation to explain the observable phenomenon. Although the cause of the origin of life remains an unobservable phenomenon, philosophers applied principles of plausible, logical explanation combined with observable phenomenon associated with being to explain the first cause or what was the first cause for the origin of life (Beebee et al., 2012)

THE ABSOLUTE PRINCIPLE

The absolute principle is another concept relevant to the study of the origin of life. The natural philosophical approach applies cause and effect as foundational principles in the scientific methodology. Philosophers apply cause and effect rationale to validate their hypothetical constructs relating to ontogeny (Adamson, 2017; Andersen & Hepburn, 2016).

According to the absolute principle, some phenomenon or being caused everything that exists or has a state of being. The absolute principle is the cause of all subsequent causes of being. The first cause is the initial cause of all subsequent causes (Adamson, 2017).

The first cause is the first absolute principle. The first absolute principle or the ultimate reality refers to the thing, being, entity, power, force, reality, presence, law, or principle that possesses the maximal ontological status that infers effect. Maximal ontological status means the absolute principle possesses all the elements required to cause all things to come into existence. The first absolute principle is the first cause. The first cause is the cause of being. All things visible and invisible emerged because of the first cause or the first absolute principle (Adamson, 2017; Lizzini, 2016).

DARWIN AND INTELLIGENT DESIGN

In an 1861 letter to Herschel[50], Darwin wrote: "One cannot look at this Universe with all living productions & man without believing that all has been intelligently designed..." (Darwin C., 1861). Darwin's conception of ID was an extension of the scientific method. The scientific method involves both inductive and deductive arguments (Snyder, 2017).

Figure 27-1 William Herschel

Causation and functionality inform philosophies concerning the use of inductive arguments and deductive inferences in scientific methodology. In the case of the origin of life and the origin of species, because of the difficulties of engaging in scientific observation of impalpable phenomena, using deductive inferential argument was an acceptable practice (Snyder, 2017).

ID is a teleological deductive inferential argument based on functionality rather than causation. Darwin used teleological deductive inference as an aspect of his theory of evolution. While Darwin engaged ID

---

[50] Figure 27-1 Lemuel Francis Abbott creator QS:P170,Q725410 (https://commons.wikimedia.org/wiki/File:William_Herschel01.jpg), „William Herschel01", marked as public domain, more details on Wikimedia Commons: https://commons.wikimedia.org/wiki/Template:PD-old

as an aspect of his evolutionary theory, it was not the first time this theoretical approach to the origin of life and the ontogeny of species appeared in philosophical thought.

Paley (1809) presented the discussion using an analogy between a stone and a watch:

> *In crossing a heath, suppose I pitched my foot against a stone, and were asked how the stone came to be there; I might possibly answer, that, for any thing I knew to the contrary, it had lain there for ever: nor would it perhaps be very easy to show the absurdity of this answer. But suppose I had found a watch upon the ground, and it should be inquired how the watch happened to be in that place; ...*
> *(Paley, 1809, p. 1).*

Paley in his argument for ID contended that upon inspection of the watch[51], it would be obvious it was designed for a purpose, and each aspect and unit of the parts are integrated to perform the purpose for which it was designed. Paley then contended that observation of the watch might lead to speculative conclusions concerning the origin of the watch. Paley argued that establishing logical inferences from the watch does not preclude the logical conclusions derived from its inspection. The

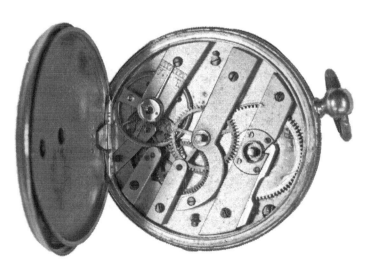

Figure 27-2 Intelligent Design: A Watch

logical conclusion is that the watch was designed for functionality or purpose (Paley, 1809).

This teleological worldview of ID was pervasive in ancient thought and literature. Two other ancient conceptualizations, the eternity of life, and that life originated somewhere in the universe other than earth were prevalent views of ancient thought. For Darwin, and other evolutionary thinkers, ID, eternity of life, and adaptation were not incompatible tenets (Darwin C., 1861; 1872; Oparin, 1957; Paley, 1809; Snyder, 2017; Thorvaldsen & Øhrstrøm, 2013).

---

[51] Figure 27-2 Hannes Grobe/Hannes Grobe (talk)
(https://commons.wikimedia.org/wiki/File:Watch_with_no_background.png),
„Watch with no background",
https://creativecommons.org/licenses/by/3.0/legalcode

Leading modern-day evolutionists furthered the concept of ID and specified complexities. Among these leading proponents, Orgel (2007) wrote:

> [L]iving organisms are distinguished by their specified complexity. Crystals are usually taken as the prototypes of simple, well-specified structures, because they consist of a very large number of identical molecules packed together in a uniform way. Lumps of granite or random mixtures of polymers are examples of structures which are complex but not specified. The crystals fail to qualify as living because they lack complexity; the mixtures of polymers fail to qualify because they lack specificity.
> (Orgel, 2007, p. 189).

ID theorists apply the scientific methodology in their study. ID theorists study and analyze a system's components to evaluate whether the system is a product of chance, natural law, ID, or a combination thereof. ID theorists neither agree with Darwin on elements of creationism, nor evolution. Instead, ID theorists apply the objective scientific methodology in their research to assess plausible, logical explanations concerning the origin of life and the origin of species (Zelenkov et al., 2011).

ID theorists hypothesize that complex and specified information comprises an ID. ID researchers contend that irreducible complexities constitute IDs. ID researchers engage in reverse-engineering of biological structures to assess whether all of these structures require all their constituents for functionality. ID researchers contend that irreducible complexity in biology indicates intelligence in design.

One of the most compelling arguments presented by ID theorists centers on irreducible complexities. ID researchers examine simple and complex organisms to assess whether all the constituents of these organisms were required for functionality; conversely, whether the organism could function without all its complexities.

Organisms function as an integrative whole. ID theorists argue that if several interacting parts are removed, then the functionality of the organisms will be seriously impaired or dysfunctional. Irreducible complexity is a proposition that some biological systems cannot evolve by successive modifications to preexisting parts or functional systems as proposed by evolutionary theorists (Mu, 2005).

REFUTATIONS OF EVOLUTIONARY THEORY

Evolutionary geneticists contend that revision of Mendel's law of inheritance extended Darwin's theory of evolution. Mendel's law of inheritance was at first rejected because it implied a static definition of the species which was in opposition to Darwin's law of incremental evolution. Although geneticists revisited and accepted Mendel's law of inheritance, these two issues of static species and improbability of incremental inheritance persist (Lönnig, 2017).

NUCLEOTIDE CONVERGENCE AND DIVERGENCE

Common descent is a foundational hypothesis of evolutionary theory. The common descent theory hinges on the postulates of genetic drift, genetic recombination, colonization and migration, mutations, and natural selection. Nevertheless, all these pathways toward phylogenetic diversity have weaknesses (Darwin C., 1882).

The conception that humans share a common ancestor with primates is a postulate of common descent. Evolutionists cite convergence of nucleotides as the evidential support of common descent. Researchers have found the independent appearance of the same genetic trait for which heredity does not account in multiple species (Christin, Weinreich, & Besnard, 2010).

These common genetic traits are responsible for many organs shared by many species. Evolutionary geneticists identify genetic convergence as supportive evidence of a common ancestor, and that the first humanoid diverged phylogenetically some six million years ago.

The main argument countering nucleotide convergence is nucleotide diversity. The nucleotide diversity of human DNA data seems too high to suggest a common ancestor with other species. Common descent proponents face challenges explaining the genetic differences, rather than the similarities with other species. However, in addition to weaknesses in the postulates upon which common descent hinges, new research findings from phylogenetic diversity studies are also not lending support to Darwin's common descent theory (Hössjer, Gauger, & Reeves, 2016; Mazel et al., 2018; O'Dwyer et al., 2012).

Nucleotides are groups of molecules that, when linked, form the building blocks of DNA and RNA. Nucleotides are hypothesized and analyzed via synthetic creations, chemical, and computational analysis.

Nucleotide convergence and divergence is a premise that species have a single nucleotide that appears to be the root or indication of a common ancestor. This single nucleotide converges or is similar in unrelated species. Nucleotides diverge or become different as part of adaptation and speciation.

HEWING THE PHYLOGENETIC TREE

The phylogenetic tree is an illustrative hypothesis showing a likely path from early evolutionary epoch to the divergence of life into different species. Darwin produced an illustration of the phylogenetic tree of life in his title "Origin of Species." Phylogeneticists use computational phylogenetic methods to construct phylogenetic trees. Convergent nucleotides and genetic distance are variables used in constructing phylogenetic trees.

GENETIC DISTANCE

Genetic distance is the measure of the genetic divergence between species or between populations within a species. Computational analysis is used to calculate estimates of genetic distance in building phylogenetic trees.

In 2000, Doolittle in an article: Uprooting the Tree of Life, cited all the mounting evidence that the concept of the phylogenetic tree was flawed. Doolittle suggested new ways to devise a phylogenetic tree but cautioned:

> *Though complicated, even this revised picture would actually be misleadingly simple, a sort of shorthand cartoon, because the fusing of branches usually would not represent the joining of whole genomes, only the transfers of single or multiple genes. The full picture would have to display simultaneously the superimposed genealogical patterns of thousands of different families of genes (the rRNA genes form just one such family).*
> *(Doolittle, 2000, p. 94).*

Doolittle indicated that new evidence was rendering the lineal theory of evolution and commonality of ancestors shaky. Doolittle lamented:

> *Some biologists find these notions confusing and discouraging. It is as if we have failed at the task that Darwin set for us: delineating the unique structure of the tree of life. But in fact, our science is working just as it should. An attractive hypothesis or model (the single tree) suggested experiments, in this case the collection of gene sequences and their analysis with the methods of molecular phylogeny. The data show the model to be too simple.*
> *(Doolittle, 2000, p. 95).*

While some scientists lamented the fall of Darwin's tree of life, others attempted to create new models to replace the fallen one. Hug et al. (2016) reiterated, "The tree of life is one of the most important organizing principles of biology." (p. 1), but "... even an approximation of the full scale of the tree has remained elusive." (p. 1) To remodel this new tree, researchers admitted that some genomes were *'abscondo'*; and so manufactured synthetic genomes to facilitate a remodeled tree (Hug et al., 2016).

MUTED MUTATIONS

Darwin C. (1872) challenged: "If it could be demonstrated that any complex organ existed, which could not possibly have been formed by numerous, successive, slight modifications, my theory would absolutely break down." (p. 146) Several evolutionary biologists seriously questioned the plausibility of "numerous, successive, slight modifications" (Lynch, 2012). Commenting on the limits of this foundational evolutionary argument

Lynch at the Proceedings of the U.S. National Academy of Science, stated: "... the simultaneous emergence of all components of a system is implausible." (p. 18851).

Darwin's theory presupposed the existence of stable protein synthesis mechanisms and processes before the appearance of mutations. A mutation is a very rare occurrence, beneficial mutation; a foundational hypothesis in evolutionary theory is even rarer. Researchers engage in mutational sensitivity to assess its implications in the formation of stable protein synthesis mechanisms and processes. Findings from one research indicated that amino acid sequences which yield stable, functional protein folds might be as rare as 1 in 1074 sequences (Axe, 2004).

The emergence of amino acid sequences would require an infinitesimal time beyond current evidence regarding the age of the earth. This suggests that the vast majority of amino acid sequences cannot be achieved through evolution without phenomenally extending the age of the earth (Axe, 2004).

JUNK DNA

Junk DNA refers to any material within the genome of a life-form that serves no functional purpose. Only 2.8% of human DNA is viable coding genes; the remaining 97.3% is junk DNA. Junk DNA is not non-coding DNA. Junk DNA is genomic material that serves no purpose and has been referred to as "genetic flotsam and jetsam" (Collins, 2007, p. 136; Lodish et al., 2000).

The conception of junk DNA stems from the idea that these sections of DNA might have served an evolutionary function no longer needed. Junk DNA is similar to vestigial organs, like the vestigial tail.

Despite the conception of junk DNA, geneticists acknowledge that species are highly functional. Although technology and science might not uncover the functions of all aspects of human genetics, increasingly research findings are confirming the functionalities of more aspects of human genetics. New evidence is showing that junk DNA, hitherto considered to be nonfunctional, has some functionality (Axe & Gauger, 2015; Douglas, Chubiz, Harcombe, & Marx, 2017; Ewert, 2015; Snoke, Cox, & Petcher, 2014).

FLAWS IN THE FITNESS MODEL

In addition to the improbability of the occurrence of a beneficial mutation , ID researchers also found serious flaws with the natural selection fitness model. According to this postulate, increasing variation for fitness also involves perpetration and increase of non-beneficial variations proportionately higher than beneficial variation for fitness.

Selection alone will not foster change. There must be the existence of genetic compositions that promote both the process of selection, as well as the process of change. Phylogeny presupposes interbreeding between closely related species. Researchers contend that interbreeding carries a risk of deleterious recessive mutations. In humans, these risks include genetic physical and psychiatric disorders (Axe & Gauger, 2015; Douglas et al., 2017; Snoke et al., 2015).

Selective mating involves interbreeding with species closely aligned genetically. Interbreeding has attendant risks. The postulate that mutation, selection, and interbreeding combined to facilitate evolution carries a high statistical improbability. Further, interbreeding and selection involve genetic predispositions suggesting that the theory of evolution incorporates in its tenets the preexistence of ID for evolutionary processes to occur (Axe & Gauger, 2015; Douglas et al., 2017).

There are increasingly overwhelming arguments against the conception of unguided evolutionary processes as the mechanisms for speciation. ID theorists posit that current research findings are causing the fitness model to increase in untenability. Currently, evolutionary researchers cite these limitations in their studies and models. Some of these limitations include the statistical improbability of a beneficial mutation occurring, deleterious consequences of selection and interbreeding, and the unlikelihood of slow evolution. Against this background, ID theorists posit alternative hypotheses to explain the origin of life (Axe & Gauger, 2015; Brisson, 2003; Douglas et al., 2017; Snoke et al., 2015).

INTELLIGENT DESIGN THEORY

TIME CONSTRAINTS: COMPLEXITIES IN FUNCTIONALITIES

Human DNA encompasses unique capabilities, complexities, and functionalities that would require the generation, and fixation of specific beneficial mutations, which cannot be explained within the constraints of long-term evolution. Using the same computational analysis used by evolutionary researchers, ID computational analysts found that computer simulations to analyze mathematically and statistically a specific string of beneficial nucleotides present significant constraints to the time element currently used in evolutionary explanations. According to carbon dating currently used in the evolutionary timeline, the emergence, generation, and fixation of only one or two strings of beneficial nucleotides would require a period that exceeds the current evolutionary timeline. For hominin evolution to occur, it would exceed the time that evolutionists contend has elapsed since the universe is purported to have first come into existence (Sanford, Brewer, Smith, & Baumgardner, 2015).

COMPLEXITIES OF EMBRYONIC BRAIN DEVELOPMENT IN PRIMATES, HOMINIDS, AND HUMANS

During embryonic development, the development of a molecule called hyperglycosylated chorionic gonadotropin (HCG) allows humans, hominid, and primates to have larger brain sizes. The molecule HCG allows increased nutrients to pass through the placenta during embryonic development, allowing primates, hominids, and humans to grow larger brains.

Many genes are implicated in brain growth and the emergence of higher intelligence. However, the evolution of chorionic gonadotropin (CG) and HCG appear to be a significant requirement for larger brain sizes and intelligence in humans, hominids, and primates. The emergence of CG and HCG would require four evolutionary events for which current evolutionary theory does not account.

Evolution hypotheses cannot account for the emergence of CG and HCG molecular structures. A random beneficial mutation is one of the explanations for functional evolutionary developments. However, statistical analysis places the odds of the emergence of these molecules as occurring at one in a trillion and one in 10 quadrillions. Consequently, beneficial random mutations cannot be applied to explain their presence as the product of evolutionary processes (Cole, 2015).

ENZYME FUNCTIONS

Evolutionary biologists use a process called co-option to substantiate that proteins can evolve to perform new functions. Using this same model, ID biologists use to analyze whether one protein can convert to perform the functions of a similarly structured protein. Researchers concluded that this conversion requires seven or more mutations. Researchers found that features which require more than two harmful mutations, or more than six neutral mutations, before providing an advantageous or beneficial mutation, 'could not arise in the entire history of the earth.' (Catazaro, Caprez, Guru, Swanson, & Powers, 2014; Reeves, Gauger, & Axe, 2014).

Further analysis of nine other closely related enzymes, to assess whether their functions can evolve, also revealed the unlikelihood of evolutionary processes involved in protein functionality conversion. Biologists using the co-opted method found that it required at least four mutations to affect enzyme conversion functionality, including mutations to duplicate the gene and over-express it. Researchers concluded that for such enzymic functionality conversion to occur, it would take 10^{15} years for the necessary mutations to arise to co-opt protein conversion function. This process would take more than 100,000 times longer than the currently estimated duration of the earth's existence (Reeves et al., 2014).

INDEPENDENT ONTOGENETIC AND EPIGENETIC INFORMATION

Genetic embryologists rely on ontogenetic information that guides the development of organisms which are non-DNA derivatives. Mutations cannot produce this information in DNA. Genetic instructions via DNA and RNA for protein synthesis are a foundational element of molecular biology and genetic studies. In molecular biological and genetic studies, DNA encoded RNA in the protein synthesis process is responsible for cell growth and replication (Wells, 2014).

Nevertheless, several non-DNA regulated processes must precede developmental gene regulatory networks, such as the sugar code and endogenous electric fields. These elements that are critical antecedents of gene regulatory functions occur outside DNA functioning. Many traits are not determined by DNA, and therefore, cannot be explained or produced by DNA encoding (Wells, 2014).

STRUCTURALISM

Structuralism was a perspective that existed in early Greek philosophy. Structuralists adhere to the view that two types of orders exist in species, a primal order generated by natural laws and one adaptive to environmental conditions. Darwin alludes to structuralism in his conception of the inherent qualities of life. Darwin further contended that these inherent qualities are functional in variation and speciation (Darwin & Wallace, 1858; Denton, 2013).

According to structuralists, homologies appear to be nonadaptive and remain unchanged in a diverse lineage. The body plan of insects is an example of homology. Recent research uncovered several homologies such as the double helix shape of DNA, the rules that generate protein folds, and the self-organization of lipid membranes (Denton, 2013).

Denton (2013) presented an argument that while the genetic code might explain the functionality of homologies such as pentadactyl and the pentamerous symmetry of echinoderms, it does not account for structure. The genetic code does explain why some structures assume their form or why these forms remain invariant in diverse lineages. While structuralism is different from ID, structuralism lends itself to deductive inferences of ID (Denton, 2013).

CONCLUSION

The ID is a theoretical approach to explaining the origin of life and the ontogeny of species, that focuses on functionality and the irreducible complexities in design. ID theorists present an overwhelming argument in support of their theoretical position. These theorists used methodology and objective scientific research approaches that validate their findings as reliable.

Philosophically, ID does not negate many of the hypotheses presented by evolutionists. However, many of the arguments that ID theorists present refute some of the claims, inconsistencies, and inconclusive generalizations applied by evolutionary researchers and practitioners.

CHAPTER REVIEW

REVIEW QUESTIONS

1. Compare ID and the theory of evolution.
2. Are ID theorists creationists?
3. Fully discuss three ID tenets.

CHAPTER TWENTY-EIGHT
AN ALTERNATIVE THEORY

CHAPTER PREVIEW

Throughout this book, there was a discussion of the relevance of evolutionary theory to the understanding of APR. Evolutionary theory was chosen because it is the foremost theoretical foundation used in almost all disciplines and research. Even when evolutionary theory is not explicitly stated, its tenets and perspectives still influence almost all disciplines, research, and studies.

Evolutionary theory is not new. Its origin could be traced back to the ancient world. Evolutionary theory is a stronghold that pervades thoughts and worldviews. The ideological framework of evolutionary theory is entrenched and intricately woven in worldviews and is seamlessly interwoven into sociocultural, political, religious, and economic systems.

Nevertheless, an up-close look at evolutionary theory reveals some deep-rooted flaws in its inferences, tenets, hypothetical assumptions, and philosophical orientation. There are a reluctance and hesitation to challenge evolutionary theory because it is held in the highest esteem in philosophy and academia.

Evolutionary theory is used to explain human aggression. However, when applied to human problems such as APR, evolutionary theory is not providing adequate answers. These inadequacies relate to its philosophical orientation and untenable underlying inferences and assumptions.

While there seem to be two polarized camps of Darwinism and anti-Darwinism, the focus of anti-Darwinists has been on criticizing the shortcomings of the theory. However, there is a need for alternative, more viable tenets that might be more applicable to human problems.

As such, the central tenets of evolution and its assumptive hypotheses will be explored in this chapter. There will be a discussion of some of the central tenets of Darwin's theory of evolution, identification of their flaws and weaknesses, and alternative tenets presented to address the flaws and weaknesses in evolutionary theory.

PURPOSE AND LEARNING OBJECTIVES

PURPOSE

The purpose of this chapter is to identify flaws and weaknesses in Darwin's theory of evolution by natural selection, and present alternative hypotheses, which might be more viable in addressing human problems such as APR.

LEARNING OBJECTIVES

After studying this chapter, the reader should

1. understand the flaws and weaknesses in attempts to apply the theory of evolution by means of natural selection to understand APR, and;
2. trace the application of the theory of evolution by means of natural selection to eugenics, genetics, and their implications for APR.

KEY TERMS AND DEFINITIONS

Feticide

Feticide is the act of causing the death of a fetus (Feticide, n.d.).

Gendercide

Gendercide is the reduction of the proportion of a particular gender, typically female, in a population, especially as a result of selective abortion (Gendercide, n.d.).

Tautology

Tautology, in logic, is a statement so framed that it cannot be denied without inconsistency. Thus, "All humans are mammals" is held to assert with regard to anything whatsoever that either it is a human or it is not a mammal. However, that universal "truth" follows not from any facts noted about real humans but only from the actual use of human and mammal and is thus purely a matter of definition (The Editors of Encyclopædia Britannica, 2015).

Truism

A truism is an undoubted or self-evident truth, especially one too obvious to mention (Truism, n.d.).

INTRODUCTION

Evolutionary theory is not new. Evolutionary philosophy can be traced back to several ancient cultures, including ancient Greece and China. Philosophers in antiquity developed the major tenets of the theory of evolution. Charles Darwin, the father of modern-day evolutionary theory, expounded on these tenets and added new dimensions to ancient evolutionary tenets. Evolution by means of natural selection theory informs the majority, if not all, modern-day science, education, and research disciplines; including physics, psychology, biology, genetics, religion, neuropsychology, neuroanatomy, and spirituality.

However, despite its widespread application, research and practice founded on evolutionary theory continue to provide conflicting answers and research findings. Despite this, the evolutionary theory continues to be widely applied in research and practice. The wide application of evolutionary theory in research and practice might be an indication of an entrenched worldview, the merits of evolutionary theory, and the absence of a viable alternative.

FOUNDATIONAL EVOLUTIONARY TENETS

Survivability is a foundational tenet upon which evolutionary theory hinges and is a principal tenet used to explain APR. However, Darwin's primary tenet of survivability has been criticized as being an untestable tautology. Additionally, the true meaning of survivability within the context of the 'battle of life,' presents disturbing realities associated with sociocultural divisiveness, oppression, eugenics, physical and psychological violence, and abuse.

SURVIVAL OF THE FITTEST AND NATURAL SELECTION

In 1864, eugenicists Herbert Spencer coined the phrase "survival of the fittest." Herbert Spencer explained that the term survival of the fittest is the same term that Darwin called "natural selection," or the preservation of the favoured races in the struggle of life. Based on Darwin's description, natural selection and survival of the fittest are synonymous terms.

In 1868 Darwin adopted the phrase. He wrote:

> *This preservation, during the battle for life, of varieties which possess any advantage in structure, constitution, or instinct, I have called Natural Selection; and Mr. Herbert Spencer has well expressed the same idea by the Survival of the Fittest. The term "natural selection" is in some respects a bad one, as it seems to imply conscious choice; but this will be disregarded after a little familiarity.*
> *(Darwin C., 1868, p. 6).*

UNTESTABLE TAUTOLOGY

In addition to being criticized as a tautology, survival of the fittest is untestable. Further, the two foundational tenets of the theory of evolution by natural selection, the concept of natural selection and the tenet that there is a force outside of human control that is directing natural selection might be little more than a spurious, arbitrary conceptualization to support an untenable philosophical orientation and belief.

The idea that a force outside of human control guides natural selection to cause some races favorable and others vulnerable is the equivalent of saying some races are designed to be superior and others vulnerable. Darwin and subsequent eugenicists identified this superior race as Europeans or people from European stock. In plain language, this is a simple assertion that Europeans, possible meaning Caucasians are superior. This superiority was predetermined by a force outside of human control.

Emanating from these two foundational tenets is the idea of orthogenesis. Again, in plain language, this presupposes that Europeans, possibly meaning Caucasians will continue to have increasing complexities to ensure their survivability. This philosophical orientation is rooted in racial bigotry that calls upon the powers of the gods or the unseen elements of the universe as the source of authority for this bigotry.

An additional claim intricated in this bigotry is that males are superior when compared with females. This foundational doctrine has found its way into many sociocultural, religious, family, and institutional systems and are identifiably at the roots of APR.

Scholars and practitioner continue to accept and defend this bigoted philosophy in the name of science. Its tenets are supported as tenable foundations of research and study and defended through academic excuses, pragmaticism, diplomacy, and political correctness.

Making the claim that survivors survive is stating the obvious and therefore represents a tautological logical argument or an empty deduction. Despite this criticism, many Darwinists make excuses to exonerate Darwin and present various explanations concerning what Darwin really meant. Darwinists posit explanations of the conceptualization of "fitness."

Currently, these apologetics offer compromising explanations for the term 'fitness' claiming that 'fitness' refers to the quality for survival. Nevertheless, Darwin and his eugenicists followers clearly enunciated that fitness meant superiority and equated fitness with racial superiority.

USE OF THE CONCEPT SURVIVAL.

In his thesis of the theory evolution by means of natural selection, Darwin clearly defined fitness as reproductive advantage. Pragmatics and eugenicists again sought to disguise Darwin's true meaning of reproductive advantage by renaming it as reproductive success. Darwin's conceptualization of reproductive advantage is equated with a modern-day interpretation of fitness as reproductive success.

FITNESS IN BIOLOGY

In biology, "fitness" is interpreted as reproductive success. Reproductive success means having the best capability for survival and the production of offspring. While this interpretation of "fitness' represents a modest effort to mask Darwin's true meaning of reproductive advantage and its underlying philosophical bigotry, the contention that fitness is reproductive success and reproductive success represent the best capability of survival as a truism.

Reproductive success is defined as the passing of 'fitness' genes from one generation to successive generations. The transmission of these genes ensures that individuals and human subspecies with the best genes have the best chance of survival. Fitness is the quantitative representation of natural selection and sexual selection. Darwin identified this as a natural selection and purposeful selection process. Darwin also associated this natural and selection process with superiority and vulnerability. This natural selection and selection process is the basis for eugenics (Wassersug & Wassersug, 1986).

Darwin resorted to pseudo biology to substantiate his theory of evolution by means of natural selection. Subsequent generations of eugenicists enlisted the support of biology as a discipline to substantiate and perpetuate the foundational elements of racism, inequality, and discrimination that was entwined in Darwin's theory of evolution by natural selection.

Social Darwinists used biology to give credence to eugenics. Scholars, thinkers, and policy makers presented eugenics as a proven theory based on the scientific study of biology. The pervasiveness and acceptance of social Darwinism and eugenics were such that Leonard (2005) wrote:

> *Histories of eugenics traditionally have focused upon movements in the United States, the United Kingdom, and in Third Reich Germany; but we now know that eugenic thought was commonplace elsewhere, influencing scholars, writers, scientists, and policymakers in virtually all non-Catholic Western countries and in many others besides: there are scholarly treatments of the eugenics movements in Canada, France, Japan, Russia, Denmark, Sweden, Norway, Finland, Romania, China, Latin America, and elsewhere. By 1933, the American demographer and eugenicist Paul Popenoe could boast that eugenic sterilization laws obtained in jurisdictions comprising 150 million people. (Leonard, 2005, p. 203).*

Genetics and natural selection were the basis of the eugenics doctrine. Natural selection, purposeful selection practices, biological theories of inheritance and genetics were the driving elements of research, policies, and practices in the race to cleanse the population of defective and unfit genes that were susceptible to vulnerability (Darwin L., 1931; Leonard, 2005).

FITNESS IN SOCIAL AND MORAL THEORIES

In social and moral theories, survivability is often equated with racial, ethnic, and cultural inequality, inequity, discrimination and other forms of social and moral injustices giving rise to eugenics, genocide, and racial cleansing under the guise of social Darwinism. Due to these perspectives rooted in inequity and injustices, research using social and moral theories as their theoretical framework tends to reinforce and perpetuate this perspective from their findings.

UNTENABLE NATURAL SELECTION AND SELECTION TENETS

Natural selection is a force that exists outside of human control. Natural selection has never been seen and cannot be sensorially observed and is therefore, unverifiable. Sexual selection is a purposeful decision to refrain from mating with persons identified as having specific phenotypic expressions. Darwin recommended purposeful selection as a mechanism to eliminate the 'unfit.' Because sexual selection targets the elimination of the unfit, Darwin referred to sexual selection as an evolutionary selection mechanism.

SURVIVABILITY, EUGENICS, AND GENDER CONCERNS

The concept of survivability is relevant to APR because of the influence of the concept on gender issues. The concept of survivability influences and continues to influence thoughts affecting male hegemony, aggression, predispositional vulnerability, genetics, and gender discrimination.

MALE HEGEMONY

Darwin concluded that males possessed superior genes when compared with females. As such, the power of choice in sexual selection was a male's privilege. The idea of males' superior eugenics influenced two key areas related to APR policies and practices, traditional gender roles, and gendercide.

The hegemonic male is a culturally accepted, socially constructed persona of male masculinity. This culturally accepted socially constructed persona delimits maleness within boundaries of behaviors. There is the exaltation of male hegemonic behaviors, and these behaviors take preeminence over other socially constructed personas, such as the subjugated, submissive female persona (Kane, 2006; Locke, 2013).

Locke (2013) stated that "hegemonic masculinity sits atop the gendered social hierarchy by embodying the culturally idealized definition of masculinity, which is constructed as both oppositional and superior to femininity." (Locke, 2013, p. 10). Males achieve ascendancy not by force, but through sociocultural practices, institutional preferences, and practices.

> *Although many of the primary traits of hegemonic masculinity facilitate physical domination, such as physical size and strength, assertiveness, aggressiveness, and skills in warfare, hegemonic masculinity does not include the use of force or violence, though those may be used to attain or maintain it. (Locke, 2013, p. 11).*

Male hegemony is traceable back to several centuries before Darwin. However, Darwin was instrumental in concretizing and legitimizing the concept when he introduced a biological basis for male superiority (Darwin C., 1882). Male hegemony and the tenets of male reproductive advantage and reproductive success are driving forces in APR and the gender-biased victimization that characterizes the phenomenon. Male hegemony was intertwined in the eugenic doctrine and practices (Kline, 2001).

EUGENICS

Eugenics *(juːˈdʒɛnɪks)* from Greek εὐγενής *eugenes* means 'well-born' from εὖ *eu*, 'good, well' and γένος *genos*, 'race, stock, kin.' (Liddell & Scott, 2007) Eugenics is a set of beliefs and practices that aim at eliminating persons and populations deemed to have undesirable or unfit genes and preserving persons and populations deemed to have favourable genes. The aim of eugenics is orthogenesis. Eugenicists aim to improve the quality of the human population (Galton, 1904)[52].

Figure 28-1 Sir Francis Galton

Positive eugenics are beliefs and practices that aim to promote a higher reproduction rate among people deemed to have desirable characteristics and traits – the *favoured* race. Negative eugenics is beliefs and practices to reduce the rate of reproduction and promote sterilization of individuals and

[52] Figure 28-1 Unknown
(https://commons.wikimedia.org/wiki/File:Sir_Francis_Galton,_circa_1905.jpg),
„Sir Francis Galton, circa 1905", marked as public domain, more details on
Wikimedia Commons: https://commons.wikimedia.org/wiki/Template:PD-old

populations with undesirable or unfit characteristics and traits (Osbourne, 1937).

Eugenicists propounded doctrines and strategies such as purposeful selection to promote positive eugenics among a human population. Hegemonic males, who according to Darwin; being of superior genes and traits of reproductive advantage, chose females with positive eugenics based on their adherence or presentment of the socially constructed femininity persona. On the other hand, women that possessed negative eugenics or traits were targets for elimination.

In the social hierarchy, hegemonic males occupied the top echelons. Females were positionally inferior and consequently faced disabilities, discrimination, and challenges. The disabilities, discrimination, and challenges that women faced because of eugenics beliefs and practices were factors involved in APR in the past, and continue to exist in the present.

TRACING EUGENICS, GENDER-BASED DISCRIMINATION, AND APR

The conception of selection and selective breeding can be traced back to Plato and cosmological philosophies as early as 400 BC. Plato promoted a state-run program of selective mating to strengthen the guardian class. Darwin expounded on the principles of selection in his theory of evolution by natural selection (Darwin C., 1872; Goering, 2014).

Like earlier religious, cosmological philosophers, Darwin presented that selective breeding, which he also referred to as selection and purposeful selection, would improve the human species. Darwin also propounded that the *favoured* races should engage in practices to eliminate unfit members of the human species and human subspecies, referred to as negative eugenics (Darwin C., 1872).

In ancient Rome, eugenics was mandated by law and included mandatory selective mating and killing of unfit children. Among Germanic tribes, cowards, disabled, unwarlike, or persons stained with abominable vices were killed by drowning in the bogs (Sanders, 2009).

Darwin, in his theory of evolution by means of natural selection, provided a biological basis for eugenics and discrimination. Because eugenics was purported to have a biological basis, it became the foundation for scientific racism and gender discrimination.

Eugenicists were among early geneticists in modern history. Eugenics theory was presented as genetic determinism, the conception that genes were the only, or the primary determinant of human characteristics, behaviors, and traits. Because APR is couched and interpreted within the framework of human characteristics, behaviors, and trait, eugenics hold relevance for current approaches to APR. Victims and perpetrators of APR are among the vulnerable populations identified under eugenic doctrines and practices.

Eugenics became a formal international organization and an academic discipline in many colleges and universities. Eugenics studies and practices were implemented in many countries globally including Britain, the US, Germany, Brazil, Belgium, Canada, Japan, Sweden, and South Africa (Rhodesia) (Allen, 2004; Black E., 2012).

With the backings of findings from genetics, biology, and scientific research, eugenics gained strength. Eugenics policies such as genetic screening, birth control, population control, measures to reduce the birth rates of vulnerable populations, abortions, marriage restrictions, segregation, sterilization, forced abortions and forced pregnancies were introduced to promote the goals of eugenics. These principles, policies, practices, and scientific research fuelled racial cleansing in Nazi Germany.

By 1925, Adolf Hitler[53] had published his autobiography, Mein Kampf outlining his political ideologies. In Mein Kampf, Adolf Hitler discussed the eugenic legislation for the sterilization of "defectives.' Legislation for sterilization of "defectives" had already been implemented in the United States. The poor, mentally ill, blind, deaf, developmentally disabled, promiscuous women, homosexuals, racial minorities, such as Blacks and Jews were among the "degenerate" and "unfit" categories of "defectives." The policy of eliminating the unfit resulted in institutionalized racism and segregation, institutionalized sterilization, euthanasia, forced abortions, maiming, and mass murder of vulnerable people (Allen, 2004; Black E., 2012).

Figure 28-2 Adolf Hitler

THE RELEVANCE OF EUGENICS TO APR

Darwin's theory of evolution by means of natural selection is founded on the conceptualization of survivability. Differential survivability under the tenets of natural selection, the survival of the fittest, and susceptibility to vulnerability are core elements of the theory of evolution by means of natural selection.

These tenets are relevant for understanding APR because vulnerable populations and individuals such as the poor, women, children, persons

---

[53] Figure 28-2 Phot-colorization
(https://commons.wikimedia.org/wiki/File:Adolf_Hitler_colorized.jpg),
https://creativecommons.org/licenses/by-sa/4.0/legalcode

with different sexual orientations, beliefs, practices, and lifestyles, the elderly, people with psychiatric disorders, and the disabled have a higher susceptibility to APR. These vulnerable populations and individuals have been the targets of eugenics.

Based on evolutionary theory, research, and practice, genes predispose vulnerable populations and individuals to susceptibility to vulnerability. Eugenics is a practical implementation of selection practices based on ancient cosmological philosophies and Darwin's theory of evolution by means of natural selection.

Research and practice related to APR are based on the foundational tenets of predispositional vulnerability. Policies, programs, and service provision to address APR are based on findings from research and practice emanating from the theory of evolution by means of natural selection.

INTELLIGENCE

Darwin contended that intelligence differentiated between the *favoured* races and the unfit such as savages and barbarians. People deemed to be of low intelligence were classified as feeble-minded, idiots, having the mental age of a child. These doctrines became the backbone and purpose of intelligence testing. It was against this background that Alfred Binet and Theodore Simon developed their intelligence test.

Eugenicist Francis Galton was instrumental in the popularization of intelligence testing, the use of the Binet-Simon scale, and the Intelligent Quotient (IQ) as eugenic tools. Intelligence scales, intelligence tests, and IQ became tools to implement overt and covert eugenic educational and psychological research, policies, and practices (Roige, 2014).

Historically, women were deemed to have, on average, a lower IQ than men. Despite efforts to extend the availability of educational opportunities to women, in many countries, educational opportunities for women lag behind men. The perception that women are of lower intelligence than men become apparent in college enrollment into academic areas purported to be the preserves of men and persons of higher intelligence.

AGGRESSION AND INTELLIGENCE

In a 1987 study, using 22 years data set of 600 subjects, Huesmann, Eron, and Yarmel (1987) reported that "aggression in childhood was shown to interfere with the development of intellectual functioning and to be predictive of poorer intellectual achievement as an adult." In a systematic review of 19 studies, Garcia-Sancho, Salguero, and Fernandez-Berrocal, (2014) reported that these studies provided strong evidence of a negative relationship between emotional intelligence and aggression. In another study on intelligence and aggression: *The role of cognitive control and test-*

related stress Zajenkowski and Zajenkowska (2015) found that higher anger was associated with poorer cognitive control.

Darwin made a link between genes, intelligence, and fitness. The idea that genes are determinants of intelligence downplayed the role of environment and the environmentalist's bias associated with intelligence assessments. Further, intelligence is linked to aggression. By implication, aggression is a genetic expression of low intelligence, which in turn is a reflection of poor genes.

EUGENICS AND THE HERITABILITY OF INTELLIGENCE

Francis Galton (1822-1911), a eugenicist and cousin of Charles Darwin, identified as the father of the "nature versus nurture" proposition, contended that intelligence is hereditary. Galton paired intelligence with educational achievement, reputation, and economic success (Roige, 2014).

Using a small sample of prominent families, Galton attempted to establish a link between heredity, intelligence, and criminality. Galton also pioneered twin studies to establish the role of heredity in the transmission of favor, fitness, or vulnerability (Roige, 2014; Tabery, 2014).

Plomin and Deary (2015) agreed with the fundamental Galtonian position concerning genetics and intelligence and reiterated eugenicist's theoretical positions concerning heredity and intelligence. Plomin and Deary reported that intelligence is one of the most heritable traits. However, the heritability of intelligence increases with age. In their review, Plomin and Deary reported that all traits show a significant genetic influence, but that no traits are 100% heritable.

Plomin and Deary (2015) based their review on associative correlation studies that used likelihood statistical association between phenotypic expressions associated with traits believed to be heritable. Plomin and Deary defined intelligence as "general cognitive ability or *g*, as discovered and defined by Spearman in 1904".

Plomin and Deary (2015) conveyed that heritability of intelligence is approximately 20% in infancy, but as persons aged, the heritability of intelligence could increase to as much as 80% in adulthood. The authors contended that intelligence is a positive model for 'positive genetics.' Because of the high heritability of intelligence, Plomin and Deary promoted selective mating among genetically similar individuals as a way to increase intelligence.

However, findings from studies relating to intelligence and aggression show that culture and environment play a role in the relationship between these two variables. In his discussion on nature versus nurture, Tabery (2014) figured that the nature versus nurture debate has two primary aims, to assess the cause and to determine intervention.

Tabery (2014) noted that scientific research concerning etiology and strategies for intervention for problems focuses on traits to determine whether they are the products of heredity or environment. Tabery further posited that the nature versus nurture debate played a central role in the eugenics movement with the emphasis on heredity as the transmitting mechanism of favor, fitness, or vulnerability, such as is evident in APR.

Tabery (2014) noted that the nature versus nurture debate continues to influence research and practice in almost all disciplines and professional fields. Roige (2014), for example, argued that eugenics became interwoven into education and psychology, and identified Spearman (1904) as being influenced by Galton.

Tabery (2014) reported that intelligence tests were used to develop educational, immigration, and segregation policies. Tabery further argued that during the 1970s a debate ensued as to whether the gap in IQ between Black Americans and White Americans was due to environmental factors including discrimination, historical experiences such as the long history of slavery, or genetics. Tabery argued that when the "science of eugenics fell out of fashion," it was replaced by disciplines such as genetics, molecular biology, sociobiology, and behavior genetics.

MEDICINE, EUGENICS, AND GENETICS

Salgirli (2011) posited that in current theory, research, and practice, eugenics came under the umbrella of medicine. In 1938, John A. Ryle, Regius professor of physic at Cambridge University in his introductions to a lecture on medicine and eugenics extolled the work of Galton and expressed his long interest in eugenics. Ryle (1938) stated that medicine and eugenics were in many respects, identical. According to Ryle (p. 9), medicine "...may be considered a sister science, with executive functions, to the science of eugenics...".

Contending that medicine in the past has played too little attention to genetics, Ryle (1938) pressed members of the medical profession to include more of this element within the scope of medicine. The medical profession is core to good and bad in all "our racial qualities."

Ryle (1938, p. 17) recommended that the long-term aim of the medical profession is "stirring of the eugenic conscience in medical students and doctors." To this end, Ryle endorsed the inclusion of eugenics in curative and preventative medicine, educational policies and programs, educational programs for individual doctors, increased role of individual doctors in public education programs, scientific education and research, a medical curriculum, and graduate training to promote eugenics.

In 1939, Haven Emerson of the DeLamar Institute of Public Health, College of Physicians and Surgeons, Columbia University mirrored and reiterated the eugenic philosophy voiced one year earlier by Ryle. Emerson (1939) stated:

> *If we lengthen our view and think not of the year after next, but of the next generation and the generations after that, we find no conflict, but rather a remarkable unity of aims in the programs of eugenics and of preventive medicine.... More than this, preventive medicine should become a potent force in the self-determination of men and women to create progeny of superior beings under those most enduring forms of social security, marriage, and the family.*
>
> *The only other professions which might function as "extension agencies" in furthering the eugenics program would be the priesthood and the bar. (Emerson, 1939, p. 553).*

In assessing the role of medicine and eugenics, Salgirli (2011) stated that eugenics is the main "unifying edifice of the medical community." Salgirli showed that eugenics went underground, but the eugenic doctrine became entwined in the curriculum, practice, and training of medical professionals. Covert eugenic doctrines and practices are accepted in mainstream medicine without question or deep thought as to those practices and policies and the way that they might be reflective of eugenics, or the origin and bases for eugenic practices and policies accepted as mainstream preventative and curative medicine.

Salgirli (2011) argued that eugenics could be found in the social reproduction practices of doctors. Eugenics play a core role in professional self-identification and transfer knowledge of medicine. Covert eugenics are the marks that distinguish members of the medical profession. Acceptance of core eugenic doctrines and practices are traits and characteristics that identify the profession. Members of the medical profession unwittingly adhere to covert eugenics within their profession and transfer these beliefs and practices within the context of social reproduction of members of the profession.

To substantiate the role of the medical profession in the eugenics movement, Emerson (1939) inculcated that human genetics should play a central role in medicine as a means to increase the idea of survival of the fittest and selection at the highest level. Eugenics strategies should be interwoven into preventative care and reproduction practices to endorse selection and survivability (Emerson, 1939; Ryle, 1938).

Eugenics is conceptually divided into two categories, positive eugenics, and negative eugenics. Positive eugenics include practices that promote reproductive advantage among the fit and negative eugenics that fosters the elimination of the unfit (Emerson, 1939; Ryle, 1938).

Ryle (1938) intimated that currently, state-mandated programs such as compulsory sterilization promoted the goals of negative eugenics. However, the involvement of physicians could be used to cause more members of the public to accept and engage in positive eugenics. Acceptance of positive eugenics would influence the public to make choices such as curbing the reproduction rates of the unfit and selective mating among the fit.

The tools available to the medical profession included their aloofness, their special knowledge, research, and education in medical genetics. Ryle (1938) and Emerson (1939) propounded the need for the medical community to lead the way for wider acceptance of eugenics through educating the public, health, social and welfare legislation, and policies. To physicians were given the responsibility of documenting the links between heredity, patient and family histories, irreversible dysgenic disorders, and social-moral practices that contribute to dysgenesis.

DNA became the stronghold of modern genetic studies. By a series of scientific inferences, DNA became equated with genes and became the backbone of associative research and study linking genes with characteristics, traits, and behaviors.

MEDICAL GENETICS, BEHAVIORAL GENETICS, AND APR

James Dewey Watson (born April 6, 1928) shared the Nobel prize in 1962 with Maurice Wilkins and Francis Crick for their 1953 mathematical calculations showing that the hypothesized DNA molecule had a double helix structure. On January 13th, (2019), the British Broadcasting Corporation (BBC) reported that the scientist was stripped of his honorary titles after repeating derogatory comments about Blacks and intelligence.

The scientist, who was the Head of the Human Genome Project, reiterated that people are born to different statuses, that genes are accountable for the difference on average between Blacks' and Whites' IQ test. Watson was vocal about abortion, stating that a woman should have a choice of abortion if she does not want a homosexual child. He was also vocal about fat shaming when he stated: "Whenever you interview fat people, you feel bad because you know you are not going to hire them."

In 2007, Watson[54] reported that he was "inherently gloomy about the prospect of Africa" because "all our social policies are based on the fact that their intelligence is the same as ours – whereas all the testing says not really" (BBC, 2019). Watson noted that while we believe everybody is equal, "people who have to deal with Black employees find this is not true."

Figure 28-3 James Dewey Watson

In 2014, Watson sold his Nobel Prize because he felt that the scientific community ostracized him because of his racial comments. Members of the academic community criticized the scientist's statements as reprehensible and unsupported by science (BBC, 2019).

Figure 28-4 Francis Crick

Crick[55], Wilkins, and Watson's mathematical calculations of the double helix structure of DNA came less than twenty years after eugenicists Emerson and Ryle outlined their strategies for the use of genetic research as a tool to promote eugenics. The scientists confessed that DNA provides proof of genetic determinism. All three scientists Crick, Wilkins, and Watson also expressed that they were eugenicists (Ridley, 2009; Schmidt, 1999). These declarations raise the questions concerning the role of genetics, and whether genetics is indeed a "back door for eugenics."

CRIMINALITY, APR, AND GENETIC DETERMINISM

James Watson, a eugenicist and anti-Semitic (Schmidt, 1999) Nobel Laureate, is reported to have said in the *Time*, March 20, 1989 "We used to think that our fate was in our stars. Now we know, in large part, that our fate is in our genes" (Gasper, 2004). This fundamental tenet of genetic

---

[54] Figure 28-3 James_D_Watson_Genome_Image.jpg: Cold Spring Harbor Laboratory derivative work: Jan Arkesteijn (talk) (https://commons.wikimedia.org/wiki/File:James_D_Watson.jpg), „James D Watson ", marked as public domain, more details on Wikimedia Commons: https://commons.wikimedia.org/wiki/Template:PD-US

[55] Figure 28-4 Francis_Crick.png: Photo: Marc Lieberman derivative work: Materialscientist (talk) (https://commons.wikimedia.org/wiki/File:Francis_Crick_crop.jpg), „Francis Crick crop", https://creativecommons.org/licenses/by/2.5/legalcode

determinism is traceable to the tenets of evolution by natural selection. Gasper 2004, propounded:

> *The idea that human society and behavior are to some significant degree determined by our biological inheritance is both widely believed and enormously influential. One version of this argument bases itself on evolutionary theory, claiming that human evolution has made such characteristics as social hierarchy, gender inequality, competition, and violence inevitable features of every social system. Claims of this kind are closely linked to arguments that claim that significant aspects of human behavior—from alcoholism to criminality – are genetically determined. (Gasper, 2004).*

GENETIC DETERMINISM

Currently, genetic determinism is accepted as a scientific fact by many. Genetic determinism guides research and practice in almost all disciplines pertinent to APR. The concept of genetic determinism is enshrined in the nature versus nurture debate.

Ryle (1938) suggested that the medical profession pay closer attention to the environment in the nature versus nurture debate. This attention to the nature versus nurture debate will strengthen the role of genetics in the phenotypic expressions of characteristics, traits, and behaviors.

Following the innovative research leading to the mathematical calculations that the DNA molecule must be double helix and the application of the theory and calculations in the Human Genome Project, genetic determinism began being presented as a more viable explanation of human problems. Scientists have increasingly vocalized the view that genetic predisposition rather than environmental conditions explain human problems; human problems are innate. As such, genetics hold the key to answering almost all life's social, mental, psychological, psychiatric, health problems, and social ills (Keller, 1992; 2002).

Early eugenicists believed that while social and political reforms could bring about some change, the sturdy support of scientific knowledge in the field of biology and medicine held great promise. The application of scientific research to support genetic determinism also reinforced racial superiority and inequity. Darwin's contention that there were superior races, that natural selection favoured and human subspecies such as barbarians and savages, whom natural selection disfavored, persisted.

Francis Galton, Darwin's cousin, who coined the phrase "survival of the fittest," pursued Darwin's idea that intelligence was one of the innate qualities that distinguished the superior and the vulnerable. Galton reinforced Darwin's conception of the biological basis of traits and claimed that "... the average intellectual standard of the negro race is some two grades below our own." (Galton, 1892, p. 338) The same sentiment voiced by Watson more than one hundred years later and that within our current historical period (BBC, 2019; Emerson, 1939; Ryle, 1938).

Figure 28-5 Charles Davenport

The scientific practice of associating phenotypic expressions as a manifestation of genes is an accepted research practice in genetics. For example, intelligence is taken to represent genetic traits. Low IQs are associated with social problems such as poverty, criminality, and aggression. The increasing acceptance of genetic determinism is rendering these conclusions valid (Black E., 2012; Chase, 1977; Kevles, 1985).

Charles Davenport[56], an evolutionary biologist, and eugenicist was instrumental in shaping eugenic policies in the United States. Those policies included forced sterilization and discriminatory immigration laws. Davenport connected social problems with heredity and wrote:

> *...though capital punishment is a crude method of grappling with the difficulty [of those with inferior genes] it is infinitely superior to that of training the feeble-minded and criminalistic and then letting them loose upon society and permitting them to perpetuate in their offspring these animal traits. (Chase, 1977; Davenport, 1911).*

Sociobiological evidence of genetic determinism continues to emerge in new fields and disciplines. Among these disciplines of high relevance to APR are the neurobiological basis of behavior, genetics, and behavioral genetics.

Lewontin (1991) presented that selective advantage could be used to explain anything, but questioned whether there was evidence to support selective advantage, superiority, survivability, or susceptibility to vulnerability.

---

[56] Figure 28-5 Unknown (https://commons.wikimedia.org/wiki/File:Charles_Benedict_Davenport.jpg), „Charles Benedict Davenport ", marked as public domain, more details on Wikimedia Commons: https://commons.wikimedia.org/wiki/Template:PD-US

> *At the very minimum, we might ask whether there is any evidence that such selective processes are going on at the present, but in fact, no one has ever measured in any human population the actual reproductive advantage or disadvantage of any human behavior. All of the sociobiological explanations of the evolution of human behavior are like Rudy Kipling's Just So stories of how the camel got his hump and how the elephant got his trunk. They are just stories. Science has been turned into a game.*
> *(Lewontin, 1991, p. 100).*

THE EVOLUTIONARY BASIS OF VIOLENCE

Natural selection, selection, survivability, vulnerable, fit, unfit, and reproductive advantage; mainstays of evolutionary theory are "just so." Ordained and predetermined by a force that exists outside of human control. However, genes, the mechanisms of survivability being an element that was breathed into life by the god Pan are predeterminants of predestined survivability or vulnerability.

Inside genes are elements such as aggression. Aggression is instinctive and the process whereby species developed into greater complexities and forms. It is this aggression that propels and continues to hurl species through the stages of evolution.

AGGRESSION, THE ENVIRONMENT, AND EVOLUTION

Evolutionary psychology is a specialty discipline seeking to provide ontogenetic explanations of human behavior. Evolutionary psychologists begin with the premise that humans evolved, and human behaviors evolved in response to difficult environments. The underlying tenet is survival of the fittest.

Evolutionary psychologists contend that harsh environments were responsible for the manifestation of violence. Aggression is innate; embedded in the genes, and violence is a phenotypic expression of aggression (Cosmides & Tooby, 1997).

As a phenotypic expression of innate aggression, violence, and abuse are contextually functional or dysfunctional. "Aggression (defined as an offensive action or procedure) and violence (defined as the exertion of any physical force to injure or abuse) stem, in part, from the need to win at any cost" (Locke, 2013, p. 51).

The conceptualization of survival of the fittest and genetic determinism hinge on two assumptions; The first is that violence is preprogrammed genetically into species and the second is that species have a long history of violence induced by harsh environmental conditions (Cosmides & Tooby, 1997).

Several criticisms could be cited with respect to this explanation concerning the etiology of aggression. The first criticism is that aggression remains constant even though evolution is about gradual and successive change.

Archaeological records inform the second criticism of aggression as an innate evolutionary principle. Archaeological records suggest that violence is culturally cultivated based on wealth accumulation, competition, and philosophies of war. Additionally, archaeological records show that violence in human societies, such as war, and largescale species-to-species violence and murder emerged within the last 10,000 years of human history, debunking the theory of centuries of violence associated with evolution (Ferguson, 2003).

BY ANY MEANS NECESSARY

Although genetic defects were the identifiable justification for eugenics, eugenicists were in favor of eliminating the unfit, whether or not genetic defects were proven to exist therein. Mehler (1997) reported that the American Eugenics Society estimated that "there were two million 'feebleminded' persons in the United States in need of institutional care and 150,000 epileptics (90,000 were actually institutionalized). Another 320,006 persons were institutionalized for insanity".

Eugenicists further argued that "even if all the criminals, epileptics and similar people were biologically desirable, their homes are rarely desirable places in which to bring up children." Common prudence "makes it advisable that even the doubtful cases should have no children." In addition to sterilization, the American Eugenics Society recommended that segregation and "vigorous promotion of birth control among the lower classes" should be pursued (Mehler, 1997).

EUGENICS POLICIES AND STRATEGIES

To reduce the population of undesirables, eugenicists recommended the provision of information and services to reduce inculcate in the unfit the need to reduce their birth rate. These included measures such as abstinence advocacy, sex-education in schools, school-based clinics, promotion of the use of contraception, and voluntary sterilization. These measures would enlist the support of the unfit to engage in eugenics practices and policies through their free will.

Eugenicists also enforced measures to create incentives for the "defectives" to have less or no children, coercion, and compulsory abortion and sterilization. Some programs produced under this initiative included incentives for sterilization, paying teenage mothers for not becoming pregnant again, payments for sterilization in developing countries, curtailment of welfare benefits, and compulsory sterilization for criminals, the feeble-minded, and imbeciles. Victims and perpetrators of APR have a high susceptibility to negative eugenics.

Positive eugenics include all measures to promote childbearing among the fit. Some measures included incentives for childbearing and eugenic migration.

HOW IT HAPPENED

Mary Meehan (2009) reported that in 1972, James Crow of the American Eugenics Society stated, 'If eugenics is a dirty word, we can find something else that means the same thing.' The American Eugenics Society changed its name to the Society for the study of Social Biology. Meehan also reported that in 1965, Frederick Osbourne (1889-1981) a founding member of the American Eugenics Society in a correspondent stated that "The term medical genetics has taken the place of the old term negative eugenics."

Meehan (2009) warned that eugenics is deeply embedded in science and research; such embeddings can remain invisible. The prejudices against "defectives" were at the roots of genetic research and the very earliest studies into prenatal testing.

Advocacy against defectives could be traced back to early cosmological philosophers such as Plato and Aristotle, who pressed for laws to kill the "offspring of the inferior, or of the better when they chance to be deformed." Darwin presented similar sentiments. Francis Galton, Darwin's cousin, contended that eugenics "must be introduced into the national conscience, like a new religion." (Meehan, 2009).

Darwin argued that when members of the superior race, through misguided sentiments of conscience, assist savages, barbarians, and unfit, they only create a burden for the government and state. Eugenicists argued that controlling the births of defectives would be tantamount to a savings to the state, reduction of the burden of welfare, and the taxpayer (Meehan, 2009).

Eugenicists further argued that it was the role of medicine and genetics to make prenatal testing with the aim of abortion of the unfit an acceptable public proposition. Meehan (2009) reported Osbourne's claim that "An advance had been made in public acceptance of the idea of controlling the birth of defectives...". This move toward public acceptance "has become an important function of medicine and public health. It is not done under the name of eugenics, but it is no less effective for that reason." (Meehan, 2009).

Figure 28-6 Margaret Sanger

ATTACK AGAINST PLANNED PARENTHOOD: A THREAT TO WOMEN'S HEALTH

In 2012, the editors of Scientific Americans discussed in an article *Political Attacks on Planned Parenthood are a Threat to Women's health* that political attacks on planned parenthood pose a threat to the well-being of millions of women in the U.S. The editors extolled the work of Margaret Sanger[57], the founder of Planned Parenthood. The editors also criticized a statement made by Senator Jon Kyl of Arizona as untrue that abortion accounts for "well over 90%" of what of Planned Parenthood does. The editors petitioned against the reduction or removal of federal funding for Planned Parenthood.

Meehan (2009) identified Margaret Sanger, a member of the Socialist Party, as a member of both the American Eugenics Society as well as a member of its British counterpart. Meehan quoted Margaret Sanger as saying:

> *In 1922 she [Margaret Sanger] complained that "the vicious circle of mental and physical defect, delinquency and beggary is encouraged, by the unseeing and unthinking sentimentality of our age, to populate asylum, hospital and prison." She spoke of people "who never should have been born at all." Malformed children, she said, were "biological and racial mistakes."*

Meehan (2009) noted that Sanger openly opposed abortion. Nevertheless, Planned Parenthood came under the leadership of another prominent eugenicist, Dr. Alan Guttmacher. Meehan also cited the role of the Rockefeller Foundation and the Carnegie Corporation in the eugenics movement. Several US presidents were also identified as supportive of eugenicists, including President Roosevelt.

---

[57] Figure 28-6 Underwood & Underwood
(https://commons.wikimedia.org/wiki/File:MargaretSanger-Underwood.LOC.jpg),
„MargaretSanger-Underwood.LOC", marked as public domain, more details on
Wikimedia Commons: https://commons.wikimedia.org/wiki/Template:PD-US

The American Society of Human Genetics (ASHG) founded in 1948 is the world's largest professional membership organization for human genetics and genomic specialists. In 2018, the ASHG issued a statement denouncing attempts to link genetics and racial supremacy (ASHG, 2018).

Eugenicists formed the backbone of the foundation of the ASHG and advocated the use of medical genetics to promote eugenic agenda. The ASHG recognized a resurgence of "groups rejecting the value of genetic diversity and using discredited or distorted genetic concepts to bolster bogus claims of White Supremacy" (ASHG, 2018).

The American Eugenics Society sponsored genetic research, funded genetics fellowships, and published information on genetic diseases. The American Eugenics Society also promoted heredity counseling. Meehan reported that in their heredity counseling report 1953-1957, the American Eugenics Society stated that they had gained "the opening wedge in the public acceptance of eugenic principles."

Abortion was one of the eugenic principles. During modern times eugenicists interests in feticides could be traced to eugenic abortions in Nazi Germany and Denmark, where there was a fostering of research in amniocentesis to analyze the fluids for Rh disease. These testing were significant in sex-selective abortions.

Based on the chromosomal theory of inheritance, females with certain diseases such as hemophilia are believed to be the carriers of the genes. This gives a 50 percent chance that the disease might be transmitted to her sons. This opened up the path for prenatal screening to determine whether the fetus was male or female. Male feticide performed because of the likelihood of genetic defects was later transferred to female feticide due to patriarchy and related sociocultural systems (Meehan, 2009).

IMPLICATIONS FOR APR

Sterilization was one of the strategies used to ensure eugenics. Specific traits, such as pauperism, criminality, and sexual immorality are eugenic targets. Consequently, vulnerable populations with the highest potentials for APR also fell within the ambit of eugenics as 'unfit.'

POLYGAMY, PATRIARCHY, AND PATRILOCALITY

Polygamous, patriarchal, and patrilocal systems present disabilities to victims of APR. Research indicates that women in polygamous, patriarchal, and patrilocal systems also experience the negative impact of negative eugenics.

Pandey (2014) reported that an estimated 37% of all married women in India are sterilized, and in 2011, the government reported that 4.6 million women had undergone tubectomy in that year. Pandey observed that patriarchy was a fundamental element in the higher number of female sterilizations when compared with males.

Pandey (2014) complained that women were coerced into sterilization programs and that the state used incentives that preyed on the lack and poverty of the nation to enforce its sterilization and family planning policies.

> *State governments regularly organise mass sterilisation camps where doctors perform serial tubectomies on dozens of women from poor families.*
>
> *The women are often promised a monetary incentive if they undergo the procedure. Health workers, who convinced a woman to undergo a tubectomy, are also sometimes rewarded.*
> *(Pandey, 2014).*

Except for the United Kingdom, UN data show disproportionately higher tubectomies than vasectomies. Tubectomies are also disproportionately higher in poorer countries when compared with first world nations.

Although eugenics and forced sterilization are thought to be things of the past, the practice is believed to be continuing up until the current period. According to a report of the Center for Investigative Reporting, nearly 150 female inmates in California prisons were sterilized between 2006 and 2010.

Sterilization, forced sterilization, planned parenthood, birth control, and abortion are continuing concerns in medicine and politics up until the present time. Disabilities against women remain an underlying theme. Statistics show that APR is gender-biased. On the matter of forced sterilization, Kline (2001) observed that women, minority groups, and persons with higher susceptibility to abuse were more often presented for forced sterilization procedures. Even during the last decade forced sterilization was performed against females without legal authority, including the use of forged signatures to enforce forced sterilization procedures against women, minorities, and persons with higher susceptibility to abuse (Johnson C. G., 2013).

> *Senator Ted Lieu, D-Redondo Beach, who oversees the Medical Board of California, stated in a letter to that board that he was troubled by "allegations that doctors violated State law, disregarded ethical guidelines, and fell well below the Standard of care".*
> *(Louv, 2013).*

The Southern Poverty Law Center (SPLC) in Alabama found that an estimated 100,000 to 150,000 poor people were sterilized annually under federally funded programs (SPLC, 1977).

> *North Carolina was a particularly egregious case: the state is recorded as having sterilized 1,110 men and 6,418 women between 1929 and 1974. 40% of those operated on were people of color, and 60% were white; a third of the women sterilized were under the age of 18, all the way down to the age of 9. (Louv, 2013).*

This pattern of sterilization of the poor with the focus on women, children, and other vulnerable targets has been found to be repeated in several countries (Pandey, 2014). There is the fear that eugenic practices continue under the guise of genetics.

NEWGENICS AND BACKDOOR EUGENICS

Troy Duster (2003) complained that the human genome project had aroused fear that the application of modern genetic technologies could bring about a resurgence of eugenics, despite the good intentions of researchers, philosophers, and geneticists. Duster's concern relates to the sociocultural contextual elements of genetic research, application, and implementation practices.

Sociocultural contextual elements are relevant to all theoretical formulations, research, practical application, and implementation of scientific study. As such, genetics, as it pertains to APR, must also be considered within the sociocultural context in which the discipline developed, and the way findings from research are applied.

An evolutionary theoretical orientation was a driving force behind the human genome project. This theoretical orientation posits tenets of survivability and vulnerability based on cosmological philosophy, a religious philosophy grounded in metaphysics.

Modern disciplines were forged out of this ancient philosophy and inculcated into science by various means of philosophical thoughts used to integrate untestable tenets that were foundational to the theory. Nevertheless, the philosophical orientation of survivability and vulnerability fashioned into theories of society and social stratification persisted throughout the development of disciplines undergirded by evolutionary theory.

Centuries of discriminatory policies and practices reinforced the doctrines of social stratification, forging a materialization of the doctrine as phenotypic expressions in the various social strata. When Darwin presented the conceptualization of pangenes as the mechanism of heredity, the concept was picked up and hurled forward by other eugenicists of the cosmological natural philosophical traditions.

As pangenetic metamorphosized into genetics and molecular genetics, its veracity and applicability to human society and human benefit increased. In the infancy of modern-day genetics, eugenicists pressed the members of the medical profession to become engaged in medical genetics because of its applicability and relevance to the eugenics movement (Emerson, 1939; Ryle, 1938).

Due to the heavy presence of eugenicists in genetics, research, application, and practice of genetics arose a justifiable fear that considering human diseases and disorders from a genetic perspective is an extension of eugenics. Ridiculous rhetoric, such as those spouted by eminent scientist James Watson, does little to allay these fears (BBC, 2019; Duster, 2003).

Generally, because the medical, scientific, and academic community are credited with having knowledge and expertise not commonly held among the general populace, members of these professions and disciplines hold the confidence of the people. As such, these professionals, educators, scientists, and researchers are held to a higher standard of ethical practice, behavior, and conduct.

Duster (2003), however, argued that considering human disease, disorders, and nature within the context of genetics is inherently racist and discriminatory. Given the origins, the philosophical orientation of genes, and genetic determinism, the application of genetics that link disorders and diseases to ethnicity could lead to eugenic abuses.

The risk of abuse becomes more imminent because of the widespread acceptance of genetic determinism and the honor in which members of the genetics and related disciplines are held. As such, Duster (2003) voiced a real fear that eugenics could emerge under the auspices of medical genetics.

QUESTIONING THE OBJECTIVITY AND VERACITY OF GENETIC RESEARCH AND APPLICATION

Because research, application, and practice occur within the context of history, economic and financial realities, sociocultural, and political practices, evolutionary theory and scientific theory, research and practice undergirded by evolutionary theory must be able to stand up to severe scrutiny. Because of the delimits of undergirding disciplines such as biology, genetics, and molecular biology, genetics are identifiable targets of ethical scrutiny.

The Human Genome Project became a backbone influence of modern genetics and DNA research. Gannett (2016) outlined that the Human Genome Project was plagued by ethical concerns very early in the program. Among the foremost concerns were gene patents, financial motives, intellectual property, social and political hegemony. Ethical concerns related to such things as cloning, genetic enhancement, and genetic testing continue to surface in the genetic debate.

Genetic screening is genetic testing carried out at the population level. The concerns with genetic testing become more immediate when genetic screening is linked with race and ethnicity; more so when the target group is financially, politically, and socially marginalized (Gannett, 2016).

The American Eugenics Society registered their concern that perpetuating an increased birth rate among "defectives and undesirables" is an added burden on public funds. Again, legislators in the very recent period reasoned that costly sterilization is a more viable prospect when weighed against the long-term costs of health and related care for persons with diseases and disorders linked to genes (Gannett, 2016; Louv, 2013; Mehler, 1997).

Those identifying genetics as newgenics cite prenatal screening as a practice highly likely to be abused. Beijing Genomics Institute, the world's largest genetics research center, was formed in 1999 to facilitate China's participation in the Human Genome Project. In 2012, the Beijing Genomics Institute spearheaded a project in search of DNA and genes believed to be linked to intelligence (Yong, 2013).

The link between intelligence and genes is traceable back to Darwin, Galton, and other early eugenicists. This thin line between gene enhancement and eugenics also has implications for gene editing, gendercide, and sex-selection.

According to the Chinese government, more than 400 million births were prevented, starting from 1970, a decade before the start of China's one-child policy. The policy was enforced using financial incentives, mandatory contraception, and sterilization. Several sociocultural issues emerged related to sex-selection practice. Among these issues were changes in the natural balance of the male-to-female ratio.

WHERE HAVE ALL THE YOUNG GIRLS GONE

The global figures for missing girls stand at 160 million. According to the United Nations Population Fund (UNFPA) data, approximately 3.5 million females representing roughly 4% of the global female population are lost each year, of this figure 1.7 million females are lost because of sex-selective abortion. About 50% of sex-selective abortions are female feticide (UNFPA, 2011).

Sex-selective abortion[58] affects human sex-ratio, which is the relative

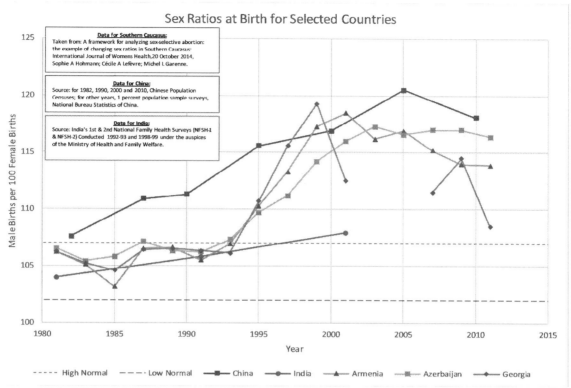

Chart 28-1 Sex Ratios at Birth for Selected Countries

number of males to females in any given age-group. Among the total human population, the ratio of men to women is 101:100 (UNFPA, 2011). Human sex-ratio that falls outside this normal range is indicative of medical, political, economic, and sociocultural practices that are influencing the patterns of live-births.

Changes in boys-to-girls birth sex-ratio were noticed in China following the implementation of China's one-child policy. These patterns were attributed to sociocultural practices related to patriarchalism. A UNFPA report (2011), indicated that prenatal sex-selection results in a distorted sex ratio at birth, in some countries reaching between 110 and

---

[58] Chart 28-1 Data from(Bhattacharya, 2012; Hohmann, Lefèvre, & Garenne, 2014)

120 males per 100 female births. Misuse of medical technology related to prenatal screening has been identified as one of the primary mechanisms

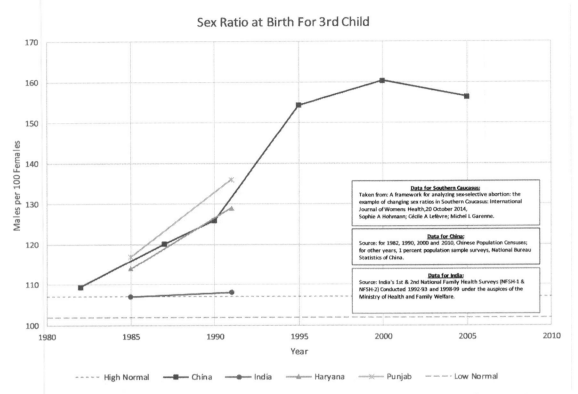

Chart 28-2   Sex Ratios at Birth of 3rd Child for Selected Countries

facilitating gender discrimination[59].

LIBERAL EUGENICS

In his book, *War against the weak: Eugenics and America's campaign to create a Master Race,* Black E. (2012) discussed the dilemma of reducing life to DNA. The critical ethical question remains concerning as to when does life begin. Related to the question of life are issues related to women's rights, rights, or non-rights of the unborn, sovereignty, and the rule of law.

On the one hand, *choice,* the rights to choose between the options of abortion and giving birth are presented as arguments to protect women's rights. On the other hand, female feticide is criticized as a violation of female rights. Within the broader context of eugenic philosophy, gendercide is only a portion of a population that could be rationalized as falling within the ambit of the vulnerable.

Liberal eugenics is a move away from compulsory, state acts of population control that target less desirable genetic traits to the program of choice. Early eugenicists proposed that eugenics should be made palatable

---

[59] Chart 28-2 Data from(Bhattacharya, 2012; Hohmann et al., 2014)

and acceptable to the target population. Through education and professional intervention, especially by members of the medical profession, individuals with undesirable traits should see the need to deter the replication of undesirable genes and participate in efforts to reduce the chances of replicating themselves (Emerson, 1939; Ryle, 1938).

Birth control education and regulation would show the benefits of curbing the population, especially among those populations with vulnerable genes. These measures should encourage the members of this population to engage in choice (Emerson, 1939; Ryle, 1938).

Ryle (1938) encouraged research and inclusion of genetics in the medical profession. Ryle also suggested that doctors should keep a detailed history that links disorders to heredity so that these data could be included in preventative care.

Goering (2014) discussed the nature and benefits of liberal eugenics. Goering identified liberal eugenics as actions taken by the individual rather than state-driven practices. The ability to choose is the emphasis of liberal eugenics. Individuals and parents should be convinced of the benefits of reproductive choice.

Agar stated, "I have argued that the addition of the word "liberal" to "eugenics" transforms an evil doctrine into a morally acceptable one" (Agar, 2004, p. 135). Whereas historical and classical eugenics were delimited by the actions of the state, liberal eugenics emphasize individual choice in decisions concerning such practices as abortion, sterilization, and prenatal testing. Whereas state-driven practices previously fell under the umbrella of historical and classical eugenics, individual choice is guided by individual acceptance of eugenic values and the individual's decision of the good life for themselves and their offspring. Liberal eugenicists argue that liberal eugenics should be backed by credible science (Agar, 2004; Goering, 2014).

The choice to engage in eugenic practices should not be construed as being vicious but should be seen as actions that are guided by scientific research (Agar, 2004; Goering, 2014). Citing the long-term policies of eugenicists as a rationale for his arguments, Duster (2003) apperceived that eugenics by the back door will increase the appropriation of genetic explanations to further eugenics.

Nevertheless, liberal eugenics boast many advantages for the general population enhancement, improvement in the lives of individuals and family, genetic enhancement, and preventative care. Prenatal testing allows parents to make a choice concerning offspring likely to have birth defects. Prenatal testing is also valuable in sex-selectivity. In vitro fertilization technology could target the best genetic traits for viable births (Agar, 2004; Parker, 2007).

Although Agar (2004) presents a case for liberal eugenics, Epstein (2003) argued that modern genetic-based practices such as prenatal screening do not equate to eugenics. Epstein argued that classical eugenics was driven by racial, discriminatory motives and intent, which cannot be found in modern-day practices of voluntary contraception, sterilization, abortion, and prenatal screening.

Advocating parental rights and the benefits of ridding the population of defective genes, Epstein (2003) argued, that while modern-day practices such as prenatal screening are founded on the same premises of eugenics, the modern-practices used to ensure good genes are devoid of the negative intents and beliefs of classical eugenics. Further, Epstein contended that modern-day practices to ensure the reproduction of good genes are not government mandated, do not have elements of discrimination, and do not provide direct financial benefits for governments.

GENES AND AGGRESSION

Association between genetics and aggression has a long history. In 1965 and 1966, researchers at the Medical Research Council Clinical and Population Cytogenetics Research Unit led by Dr. Court Brown concluded that their research indicated that aggression was linked to chromosomal abnormalities. These findings were later found to be erroneous (Johnson R. N., 1972).

Ethological studies have been used to examine whether there is a link between genes and aggression. Selective breeding was among earlier models. Researchers interbred strains of animals, such as mice, dogs, and birds that seem to be more aggressive to assess whether genes might be responsible for aggression.

Researchers used mice models for selective breeding of mice showing aggression. In one study, both male and female offspring from highly aggressive strains of mice showed aggressive behavioral expressions during the middle-age period. These mice were not observed to be more aggressive than other strains of mice during the early and later stages of development (Brain & Benton, 1981).

Thus far, researchers in molecular genetics have established a molecular basis for aggression. Researchers have concluded that several neurotransmitters, including dopamine and serotonin, are implicated in aggression. Through extrapolatory calculations, these neurotransmitters have been linked to the DNA molecule (Nelson & Chiavegatto, 2001).

Scientists identify and believe that DNA, an acid in the nuclei of cells, is implicated in the production of brain and body chemicals. Molecular biologists identify very specific changes in DNA and associate these with the production of brain and body chemicals.

Scientists make an inference that DNA reflects genes. Because genes have and cannot be seen, genetic analysis makes use of DNA to make extrapolations and draw conclusions about hypothesized genes and gene behavior.

Scientists hypothesized that all organisms have genes. DNA is an acid that interacts with four proteins. When DNA interacts with proteins, cell replication occurs. Scientists infer that genes exist and that genes are giving instructions to DNA on how to replicate.

Nucleotides are the constituent parts of DNA. A nucleotide is a group of molecules, that when linked together form the building block of DNA or RNA.

Monomers are the constituent part of nucleotides. A monomer is a molecule that can combine with other molecules of the same kind. A molecule is an electrically neutral group of two or more atoms held together by chemical bonds. A polymer comprises bonded molecules.

A single nucleotide polymorphic unit is a specific unit within DNA. Using computer analysis, molecular geneticists identified a single nucleotide polymer that they believe is associated with aggression.

Polymorphism means to occur in different forms. Molecular geneticists believe that nucleotide polymers are configured differently and that the differences in configurations cause differences in the production of neurochemicals.

In mice models, it has been observed that serotonin, dopamine, and other neurotransmitters play a role in the expression of aggressive behaviors. Geneticists figured that differences in neurochemicals such as dopamine and serotonin might be due to differences in nucleotide polymers.

Nucleotide polymers are inferred to be a reflection of genes. Based on this inference, molecular geneticists believe that aggression is the product of genes. Although molecular geneticists associate differences in nucleotide polymers with aggression, Nehrenberg, Wang, Buus, Perkins, Pardo-Manuel de Villena and Pomp in a study *Genomic mapping of social behavior traits in a F2 cross derived from mice selectively bred for high aggression*, reported that "No evidence for a locus with major effect on aggressive behavior in mice was identified." (2010, p. 1)

Nehrenberg et al. (2010) stated that selective breeding programs indicated significant differences in aggression levels within five generations of mice offspring of selective breeding between mice with strong aggression. These researchers engaged in a comparative study of a mouse line selectively bred for higher levels of attack behavior. Nehrenberg et al. (2010) used selectively bred high and low aggression mouse lineages in their study. The researchers reported that all mice in their study exhibited both affiliative and aggressive behaviors.

Several other mice model studies using knockout techniques have explored whether there is a link between nucleotide polymers and aggression. While these studies confirm a neurophysiological basis of aggression, a causative link between nucleotide polymers and aggression have not been established (Garratt & Brooks, 2015).

CRITICISM OF GENETIC APPROACH

Some scholars criticize the approach that uses genes to explain behavior. The philosophical orientation of the theory of evolution by means of natural selection is often cited as the reason for these criticisms. The conceptualization of genes, social stratification, racism, and discriminatory undertones of the theory of evolution by means of natural selection is at the root of criticisms of the approach that uses genes to explain behavior.

Thus far, molecular scientists have identified DNA, RNA, and their constituents. The contention that DNA represents genes is an inference or hypothetical assumption based on the existence of genes, and that DNA represents genes. Some scientists argue that while DNA and RNA might be chemicals found in the nuclei of cells, contending that DNA and RNA are genes are hypothetical assumptions that have not been substantiated. Further, these scientists contend that inferring the existence of genes based on the existence and functions of DNA have not proven the existence of genes (Barbieri, 2007).

Additionally, Genome-wide association studies (GWAS) have not been able to explain heritability, disease, and disorders. In February 2009, a group of experts convened by the National Human Genome Research Institute to address the reasons GWAS have not been able to explain heritability, disease, and disorders. The expert reported that "Genome-wide association studies (GWAS), in which several hundred thousand to more than a million SNPs are assayed in thousands of individuals, represent a powerful new tool for investigating the genetic architecture of complex diseases" (Manolio et al., 2010, p. 2).

The experts stated that "Many common human diseases and traits are known to cluster in families and are believed to be influenced by several genetic and environmental factors, but until recently the identification of genetic variants contributing to these 'complex diseases' has been slow and arduous" (Manolio et al., 2010, p. 2). The purpose of the group was to come up with an explanation as to why so much of the heritability inferences are apparently unexplained by findings from GWAS (Manolio et al., 2010).

Some scholars have argued that genetic determinism is not a viable explanation for disease and disorders. In addition to the controversial ideological underpinning of the theory undergirding genetic determinism that some scholars use to undermine heritability and disorders, some scholars cite polygenetic variants, epigenetic mechanisms, and sociocultural influences on behavior.

In defense of the connectivity between heritability and disorders, Manolio et al., (2010) indicated that gene manifestation, functions, and interactions are complex phenomena. As such GWAS have failed in making a link between heritability and disorders because of technological limitations and the complexities of genes.

Key to understanding the challenges associating genes and heritability of diseases and disorders is distinguishing between genes and DNA. DNA in molecular genetics is not the same as genes in classical genetics. DNA is a chemical substance found in replicating cells. Information theory facilitates the association of DNA as a manifestation of genes in molecular genetics. Likelihood statistical analysis and simulated computer models are used to infer the connections between DNA and genes (Barbieri, 2007; Manolio et al., 2010).

Because of the current methodology and models used in molecular genetic research, DNA, gene-expressions, variations of phenotypic expressions, and the manifestations of diseases and disorders are predictive models. Very often, predictability is low (Barbieri, 2007; Manolio et al., 2010).

The Council for Responsible Genetics (CRG) is a nonprofit, nongovernmental organization based in Cambridge, Massachusetts. The CRG was founded in 1983 with a stated aim of providing clear and understandable information on the social, ethical, and environmental implications of genetic technologies.

Hubbard and Wald (1999) stated that initially many biologists favored the idea that DNA was a framework within which naturally occurring proteins combined in different shapes and sizes for the transmission of various molecular characteristics, traits, and behaviors. With the discovery of the double helix DNA structure, there also came a shift in thought in the role of DNA.

This shift in thought is the paradigm within which modern-day genetic research is conducted. However, Hubbard and Wald (1999) suggest that this shift in thought represented a pre-mindset of the theorists presenting the DNA hypothesis and the calculations showing that DNA has a double helix structure that DNA holds the 'secret of life.'

This perspective does not fully incorporate that DNA is a complex structure with multifaceted and multifunctional interactions within a very complex internal cellular environment. This approach to using DNA to explain genetic manifestations also does not fully take into account the complexities of the external environment and individual differences in trait manifestation and transmission (Hubbard & Wald, 1999).

Although there are much-publicized research findings identifying an association between genes and behavior, Joseph and Ratner (2013) observed that scholars have not been able to replicate these studies. Genetic researchers hold that genes that influence psychiatric conditions and psychological behavior exist. However, the failure to discover these genes is due to their small effect size, shortcomings in methods, and sample size (Joseph & Ratner, 2013).

Joseph and Ratner (2013) argued that genetic studies associating genes, psychiatric conditions, and behaviors could not be found because they do not exist. Having explored weaknesses in methodology, Joseph and Ratner (2013) posited that genes research in psychiatry and psychology is contaminated by environmental confounders and biases. Joseph and Ratner (2013) implored genetic researchers to reevaluate their assumptions and seek out a more viable explanation for human psychology.

MONOGENETIC THEORY OF COMMON DESCENT

The concept of common genes; common disorder, is based on the Mendelian law of inheritance. Mendelian inheritance forms the basis for explaining genetic diseases and disorders. However, in the absence of findings to support the common genes, common disorder heritability model, geneticists are beginning to favor genetic heterogeneity (Manolio et al., 2010; Ringman et al., 2014; Varol, Sotiras, & Davatzikos, 2017).

Roots of the Mendelian law of inheritance could be found in the tenets of Common Descent, a foundational tenet of evolutionary theory. According to Darwin's hypothesis, humans emerged from a common ancestor and branched off into different human subspecies. Susceptibility or superiority of the subspecies is due to the evolutionary process, whereby mutations play a significant role.

The validity of mutation as a mechanism of evolution has been criticized as being flawed and statistically improbable. Keller (2013) showed that a two-step inference has to be made to facilitate the case for mutation. The first inference is that phenotypic difference is indicative of changes in the underlying mechanisms or genes. The second inference is that the existence and identity of the genes are inferred from the mutation (Keller, 2013).

Keller (2013) argued that "a certain confounding of traits and trait differences was built into the science of genetics from the very beginning." The study of genetics, therefore, is built on the foundation that phenotypic differences are indicative of changes in some underlying internal mechanism(s). This inferential assumption, though accepted as fact, is yet to be proven (Keller, 2013).

Jablonka and Lamb (2014) argued that the problem of the illusive heritability "maybe part of the answer to this puzzle is that it resides not in the genotype, but rather in the epigenotype." Newman (2013) argued several flaws exist in Darwin's theory of evolution by means of natural selection. These flaws require leaps in thinking, which current technology and knowledge have not substantiated (Jablonka & Lamb, 2014; Newman, 2013).

Counter-evolutionists continue to question natural selection as a mechanism of evolution. Although geneticists and modern-day evolutionary biologists accept that genes are the internal mechanism of change, thus far, genetic effects have been deduced to only have small effects on change. However, Mendel's law of inheritance is based on large effect, and genes of large effect will be rare in any natural population (Newman, 2013).

Newman (2013) also observed that in the process of imperceptible change for each stage of speciation to occur, the new species could not engage in viable reproduction with species on the preceding rung of the ladder. This negates the tenet of pangenes as the internal mechanism of evolution by natural selection.

Even if one were to accept all the tenets of Darwin's theory of evolution by natural selection, Newman (2013) argued that no explanation has ever been given to explain the existence of matter in a form to facilitate the process of natural selection. This troubling reality falls under the broad umbrella of the ontogeny of life and ontogeny of species which remain unexplained.

CONCLUSION: A BETTER WAY

The theory of evolution by natural selection continues to be plagued by flaws and weaknesses. Efforts to validate the theory, especially through research in genetics and evolutionary biology remain fraught with problems. Moreover, the foundation of the theory is strongly linked to aggression, discrimination, and inequity. The most damaging criticisms of the theory of evolution by means of natural selection might be its link with eugenics.

Indoctrination is the process of inculcating a person with ideas, attitudes, cognitive strategies, and professional methodologies. A Pew report from July (2015-7) indicated that 35% of US adults believe that humans evolved by means of natural processes, and 24 % believe that evolution was or is guided by a supreme being.

Darwin's theory of evolution by natural selection combine both elements of natural selection and a force outside of human control, possibly under the auspices of the god Pan. An earlier Pew report from January (2015-1) also reported that 98% of scientists connected to the American Association for the Advancement of Science believe that humans evolved.

The controversy over the theory of evolution by means of natural selection is usually presented within the framework of religion and science.

However, any theory, including the theory of evolution by natural selection is not tailored by religious beliefs, but by scientific processes.

The flaws and weaknesses associated with the theory of evolution by means of natural selection continue to mount. Upheld under the light of scientific scrutiny, these weaknesses and flaws are undeniable. As such, objections to the theory of evolution by means of natural selection based on this scrutiny cannot be dismissed as a religious persuasion but must be evaluated within scientific credibility.

Survivability, selection, superiority, vulnerability, and aggression are ideological tenets of the theory of evolution by means of natural selection. An ideology is a collection of normative beliefs and values that an individual or group holds for other than purely epistemic value. As such, superiority, selection, survivability, vulnerability, and aggression, the core tenets of evolution by means of natural selection must be evaluated within the context of epistemic values. If the core tenets of evolution by means of natural selection, including survivability, selection, superiority, aggression, innateness, and vulnerability do not stand the test of epistemic value, they must be revisited.

The theory of planned behavior indicates that beliefs affect behavior. Beliefs become the filter through which actions and behaviors emerge. As such, beliefs shape reality.

Beliefs concerning survivability, selection, superiority, innateness shape individual and group aggression. As such, to correctly intervene in APR, there must be a reevaluation and abandonment of core elements that shape beliefs.

An antithesis to the theory of evolution by natural selection must abandon theories and beliefs of aggression and survival of the fittest and redirect individual and group processing to internal and group strengths of resilience and resourcefulness, as opposed to aggression. Additionally, the theory of genetic predisposition should be reassessed within the context of the environment and phenotypic expression.

CHAPTER REVIEW

REVIEW QUESTIONS
1. What are the main objections to the theory of evolution by means of natural selection?
2. Offer an alternative explanation for APR.

GLOSSARY

Key Term	Definition
Absolute Principle	The first absolute principle or the Ultimate Reality refers to the thing, being, entity, power, force, reality, presence, law, or principle that possesses the maximal ontological status that infers effect.
Abstraction	The act of considering something as a general quality or characteristic, apart from concrete realities or beings. Abstraction in scientific research often pertains to things that do not have a concrete existence, such as atoms and molecules. Things such as atoms and molecules that do not have a concrete existence are given specific identifying properties and qualities. These characteristics are used to study hypothetical constructs of phenomena. 1 The act or process of abstracting: the state of being abstracted. 2 An abstract idea or term. 3 Abstract quality or character. 4 An abstract composition or creation in art.
Aggression in Proximity Relationships (APR)	APR is an all-encompassing definition to include all forms of aggression, including violence and abuse perpetrated by and between persons related through nearness.
Allele	Allele has two definitions, a traditional and a more loosely word usage. Traditional definition: alternate forms of a gene, composed of one or more single nucleotide polymorphisms (SNPs). More loosely: an SNP. For example, at a given position along a chromosome, most people might have the DNA base "A". A few might have an alternative sequence. Each defined type is an allele.
Antiquities	Matters relating to the life or culture of ancient times.
Antiquity	Antiquity is a period of history prior to the Middle Ages. Ancient time.
Being	Being is the fact of existence. The substance or nature of living organisms.
Bio-Epigenetic or Nongenetic Transmissions	Bio-epigenetic or nongenetic transmissions are the transmissions of heritable characteristics, traits, and behaviors from progenitors to offspring that occurs outside genetic mechanisms.
Biogenesis	Biogenesis originally meant the emergence of life from nonliving things. This conceptualization was aligned with some theories that original life-form or organic life-form emerged from inorganic or nonliving life-forms, such as rocks.
Biogenetic Transmissions	Biogenetic transmission is defined as the occurrence of similarities in DNA sequencing among progenitors and offspring accompanied by similarities in characteristics, traits, and behaviors.
Causation	Causation is anything that causes an effect. 1 The act or process of causing. 2 The act or agency which produces an effect.

Key Term	Definition
Chimerism	Chimerism stemmed from the Greek mythological god known as Chimaera, a fire-breathing Greek god with a lion's head, goat's body, and a serpent's tail.
Common Descent	According to the common descent hypothesis, species descended from either one or a few common ancestors.
Correlation	Correlation is the mutual relation between two or more things.
Cosmology	Cosmology is a branch of philosophy dealing with the origin and general structure of the universe, with its parts, elements, and laws, and especially with such of its characteristics as space, time, causality, and freedom. Cosmology is also a branch of astronomy that deals with the general structure and evolution of the universe.
Cosmozoë	Cosmozoë is a branch of philosophy that can be traced back to ancient Greece. Cosmozoë philosophers hypothesized explanations of the origin and general structure of the universe. Cosmozoë philosophers believed that stars were gods and that stars were responsible for ontogeny. Cosmozoë philosophers attempted to remove mythical elements from cosmology and establish metaphysics as a scientific discipline. The present-day discipline of cosmology has its origin in cosmozoë.
Demyelination	Demyelination is the loss of myelin from the nerve sheaths.
Domestic Violence (DV)	DV is: 1 The inflicting of physical injury by one family or household member on another 2 A repeated or habitual pattern of such behavior.
Embryology	Embryology is a branch of biology where the focus of the study is on the fertilization process of gametes, and prenatal development of fetuses.
Empiricism	Empiricism is a philosophy concerning the theory of knowledge. Empiricists claim knowledge can only be achieved through sensorial observation of a phenomenon.
Epigenetics	Epigenetics is the study of heritable phenotypic changes that do not involve alterations in the deoxyribonucleic acid (DNA) molecule. Epigenetics refers to the process related to or produced by the chain of developmental processes in epigenesis that lead from genotype to phenotype after the initial actions of the genes. Epigenetics also means related to, being, or involve changes in gene functions that do not involve changes in the DNA molecular sequence.
Epistemology	Epistemology is a branch of philosophy concerned with the origin, nature, methods, and scope of human knowledge.
Etiology	Etiology is a branch of knowledge concerned with causes.
Eugenics	Eugenics is a targeted practice or policy aimed at reducing those persons and populations with genetic defects or those perceived to possess undesirable traits or negative eugenics. Eugenics emerged out of Darwinism, tenets of evolution, and neo-evolutionary theories. Eugenics is a belief system based on the tenets of survivability, the survival of the fittest, vulnerability, and reproductive advantage.

Key Term	Definition
Existentialism	Existentialism is a chiefly 20th-century philosophical movement embracing diverse doctrines but centering on analysis of individual existence in an unfathomable universe and the plight of the individual who must assume ultimate responsibility for acts of free will without any certain knowledge of what is right or wrong or good or bad.
Fatalism	Fatalism is the acceptance of all things and events as inevitable: submission to fate.
Feticide	Feticide is the act of causing the death of a fetus.
First Cause	The first cause is the first absolute principle. The first cause is the cause of the existence of the first thing or being.
Gendercide	Gendercide is the reduction of the proportion of a particular gender, typically female, in a population, especially as a result of selective abortion.
Genes	The word genes is a terminology used in the Genome Project to explain genetics. The stereochemistry or spatial relations of atoms and subatomic particles of conjoined deoxyribose and ribose that regulate protein synthesis and cell replication in a controlled cloned or asexual reproductive experiment. Stable, heritable characteristics, traits, and behaviors.
Genetic Hybridization	Genetic hybridization is a scientific creation of an intraspecies from which a new species is created.
Genetics	Genetics is a branch of study that uses a predictive model that establishes an association between DNA and RNA mechanisms and sequences.
Genotype	The genotype is all or part of the genetic constitution of an individual or group.
Germline Theory	Some cells, such as sperms and eggs, are called germline cells. Germline cells are purported to be involved in transmitting genetic materials. Germline theory is an emergent theory from Darwin's pangenesis.
Homology	Homology is the state of having the same or similar relation, relative position, or structure.
Hypothesis	1 A hypothesis is a proposed explanation for a phenomenon. It forms the basis of research or experiment that is designed to test whether the hypothetical assumptions undergirding the hypothesis are true. Scientists generally base their hypothesis on previous observations that cannot satisfactorily be explained with the available scientific theories. 2 A hypothesis is a supposition or proposed explanation made based on limited information or evidence as the starting point for further research.
Hypothetical Assumption	A hypothetical assumption is an assumptive statement that forms the basis of a hypothesis. A hypothetical assumption is a statement based on beliefs concerning the way the world and things in the world function.
Hypothetical Construct	A hypothetical construct in the philosophy of science is an object that exists in the mind of the theorist. A hypothetical construct is an explanatory variable that is not directly observable.

Glossary

Key Term	Definition
Impalpable Entities and Phenomena	An entity, concept, or phenomenon whose existence, nature, properties, qualities, or relations are not directly observable by humans. Examples of impalpable entities and concepts are atoms, atomic particles, the force of gravity, causation, beliefs, and desires.
Intelligent Design	The theory of ID is a scientific theory that certain features of the universe and living things are best explained by an intelligent cause, not an undirected process.
Intervening Variables	An intervening variable is a hypothetical construct used to measure differences and explain causal relationships between other variables.
Intimate Partner Violence (IPV)	IPV describes physical violence, sexual violence, stalking and psychological aggression (including coercive acts) by a current or former intimate partner.
Intragenerational	Intragenerational phenomena are the existences or occurrences of characteristics, traits, and behaviors among members of the same generation.
Maladaptive Aggression	According to evolutionary conceptualization, aggression can be either functional or dysfunctional behavior. While functional aggression is adaptive, dysfunctional aggression is maladaptive. Maladaptive aggression is harmful behaviors that violate social conventions. Maladaptive aggression is any behavior that is an intentional and deliberate choice to cause harm and hurt to another person.
Metaphysical	Metaphysical means pertaining to metaphysics.
Metaphysics	Metaphysics is a branch of philosophy that is concerned with the fundamental nature of reality and being. Metaphysics philosophy includes ontology, cosmology, and epistemology. In ontology, metaphysical disciplines are abstract philosophical studies: a study of what is outside of objective experience. "'Metaphysics analyzes the generic traits manifested by existences of any kind' J. H. Randall."
Mythical	Mythical means pertaining to a myth. A myth is a traditional story, especially one concerning the early history of a people or explaining a natural or social phenomenon, and typically involving supernatural beings or events.
Natural Selection	Natural Selection is an element that exists outside the control of humans.
Neurodynamics	Neurodynamics refers to the neurological processes activated through cognitive, emotional, and behavioral interactions between the individual and others. The activation of these neurological processes serves the purpose of self-management.
Nonsensorially Observable Phenomena	Nonsensorially observable phenomena are phenomena that cannot be literally observed using the five senses (see Impalpable).
Ontogeny	Ontogeny is the developmental history of an organism, individual, or species. Ontogenesis, also called morphogenesis, is the study of the origination and development of individual organisms. Embryology is also referred to as ontogeny.

Key Term	Definition
Ontology	Ontology is a branch of philosophy concerned with the nature of being.
Orthogenesis	Orthogenesis is a combined form of two Greek words ὀρθός orthós, meaning straight, and γένεσις genesis meaning origin. Orthogenesis is one of the hypothetical tenets of evolution by natural selection. The orthogenesis premise states that successive generations of some organisms, species, subspecies, and species members become increasingly modified or progressively evolve into higher forms and complexities. The governing force of natural selection has an orthogenetic straight-line goal.
Palpable	Palpable means to be capable of being touched or felt: tangible. Easily perceived: noticeable. Easily perceptible by the mind: manifest.
Panspermia	Panspermia is the theory that life exists and is distributed throughout the universe in forms that permit development based on the planetary atmosphere.
Patriarchy	Patriarchy is a social system in which males hold primary power and predominate in roles of political leadership, moral authority, social privilege, and control of property.
Phenomenology	Phenomenology is the study of the development of human consciousness and self-awareness as a preface to or a part of philosophy.
Phenotype	A phenotype is the observable properties of an organism that are produced by the interaction of the genotype and the environment.

Philosophy	Merriam-Webster Dictionary provides several definitions of philosophy.
	 1 Disciplinary
	  a) Philosophy underpins all disciplines and subdisciplines, including philosophy, ethics, biology, sociology, law, politics, economics, logic, metaphysics, religion, and aesthetics. Philosophy also refers to a course of higher learning, such as a Ph.D.
	 2 Beliefs, Concepts, and Attitudes
	  a) Philosophy also refers to fundamental beliefs, concepts, attitudes, and practices of individuals and groups, such as religious philosophy.
	 3 Wisdom
	  a) Philosophy also refers to the pursuit of wisdom, a search for a general understanding, or the fundamental beliefs that undergird hypothetical formulations.

Phylogeny	A phylogeny is a hypothetical reconstruction of the evolutionary relationships or the sequential evolutionary steps of a group of organisms. These sequences (nucleotide or amino acid) can explain the origin of a species and its development to its current state of existence or being. The phylogeny of species is often represented graphically in the form of a tree and enables scientists to find new relationships between organisms.

Key Term	Definition
Pragmaticism	Pragmaticism is the philosophic doctrine of C. S. Peirce.
Pragmatism	1. A practical approach to problems and affairs 2. An American movement in philosophy founded by C. S. Peirce and William James and marked by the doctrines that the meaning of conceptions is to be sought in their practical bearings, that the function of thought is to guide action, and that truth is preeminently to be tested by the practical consequences of belief.
Predestination	Predestination is the belief that the eventual fate is predetermined and willed by a force outside of human control.
Predeterminism	Predeterminism is the belief that all events that occur have already been determined.
Proximity Relationship	A proximity relationship is a relationship established based on such ties as biological, geographical, legal, community, or sociocultural. Biological proximity relationships, for example, include such relationships as child/children, parents, siblings, or anyone in a familial relationship based on blood ties.
Quantum Mechanics	Quantum mechanics is a field of study dealing with the behavior of matter and light on atomic and subatomic scales.
Rationality	Rationality is the rational process that refers to the steps involved in arriving at a reasonable, logical thought or belief. 1. the quality or state of being rational, 2. the quality or state of being agreeable to reason, or 3. a rational opinion, belief, or practice—usually used in the plural.
Recapitulation	The biogenetic law is a theory of recapitulation. According to the theory of recapitulation, the embryo goes through stages of development that the adult organism underwent throughout the evolutionary process. Each stage of embryonic development from fertilization to birth is reflective of a different stage of evolution.
Scientific Objectivity	Scientific objectivity is a claim that the methods, claims, and results of research or studies that apply the scientific method are free from bias.
Social Darwinism	The concept of social Darwinism stemmed from the application of natural selection and reproductive advantage to the socioeconomic systems. Social Darwinists contend that within the context of society and the economy, the implementation of programs, measures, and policies should aim at eliminating the weak and the unfit by promoting the interest and well-being of the favoured races.
Spontaneous Generation	Spontaneous Generation is a hypothetical construct that living organisms developed from nonliving objects. Another aspect of this hypothesis is that several types of organisms or species appeared at the same time.
Susceptibility	Susceptibility is the extent to which an individual or organism possesses the capacity or the tendency to be impressed.

Key Term	Definition
Tautology	Tautology, in logic, is a statement so framed that it cannot be denied without inconsistency. Thus, "All humans are mammals" is held to assert with regard to anything whatsoever that either it is a human or it is not a mammal. But that universal "truth" follows not from any facts noted about real humans but only from the actual use of human and mammal and is thus purely a matter of definition.
The Biogenetic Law	Ernst Haeckel posited the biogenetic law in the 1860s. According to Haeckel, the chronological development of the embryo is indicative of stages in the evolutionary development. The biogenetic law is often stated as ontogeny recapitulates phylogeny.

Theory	Merriam-Webster Dictionary provides several definitions of theory
	
	1
	
	   a) A plausible or scientifically acceptable general principle or body of principles offered to explain phenomena
	
	2
	
	   a) A belief, policy, or procedure proposed or followed as the basis of action
	   b) an ideal or hypothetical set of facts, principles, or circumstances —often used in the phrase in theory
	
	3
	
	   a) a hypothesis assumed for the sake of argument or investigation
	   b) an unproved assumption: conjecture
	   c) a body of theorems presenting a concise, systematic view of a subject
	
	4
	
	   a) the general or abstract principle of a body of fact, a science, or an art
	
	5
	
	   a) abstract thought: speculation
	
	6
	
	   a) the analysis of a set of facts in their relation to one another.

Transgenerational Epigenetic Inheritance	Transgenerational epigenetic inheritance is evident by changes in protein synthesis mechanisms and processes in third and fourth generation progenies occurring without alterations of the structure of ancestral DNA.
Transgenerational Transference	Transgenerational transference refers to changes in manifested characteristics, traits, and behaviors that occur because of environmental conditions that resulted in changes in biogenetic mechanisms.
Truism	A Truism is an undoubted or self-evident truth, especially one too obvious to mention.
Validity	Validity is the extent to which a concept, conclusion, or measurement is well-founded and likely corresponds to the real world based on probability. The quality or state of being valid such as 1 the state of being acceptable according to the law; or 2 the quality of being well-grounded, sound, or correct.

Glossary

Key Term	Definition
Vulnerable Population	A vulnerable population is a population, individual, group, or organization with impaired capacity or ability to anticipate, cope with, resist, and recover from the impacts of disasters.
Worldview	The term worldview refers to any ideological, philosophical, theological, or religious perspective that provides an overarching understanding of God, the world, man's relations to God and the world. 1 A comprehensive conception or apprehension of the world, especially from a specific standpoint.

REFERENCES

Abstraction. (n.d.). In *Merriam-Webster's online dictionary*. Retrieved from https://www.merriam-webster.com/dictionary/abstraction

Adamson, P. (2017). The theology of Aristotle. In E. N. Zalta (Ed.), *The Stanford Encyclopedia of Philosophy* (Summer 2017 ed.). Retrieved from https://plato.stanford.edu/archives/sum2017/entries/theology-aristotle/

Agar, N. (2004). *Liberal eugenics: In defence of human enhancement*. Oxford, UK: Blackwell Publishing.

Ågren, J. A. (2016). Selfish genetic elements and the gene's-eye view of evolution. *Current Zoology, 62*(6), 659–665. doi:10.1093/cz/zow102

Aho, K. (2014). *Existentialism: An introduction*. Cambridge, England: Polity Press.

Albee, G. W. (1996). The psychological origins of the white male patriarchy. *Journal of Primary Prevention, 17*(1), 75–97. doi:10.1007/BF02262739

Alberts, B., Johnson, A. D., Lewis, J., Raff, M., Roberts, K., & Walter, P. (2002). Chapter 17. The cell cycle and programmed cell death: Extracellular control of cell division, cell growth, and apoptosis. In B. Alberts, A. D. Johnson, J. Lewis, M. Raff, K. Roberts, & P. Walter, *Molecular Biology of the Cell* (4th ed.). New York, NY: Garland Science.

Alexandria, P. (1981). On the account of the world's creation given by Moses. In G. P. Goold (Ed.), *Philo Volume 1* (F. H. Colson, & Whitaker, Trans., pp. 2-137). Cambridge, MA: Harvard University Press. Retrieved from https://ryanfb.github.io/loebolus/

Allen, G. E. (2004). Was Nazi eugenics created in the US. *EMBO Reports, 5*(5), 451-452. doi:10.1038/sj.embor.7400158

American Psychological Association. (2017, July). *Ethnic and racial minorities and socioeconomic status (Fact Sheet)*. Retrieved from American Psychological Association: https://www.apa.org/pi/ses/resources/publications/minorities.aspx

Andersen, H., & Hepburn, B. (2016). Scientific method. In E. N. Zalta (Ed.), *The Stanford Encyclopedia of Philosophy* (Summer 2016 ed.). Retrieved from https://plato.stanford.edu/archives/sum2016/entries/scientific-method/

Antiquity. (n.d.). In *Merriam-Webster's online dictionary*. Retrieved from https://www.merriam-webster.com/dictionary/antiquity

Aristotle. (1999). *The metaphysics* (Revised ed.). (H. Lawson-Tancred, Trans.) London, England: Penguin Books Ltd. Retrieved from Africahead.

ASHG. (2018). ASHG denounces attempts to link genetics and racial supremacy. *The American Journal of Human Genetics, 103*(5), 636. doi:10.1016/j.ajhg.2018.10.011

Axe, D. D. (2004). Estimating the prevalence of protein sequences adopting functional enzyme folds. *Journal of Molecular Biology, 341*(5), 1295-1315. doi:10.1016/j.jmb.2004.06.058

Axe, D. D., & Gauger, A. K. (2015). Model and laboratory demonstrations that evolutionary optimization works well only if preceded by invention--Selection itself is not inventive. *BIO-Complexity, 2015*(2), 1-13. doi:10.1146/annurev-immunol-020711-075032

Bailey, C. (1928). *The Greek atomists and Epicurus*. New York, NY: Russell & Russell.

Bailey, N. W., & Moore, A. J. (2012). Runaway sexual selection without genetic correlations: Social environment and flexible mate choice initiate and enhance the Fisher process. *Evolution, 66*(9), 2674–2684. doi:10.1111/j.1558-5646.2012.01647.x

Banaszak, L. J. (2000). *Foundations of structural biology* (1st ed.). San Diego, CA: Academic Press.

Barbieri, M. (Ed.). (2007). *Introduction to biosemiotics: The new biological synthesis*. Dordrecht, The Netherlands: Springer.

Barnes, M. E. (2014). Ernst Haeckel's biogenetic law (1866). *The Embryo Project Encyclopedia (2014-05-03)*. Retrieved from http://embryo.asu.edu

Bastian, H. C. (1887). The "muscular sense"; its nature and cortical localisation. *Brain, 10*(1), 1-89. doi:10.1093/brain/10.1.1

BBC. (2019, January 13). James Watson: Scientist loses titles after claims over race. Retrieved January 25, 2019, from https://www.bbc.com/news/world-us-canada-46856779

References

Beebee, H., Hitchcock, C., & Menzies, P. (2012). *The Oxford handbook of causation* (Reprint ed.). Oxford, England: Oxford University Press.

Being. (n.d.). In *Merriam-Webster's online dictionary.* Retrieved from https://www.merriam-webster.com/dictionary/being

Belsky, J. (2013). Differential susceptibility to environmental influences. *International Journal of Child Care and Education Policy, 7*(2), 15-31. doi:10.1007/2288-6729-7-2-15

Belsky, J., & Pluess, M. (2009). Beyond diathesis stress: Differential susceptibility to environmental influences. *Psychological Bulletin, 135*(6), 885-908. doi:10.1037/a0017376

Belsky, J., Jonassaint, C. R., Pluess, M., Stanton, M. V., Brummett, B., & Williams, R. B. (2009). Vulnerability genes or plasticity genes? *Molecular Psychiatry, 14*, 746-754. doi:10.1038/mp.2009.44

Beutel, R. G., Friedrich, F., & Leschen, R. A. (2009). Charles Darwin, beetles and phylogenetics. *Naturwissenschaften, 96*(11), 1293-1312. doi:10.1007/s00114-009-0601-2

Bhattacharya, P. C. (2012). *Gender inequality and the sex ratio in three emerging economies: Working paper No. 2012-01.* Heriot-Watt University Economics Discussion Papers 1201, Department of Economics, School of Management and Languages, Heriot Watt University. Retrieved from http://www2.hw.ac.uk/sml/downloads/economics/HW_DP_2012_01.pdf

Bierer, L. M., Bader, H. N., Daskalakis, N. P., Lehrner, A. L., Makotkine, I., Seckl, J. R., & Yehuda, R. (2014). Elevation of 11β-hydroxysteroid dehydrogenase type 2 activity in Holocaust survivor offspring: Evidence for an intergenerational effect of maternal trauma exposure. *Psychoneuroendocrinology, 48*, 1-10. doi:10.1016/j.psyneuen.2014.06.001

Black, D. S., Sussman, S., & Unger, J. B. (2009). A further look at intergenerational transmission of violence: Witnessing interparental violence in emerging adulthood. *Journal of Interpersonal Violence, 25*(6), 1022-1042. doi:10.1177/0886260509340539

Black, E. (2012). *War against the weak: Eugenics and America's campaign to create a Master Race* (Expanded ed.). Washington, DC: Dialog Press.

Bliss, R., & Trogdon, K. (2016). Metaphysical grounding. In E. N. Zalta (Ed.), *The Stanford Encyclopedia of Philosophy* (Winter 2016 ed.). Retrieved from https://plato.stanford.edu/archives/win2016/entries/grounding

Bodnar, I. (2018). Aristotle's natural philosophy. In E. N. Zalta (Ed.), *The Stanford Encyclopedia of Philosophy* (Summer 2018 ed.). Retrieved from https://plato.stanford.edu/archives/spr2018/entries/aristotle-natphil/

Bohacek, J., & Mansuy, I. M. (2015). Molecular insights into transgenerational non-genetic inheritance of acquired behaviours. *Nature Reviews. Genetics, 16*, 641-652. doi:10.1038/nrg3964

Boulay, R. A. (2003). *Flying serpents and dragons: The story of mankind's reptilian past.* San Diego, CA: The Book Tree.

Bourget, D., & Mendelovici, A. (2017). Phenomenal intentionality. In E. N. Zalta (Ed.), *The Stanford Encyclopedia of Philosophy* (Spring 2017 ed.). Retrieved from https://plato.stanford.edu/archives/spr2017/entries/phenomenal-intentionality/

Bowlby, J. (1984). Violence in the family as a disorder of the attachment and caregiving systems. *American Journal of Psychoanalysis, 44*(1), 9-27. doi:10.1007/BF01255416

Bradie, M., & Harms, W. (2017). Evolutionary epistemology. In E. N. Zalta (Ed.), *The Stanford Encyclopedia of Philosophy* (Spring 2017 ed.). Retrieved from https://plato.stanford.edu/archives/spr2017/entries/epistemology-evolutionary/

Brain, P. F., & Benton, D. (Eds.). (1981). *The biology of aggression.* Dordrecht, The Netherlands: Springer.

Brandon, R. (2014). Natural selection. In E. N. Zalta (Ed.), *The Stanford Encyclopedia of Philosophy* (Spring 2014 ed.). Retrieved from https://plato.stanford.edu/archives/spr2014/entries/natural-selection

Brigandt, I., & Love, A. (2017). Reductionism in biology. In E. N. Zalta (Ed.), *The Stanford Encyclopedia of Philosophy* (Spring 2017 ed.). Retrieved from https://plato.stanford.edu/archives/spr2017/entries/reduction-biology/

Brisson, D. (2003). The directed mutation controversy in an evolutionary context. *Critical Reviews in Microbiology, 29*(1), 25-35. doi:10.1080/713610403

Brücher, B. L., & Jamall, I. S. (2016). Somatic mutation theory - why it's wrong for most cancers. *Cellular Physiology and Biochemistry, 38*, 1663-1680. doi:10.1159/000443106

Burke, J. G. (1986). *Cosmic debris: Meteorites in history.* New York, NY: University of California Press.

Buss, D. M. (2005). *The murderer next door: Why the mind is designed to kill.* New York, NY: The Penguin Press.

Buss, D. M. (2009). The great struggles of life: Darwin and the emergence of evolutionary psychology. *American Psychologist, 64*(2), 140-148. doi:10.1037/a0013207

Buss, D. M., & Shackelford, T. K. (1997). Human aggression in evolutionary psychological perspective. *Clinical Psychology Review, 17*(6), 605-619. Retrieved from https://www.journals.elsevier.com/clinical-psychology-review/

Carnes, N. C., & Winer, J. P. (2017). Do unto others: How cognitive fusion shapes the transmission of moral behavior. *Journal of Experimental Psychology: General, 146*(4), 472-484. doi:10.1037/xge0000294.

Caspi, A., Sugden, K., Moffitt, T., Taylor, A., Craig, I. W., Harrington, H., . . . Poulton, R. (2003). Influence of life stress on depression: Moderation by a polymorphism in the 5-HTT gene. *Science, 301*(5631), 386-389. Retrieved from https://www.jstor.org/journal/science

Catazaro, J., Caprez, A., Guru, A., Swanson, D., & Powers, R. (2014). Functional evolution of PLP-dependent enzymes based on active-site structural similarities. *Proteins, 82*(10), 2597-2608. doi:10.1002/prot.24624

Causation. (n.d.). In *Merriam-Webster's online dictionary.* Retrieved from https://www.merriam-webster.com/dictionary/causation

CDC. (2018, October 23). *Violence Prevention: Intimate Partner Violence : Definition.* Retrieved from CDC: https://www.cdc.gov

Chalmers, A. (2014). Atomism from the 17th to the 20th century. In E. N. Zalta (Ed.), *The Stanford Encyclopedia of Philosophy* (Winter 2014 ed.). Retrieved from https://plato.stanford.edu/archives/win2014/entries/atomism-modern/

Chase, A. (1977). *The legacy of Malthus: The social costs of the new scientific racism* (1st ed.). New York: Alfred A. Knopf.

Chen, J.-Y. (2014). Review of the book 'Genetic explanations: Sense and nonsense', by S. Krimsky & J. Gruber Eds. *Yale Journal of Biology and Medicine, 87*(1), 95-96. Retrieved from https://medicine.yale.edu/yjbm/index.aspx

Choi, C. Q. (2018, June 27). Ingredients for life found on Saturn's moon Enceladus. *Scientific American.* Retrieved from https://www.scientificamerican.com

Choi, J. K., & Kim, S. C. (2007). Environmental effects on gene expression phenotype have regional biases in the human genome. *Genetics, 175*(4), 1607-1613. doi:10.1534/genetics.106.069047

Christin, P.-A., Weinreich, D. M., & Besnard, G. (2010). Causes and evolutionary significance of genetic convergence. *Trends in Genetics, 26*(9), 400-405. doi:10.1016/j.tig.2010.06.005

Claeys, G. (2000). The "Survival of the Fittest" and the origins of social Darwinism. *Journal of the History of Ideas, 61*(2), 223-240. doi:10.1353/jhi.2000.0014

Cofre, J., & Abdelhay, E. (2017). Cancer Is to embryology as mutation Is to genetics: Hypothesis of the cancer as embryological phenomenon. *The Scientific World Journal, 2017,* 3578090, 1-17. doi:10.1155/2017/3578090

Colbert, M. W., & Rowe, T. (2008). Ontogenetic sequence analysis: Using parsimony to characterize developmental sequences and sequence polymorphism. *Journal of Experimental Zoology. Part B, Molecular and developmental evolution, 310*(5), 398–416. doi:10.1002/jez.b.21212.

Cole, L. A. (2015). The evolution of the primate, hominid, and human brain. *Journal of Primatology, 4*(1), 1-8. doi:10.4172/2167-6801.1000124

Coleman, K. J., Stewart, C., Waitzfelder, B. E., Zeber, J. E., Morales, L. S., Ahmed, A. T., . . . Simon, G. E. (2016). Racial-ethnic differences in psychiatric diagnoses and treatment across 11 health care systems in the Mental Health Research Network. *Psychiatric Services, 67*(7), 749-757. doi:10.1176/appi.ps.201500217

Collins, F. S. (2007). *The language of God: a scientist presents evidence for belief* (Reprint edition ed.). New York, NY: Free Press.

References

Cook, D. L., Bookstein, F. L., & Gennari, J. H. (2011). Physical properties of biological entities: An introduction to the ontology of physics for biology. *PLoS One, 6*(12), e28708. doi:10.1371/journal.pone.0028708

Cosmides, L., & Tooby, J. (1997). *Evolutionary psychology: A primer.* Santa Barbara, CA: University of California. Retrieved January 26, 2019, from https://www.cep.ucsb.edu/primer.html

Craver, C., & Tabery, J. (2017). Mechanisms in science. In E. N. Zalta (Ed.), *The Stanford Encyclopedia of Philosophy* (Spring 2017 ed.). Retrieved from https://plato.stanford.edu/archives/spr2017/entries/science-mechanisms/

Crowell, S. (2012). *The Cambridge companion to existentialism.* Cambridge, England: Cambridge University Press.

Crowell, S. (2017). Existentialism. In E. N. Zalta (Ed.), *The Stanford Encyclopedia of Philosophy* (Winter 2017 ed.). Retrieved from https://plato.stanford.edu/archives/win2017/entries/existentialism/

Dall, S. R., Bell, A. M., Bolnick, D. I., & Ratnieks, F. L. (2012). An evolutionary ecology of individual differences. *Ecology Letters, 15*(10), 1189-1198. doi:10.1111/j.1461-0248.2012.01846.x

Darwin, C. (1861, May 23). Letter to John F W Herschel. *Darwin Correspondence Project.* University of Cambridge. Retrieved from https://www.darwinproject.ac.uk/letter/DCP-LETT-3154.xml

Darwin, C. (1867, October 16). Letter to Asa Gray. University of Cambridge. Retrieved from Darwin Correspondence Project: https://www.darwinproject.ac.uk/letter/DCP-LETT-5649.xml

Darwin, C. (1868). *The variation of animals and plants under domestication* (1st ed., Vol. 1). London, England: John Murray.

Darwin, C. (1872). *On the origin of species by means of natural selection, or the preservation of favoured races in the struggle for life* (6th with additions and corrections ed.). London, England: John Murray.

Darwin, C. (1882). *The descent of man and selection in relation to sex* (2nd ed.). London, England: John Murray.

Darwin, C., & Wallace, A. R. (1858). On the tendency of species to form varieties; And on the perpetuation of varieties and species by natural means of selection. *Journal of the Proceedings of the Linnean Society of London. Zoology, 3*(9), 45-62. doi:10.1111/j.1096-3642.1858.tb02500.x

Darwin, L. (1931). Biology and eugenics. *The Eugenics Review, 23*(1), 21-23. Retrieved January 20, 2019, from https://www.ncbi.nlm.nih.gov/pmc/articles/PMC2985004/pdf/eugenrev00302-0031.pdf

Davenport, C. B. (1911). *Heredity in relation to eugenics.* New York, NY: Henry Holt and company.

Dawkins, R. (1989). *The extended phenotype: The long reach of the gene.* New York, NY: Oxford University Press.

de Almeida, R. M., Cabral, J. C., & Narvaes, R. (2015). Behavioural, hormonal and neurobiological mechanisms of aggressive behaviour in human and nonhuman primates. *Physiology and Behavior, 143*, 121- 135. doi:10.1016/j.physbeh.2015.02.053

Del Soldato, E. (2016). Natural philosophy in the renaissance. In E. N. Zalta (Ed.), *The Stanford Encyclopedia of Philosophy* (Fall 2016 ed.). Retrieved from https://plato.stanford.edu/archives/fall2016/entries/natphil-ren/

Dennis, R. M. (1995). Social Darwinism, scientific racism, and the metaphysics of race. *The Journal of Negro Education, 64*(3), 243-252. doi:10.2307/2967206

Denton, M. J. (2013). The types: A persistent structuralist challenge to Darwinian pan- selectionism. *BIO-Complexity, 2013*(3), 1-18. doi:10.5048/BIO-C.2013.3

Dias, B. G., & Ressler, K. J. (2014). Parental olfactory experience influences behavior and neural structure in subsequent generations. *Nature Neuroscience, 17*(1), 89-96. doi:10.1038/nn.3594

Dikmenli, M., Cardak, O., & Kiray, S. A. (2011). Science student teachers' ideas about the 'Gene' concept. *Procedia - Social and Behavioral Sciences, 15*, 2609-2613. doi:10.1016/j.sbspro.2011.04.155

Dodd, A. N., Belbin, F. E., Frank, A., & Webb, A. A. (2015). Interactions between circadian clocks and photosynthesis for the temporal and spatial coordination of metabolism. *Frontiers in Plant Science, 6*(245), 1 - 7. doi:10.3389/fpls.2015.00245

Domestic Violence. (n.d.). In *Merriam-Webster's online dictionary*. Retrieved from https://www.merriam-webster.com/dictionary/domestic%20violence

Doolittle, W. F. (2000). Uprooting the tree of life. *Scientific American, 282*(2), 90-95. Retrieved from https://www.scientificamerican.com

Douglas, S. M., Chubiz, L. M., Harcombe, W. R., & Marx, C. J. (2017). Identification of the potentiating mutations and synergistic epistasis that enabled the evolution of inter-species cooperation. *PLoS One, 12*(5), e0174345. doi:10.1371/ journal.pone.0174345

Duster, T. (2003). *Backdoor to eugenics* (2nd ed.). New York, NY: Routledge.

Ellis, B. J., Boyce, W. T., Belsky, J., Bakermans-Kranenburg, M. J., & van IJzendoorn, M. H. (2011). Differential susceptibility to the environment: An evolutionary–neurodevelopmental theory. *Development and Psychopathology, 23*(1), 7-28. doi:10.1017/S0954579410000611

Emerson, H. (1939). Eugenics in relation to medicine. *Journal of Heredity, 30*(12), 553-556. doi:10.1093/oxfordjournals.jhered.a104659

Epigenetics. (n.d.). In *Merriam-Webster's online dictionary*. Retrieved from https://www.merriam-webster.com/dictionary/epigenetics

Epstein, C. J. (2003). Is modern genetics the new eugenics? *Genetics in Medicine, 5*, 469-475. doi:10.1097/01.GIM.0000093978.77435.17

Etiology. (n.d.). In *Merriam-Webster's online dictionary*. Retrieved from https://www.merriam-webster.com/dictionary/etiology

Evans, J. (2009). Anaximander. In *Encyclopædia Britannica On Line*. Retrieved from https://www.britannica.com/

Evans, J. S., Newstead, S. E., & Byrne, R. M. (2004). *Human reasoning: The psychology of deduction*. East Sussex, England: Lawrence Erlbaum Associates Ltd.

Ewert, W. (2015). Overabundant mutations help potentiate evolution: The effect of biologically realistic mutation rates on computer models of evolution. *BIO-Complexity, 2015*(1), 1-11. doi:10.5048/BIO-C.2015.1

Existentialism. (n.d.). In *Merriam-Webster's online dictionary*. Retrieved from https://www.merriam-webster.com/dictionary/existentialism

Ezcurra, M. D., Scheyer, T. M., & Butler, R. J. (2014). The origin and early evolution of Sauria: Reassessing the Permian Saurian fossil record and the timing of the crocodile-lizard divergence. *PLos One, 9*(2), e89165. doi:10.1371/journal.pone.0089165. eCollection 2014.

Fatalism. (n.d.). In *Merriam-Webster's online dictionary*. Retrieved from https://www.merriam-webster.com/dictionary/fatalism

Ferguson, R. B. (2003). The birth of war. *Natural History, July/August*, 28-35. doi:10.13140/2.1.3660.6088

Feticide. (n.d.). In *Merriam-Webster's online dictionary*. Retrieved from https://www.merriam-webster.com/dictionary/feticide

Fisher, R. A. (1915). The evolution of sexual preference. *Eugenics Review, 7*(3), 184-192. Retrieved from https://www.ncbi.nlm.nih.gov/pmc/articles/PMC2987134/

Fisher, R. A. (1930). *The genetical theory of natural selection*. Oxford, UK: The Clarendon Press.

Forth, C. E. (2005). Breeding superman: Nietzsche, race, and eugenics in Edwardian and Interwar Britain (Review). *Journal of Nietzsche Studies, 29*(1), 79-80. doi:10.1353/nie.2005.0005

Freeman, R. B. (1978). *Charles Darwin: A companion*. Folkestone, Kent, England: Wm Dawson & Sons Ltd.

Frisell, T., Lichtenstein, P., & Långström, N. (2010). Violent crime runs in families: A total population study of 12.5 million individuals. *Psychological Medicine, 41*(1), 97-105. doi:10.1017/S0033291710000462.

Gaidos, E., & Selsis, F. (2007). From protoplanets to protolife: The emergence and maintenance of Life. In B. Reipurth, D. Jewitt, & K. Keil (Eds.), *Protostars and Planets V* (2 ed., pp. 929-944). University of Arizona Press. Retrieved from https://www.lpi.usra.edu/books/PPV/8004.pdf

Galton, F. (1892). *Hereditary genius: An inquiry into its laws and consequences* (2nd ed.). London and New York: MacMillan and Co. .

References

Galton, F. (1904). Eugenics; its definition, scope and aims. *Nature, 70*(1804), 82. doi:10.1038/070082a0

Gannett, L. (2016). The human genome project. In E. N. Zalta (Ed.), *Stanford Encyclopedia of Philosophy* (Summer 2016 ed.). Retrieved from https://plato.stanford.edu/archives/sum2016/entries/human-genome

García-Sancho, E., Salguero, J. M., & Fernandez-Berrocal, P. (2014). Relationship between emotional intelligence and aggression: A systematic review. *Aggression and Violent Behavior, 19*(5), 584-591. doi:10.1016/j.avb.2014.07.007

Gardner, A. (2016). The strategic revolution. *Cell, 166*(6), 1345-1348. doi:10.1016/j.cell.2016.08.033

Garratt, M., & Brooks, R. C. (2015). A genetic reduction in antioxidant function causes elevated aggression in mice. *The Journal of Experimental Biology, 218*, 223-227. doi:10.1242/jeb.112011

Garson, J. (2016). Modal logic. In E. N. Zalta (Ed.), *The Stanford Encyclopedia of Philosophy* (Spring 2016 ed.). Retrieved from https://plato.stanford.edu/archives/spr2016/entries/logic-modal/

Gasper, P. (2004). Genes, evolution, and human nature: Is biology destiny? *International Socialist Review (Online Edition)*(38). Retrieved January 25, 2019, from http://www.isreview.org/issues/38/genes.shtml

Gendercide. (n.d.). In *Oxford English Dictionary (US) On-Line*. Retrieved from https://en.oxforddictionaries.com/

Genetics Society of America. (2015, April). Hidden burden: Most people carry recessive disease mutations. *ScienceDaily*. Retrieved from https://www.sciencedaily.com/

Genotype. (n.d.). In *Merriam-Webster's online dictionary*. Retrieved from https://www.merriam-webster.com/dictionary/genotype

Georgia State University. (2016, May 18). *Racial, ethnic differences found in psychiatric diagnoses, treatment, according to researchers*. Retrieved from ScienceDaily: https://www.sciencedaily.com/

Glansdorff, N., Xu, Y., & Labedan, B. (2008). The last universal common ancestor: Emergence, constitution, and genetic legacy of an elusive forerunner. *Biology Direct, 3*(29). doi:10.1186/1745-6150-3-29

Goering, S. (2014). Eugenics. In E. N. Zalta (Ed.), *The Stanford Encyclopedia of Philosophy* (Fall 2014 ed.). Retrieved from https://plato.stanford.edu/archives/fall2014/entries/eugenics/

Gong, W., Liang, Q., Zheng, D., Zhong, R., Wen, Y., & Wang, X. (2017). Congenital heart defects of fetus after maternal exposure to organic and inorganic environmental factors: A cohort study. *Oncotarget, 8*(59), 100717-100723. doi:10.18632/oncotarget.20110

Greaves, M. (2014). Was skin cancer a selective force for black pigmentation in early hominin evolution? *Proceedings of the Royal Society of London B: Biological Sciences, 281*(1781), 1-10. doi:10.1098/rspb.2013.2955

Green, S. (2018). Philosophy of systems and synthetic biology. In E. N. Zalta (Ed.), *The Stanford Encyclopedia of Philosophy* (Summer 2018 ed.). Retrieved from https://plato.stanford.edu/archives/sum2018/entries/systems-synthetic-biology/

Grimm, S. R. (2008). Epistemic goals and epistemic values. *Philosophy and Phenomenological Research, 77*(3), 725-744. doi:10.1111/j.1933-1592.2008.00217.x

Guthrie, S. E. (2008, April 15). Anthropomorphism. In *Encyclopædia Britannica On Line*. Retrieved from https://www.britannica.com/

Gyngell, C., Douglas, T., & Savulescu, J. (2017). The ethics of germline gene editing. *Journal of Applied Philosophy, 34*(4), 498-513. doi:10.1111/japp.12249

Haig, D. (2012). The strategic gene. *Biology & Philosophy, 27*(4), 461–479. doi:10.1007/s10539-012-9315-5

Hall, N. (2016). David Lewis's metaphysics. In E. N. Zalta (Ed.), *The Stanford Encyclopedia of Philosophy* (Winter 2016 ed.). Retrieved from https://plato.stanford.edu/archives/win2016/entries/lewis-metaphysics/

Hamilton, R. J., & Bowers, B. J. (2007). The theory of genetic vulnerability: A Roy model exemplar. *Nursing Science Quarterly, 20*(3), 254-264. doi:10.1177/0894318407303127

Helix. (n.d.). In *American Heritage® Dictionary of the English Language, Fifth Edition. (2011)*. Retrieved from https://www.thefreedictionary.com/helix

Hesiod. (1914). Theogeny. In Hesiod, *The Homeric Hymns And Homerica* (H. G. Evelyn-White, Trans., pp. 137-139). London, England: William Heinemann.

Hofweber, T. (2018). Logic and ontology. In E. N. Zalta (Ed.), *The Stanford Encyclopedia of Philosophy* (Summer 2018 ed.). Retrieved from https://plato.stanford.edu/archives/sum2018/entries/logic-ontology/

Hohmann, S. A., Lefèvre, C. A., & Garenne, M. L. (2014). A framework for analyzing sex-selective abortion: The example of changing sex ratios in Southern Caucasus. *International Journal of Women's Health, 6*, 889–897. doi:10.2147/IJWH.S66333

Holterhoff, K. (2014). The history and reception of Charles Darwin's hypothesis of pangenesis. *Journal of the History of Biology, 47*(4), 661-695. doi:10.1007/s10739-014-9377-0

Hössjer, O., Gauger, A., & Reeves, C. (2016). Genetic modeling of human history part 1: Comparison of common descent and unique origin approaches. *BIO-Complexity, 2016*(3), 1-15. doi:10.5048/BIO-C.2016.3.

Huang, T., Shu, Y., & Cai, Y.-D. (2015). Genetic differences among ethnic groups. *BMC Genomics, 16*(1093), 1-10. doi:10.1186/s12864-015-2328-0

Hubbard, R., & Wald, E. (1999). *Exploding the gene myth: How genetic information is produced and manipulated by scientists, physicians, employers, insurance companies, educators, and law enforcers.* Boston, MA: Beacon Press.

Huesmann, L. R., Eron, L. D., & Yarmel, P. W. (1987). Intellectual functioning and aggression. *Journal of Personality and Social Psychology, 52*(1), 232-240. doi:10.1037//0022-3514.52.1.232

Hug, L. A., Baker, B. J., Anantharaman, K., Brown, C. T., Probst, A. J., Castelle, C. J., . . . Banfield, J. F. (2016). A new view of the tree of life. *Nature Microbiology, 1*(16048), 1-6. doi:10.1038/nmicrobiol.2016.48

Hutson, M. (2012). *The 7 laws of magical thinking: How irrational beliefs keep us happy, healthy, and sane* (Reprint ed.). London, England: Oneworld Publications.

Hypothesis. (n.d.). In *Merriam-Webster's online dictionary.* Retrieved from https://www.merriam-webster.com/dictionary/hypothesis

Ichikawa, J. J., & Steup, M. (2018). The analysis of knowledge. In E. N. Zalta (Ed.), *The Stanford Encyclopedia of Philosophy* (Summer 2018 ed.). Retrieved from https://plato.stanford.edu/archives/sum2018/entries/knowledge-analysis/

Impalpable. (n.d.). In *Merriam-Webster's online dictionary.* Retrieved from https://www.merriam-webster.com/dictionary/impalpable

Intragenerational. (n.d.). In *Merriam-Webster's online dictionary.* Retrieved from https://www.merriam-webster.com/dictionary/intragenerational

Jablonka, E., & Lamb, M. J. (2014). *Evolution in four dimensions: Genetic, epigenetic, behavioral, and symbolic variation in the history of life* (Revised ed.). Boston, MA: The MIT Press.

Janiak, A. (2016). Newton's philosophy. In E. N. Zalta (Ed.), *The Stanford Encyclopedia of Philosophy* (Winter 2016 ed.). Retrieved from https://plato.stanford.edu/archives/win2016/entries/newton-philosophy/

Johnson, C. G. (2013, July 7). *Female inmates sterilized in California prison without approval.* Retrieved from Reveal: https://www.revealnews.org/

Johnson, R. C., McClearn, G. E., Yuen, S., Nagoshi, C. T., Ahern, F. M., & Cole, R. E. (1985). Galton's data a century later. *American Psychologist, 40*(8), 875-892. doi:10.1037//0003-066X.40.8.875

Johnson, R. N. (1972). *Aggression in man and animals* (3rd ed.). Philadephia, PA: W. B. Saunders Company.

Joober, R., Sengupta, S., & Boksa, P. (2005). Genetics of developmental psychiatric disorders: Pathways to discovery. *Journal of Psychiatry and Neuroscience, 30*(5). Retrieved from https://jpn.ca/

Joseph, J., & Ratner, C. (2013). The fruitless search for genes in psychiatry and psychology: Time to reexamine a paradigm. In S. Krimsky, & J. Gruber (Eds.), *Genetic Explanations: Sense and Nonsense.* Cambridge, MA: Harvard University Press.

Joshi, S. S. (2008). Origin of life: Panspermia theory. *Helix Magazine.* Retrieved from Helix Magazine: North Western University, Department of Science: https://helix.northwestern.edu

Kahn, C. H. (2003). Xenophanes. In S. Hornblower, & T. Spawforth (Eds.), *Who's Who in the Classical World.* Oxford University Press. doi:10.1093/acref/9780192801074.001.0001

Kane, E. W. (2006). "No way my boys are going to be like that!" Parents responses to children's gender nonconformity. *Gender and Society, 20*(2), 149-176. doi:10.1177/0891243205284276

References

Kaspin-Powell, L. (2018, April 27). Why formamide may have been early life's alternative to water. *Astrobiology Magazine: Exploring the Solar System and Beyond*. Retrieved from https://www.astrobio.net/

Keller, E. F. (1992). Nature, nuture, and the human genome project. In D. J. Kevles, & L. Hood (Eds.), *The Code of Codes* (pp. 281-299). Cambridge, MA: Harvard University Press.

Keller, E. F. (2002). *The century of the gene.* Cambridge, MA: Harvard Univeristy Press.

Keller, E. F. (2013). Genes as difference makers. In S. Krimsky, & J. Gruber (Eds.), *Genetic Explanations: Sense and Nonsense.* Cambridge, MA: Harvard University Press.

Kendler, K. S., Kuhn, J. W., Vittum, J., Prescott, C. A., & Riley, B. (2005). The interaction of stressful life events and a serotonin transporter polymorphism in the prediction of episodes of major depression. *Archives of General Psychology, 62*(5), 529-535. doi:10.1001/archpsyc.62.5.529

Kevles, D. J. (1985). *In the name of eugenics: Genetics and the uses of human heredity.* Berkeley, CA: University of California Press.

Kido, T., Sikora-Wohlfeld, W., Kawashima, M., Kikuchi, S., Kama, N., Patwardhan, A., . . . Butte, A. J. (2018). Are minor alleles more likely to be risk alleles? *BMC Medical Genomics, 11*(3), 1-11. doi:10.1186/s12920-018-0322-5

Klengel, T., Dias, B. G., & Ressler, K. (2015). Models of inter- and transgenerational transmission of risk for psychopathology in mice. *Neuropsychopharmacology, 41*(1), 219-231. doi:10.1038/npp.2015.249

Kline, W. (2001). *Building a better race: Gender, sexuality, and eugenics from the turn of the century to the baby boom.* Berkeley, CA: University of California Press.

Kragh, H. (2017). Cosmology and the origin of the universe: Historical and conceptual perspectives. In Á. Díaz de Rada (Ed.), *Orígenes.*

Kulminski, A. M., Arbeev, K. G., Christensen, K., Stallard, E., Miljkovic, I., Barmada, M., & Yashin, A. I. (2012). Biogenetic mechanisms predisposing to complex phenotypes in parents may function differently in their children. *The Journals of Gerontology Series A Biological Sciences and Medical Sciences, 68*(7), 760-768. doi:10.1093/gerona/gls243

Lacourse, E., Boivin, M., Brendgen, M., Petitclerc, A., Girard, A., Vitaro, F., . . . Tremblay, R. (2014). A longitudinal twin study of physical aggression during early childhood: Evidence for a developmentally dynamic genome. *Psychological Medicine, 44*(12), 1-11. doi:10.1017/S0033291713003218

Ladyman, J., Ross, D., Spurrett, D., & Collier, J. (2007). Ontic structural realism and the philosophy of physics. In J. Ladyman, D. Ross, D. Spurrett, & J. Collier, *Every thing must go: Metaphysics naturalized.* Oxford Scholarship Online. doi:10.1093/acprof:oso/9780199276196.003.0003

Lakadamyali, M., & Cosma, M. P. (2015). Advanced microscopy methods for visualizing chromatin structure. *FEBS Letters, 589*(20), 3023-3030. doi:10.1016/j.febslet.2015.04.012

Larsson, H. C. (2001). Endocranial anatomy of Carcharodontosaurus saharicus (Theropoda: Allosauroidea) and its implications for theropod brain evolution. In K. Carpenter, D. Tanke, K. Carpenter, & M. W. Skrepnick (Eds.), *Mesozoic Vertebrate Life* (pp. 19-33). Bloomington, IN: Indiana University Press.

Laurent, G., Fournier, J., Hemberger, M., Müller, C., Naumann, R., Ondracek, J. M., . . . Yamawaki, T. (2016). Cortical evolution: Introduction to the reptilian cortex. In G. Buzsáki, & Y. Christen (Eds.), *Micro-, Meso- and Macro-Dynamics of the Brain. Research and Perspectives in Neurosciences* (pp. 23-33). Cham, Netherlands: Springer. doi:10.1007/978-3-319-28802-4_2

Leibnitz, G. W. (1989). *Philosophical papers and letters: A selection* (2nd ed.). (L. E. Loemker, Ed., & L. E. Loemker, Trans.) Dordrecht, Netherlands: Springer. doi:10.1007/978-94-010-1426-7

Le-Niculescu, H., Kurian, S. M., Yehyawi, N., Dike, C. A., Patel, S. D., Edenberg, H. J., . . . Niculescu, A. B. (2009). Identifying blood biomarkers for mood disorders using convergent functional genomics. *Molecular Psychiatry, 14*, 156-174. doi:10.1038/mp.2008

Leonard, T. C. (2005). Mistaking eugenics for Social Darwinism: Why eugenics is missing from the history of American economics. *History of Political Economy, 37*(Suppl_1), 200-233. doi:10.1215/00182702-37-Suppl_1-200

Levine, R. S., Williams, J. C., Kilbourne, B. A., & Juarez, P. D. (2012). Tuskegee redux: Evolution of legal mandates for human experimentation. *Journal of Health Care for the Poor and Underserved, 23*(4 Suppl), 104-125. doi:10.1353/hpu.2012.0174

Lewis, J., & Kattmann, U. (2004). Traits, genes, particles and information: Re-visiting students understandings of genetics. *International Journal of Science Education, 26*(2), 195-206. doi:10.1080/0950069032000072782

Lewis, P. J. (2016). *Quantum ontology: A guide to the metaphysics of quantum mechanics.* Oxford, England: Oxford University Press.

Lewkowicz, D. J. (2011). The biological implausibility of the nature-nurture dichotomy & what it means for the study of infancy. *Infancy, 16*(4), 331-367. doi:10.1111/j.1532-7078.2011.00079.x

Lewontin, R. C. (1991). *Biology as ideology: The doctrine of DNA* (Reprint ed.). New York, NY: Harper Perennial.

Liddell, H. G., & Scott, R. (2007). *Liddell and Scott's Greek-English lexicon* (Abridged ed.). London, England: Simon Wallenberg Press.

Liu, C. (2013). Strategies for designing transgenic DNA constructs. In L. A. Freeman (Ed.), *Lipoproteins and Cardiovascular Disease. Methods in Molecular Biology (Methods and Protocols)* (Vol. 1027, pp. 183-201). Totowa, NJ: Humana Press. doi:10.1007/978-1-60327-369-5_8

Liu, C., Du, Y., Xie, W., & Gui, C. (2013). Purification of plasmid and BAC transgenic DNA constructs. *Methods in Molecular Biology, 1027,* 203-215. doi:10.1007/978-1-60327-369-5_9.

Liu, Y., & Li, X. (2012). Does Darwin's Pangenesis have fatal flaws? *International Journal of Epidemiology, 41*(5), 1492–1493. doi:10.1093/ije/dys132

Liu, Y., & Li, X. (2014). Has Darwin's Pangenesis been rediscovered. *BioScience, 64*(11), 1037–1041. doi:10.1093/biosci/biu151

Lizzini, O. (2016). Ibn Sina's metaphysics. In E. N. Zalta (Ed.), *The Stanford Encyclopedia of Philosophy* (Fall 2016 ed.). Retrieved from https://plato.stanford.edu/archives/fall2016/entries/ibn-sina-metaphysics/

Locke, B. T. (2013). *The military-masculinity complex: Hegemonic masculinity and the United States armed forces, 1940-1963.* (Master's thesis). Retrieved from https://digitalcommons.unl.edu/cgi/viewcontent.cgi?article=1065&context=historydiss

Lodish, H., Berk, A., Zipursky, S. L., Matsudaira, P., Baltimore, D., & Darnell, J. (2000). Section 9.2, Chromosomal organization of genes and noncoding DNA. In *Molecular Cell Biology.* W. H. Freeman.

Loewe, L., & Hill, W. G. (2010). The population genetics of mutations: Good, bad and indifferent. *Philosophical transactions of the Royal Society of London. Series B, Biological sciences, 365*(1544), 1153-1167. doi:10.1098/rstb.2009.0317

Lohoff, F. W. (2010). Overview of the genetics of major depressive disorder. *Current Psychiatry Reports, 12*(6), 539–546. doi:10.1007/s11920-010-0150-6

Lönnig, W.-E. (2017). Mendel's paper on the laws of heredity (1866): Solving the enigma of the most famous 'Sleeping Beauty' in science. *eLS,* 1-10. doi:10.1002/9780470015902.a0026823

Louv, J. (2013, October 24). *The dark history (and reality) of eugenics in America and the forced sterilization of women.* Retrieved from Ultraculture: https://ultraculture.org

Love, A. (2015). Developmental biology. In *The Stanford Encyclopedia of Philosophy* (Fall 2015 ed.). Retrieved from https://plato.stanford.edu/archives/fall2015/entries/biology-developmental/

Lü, J., Xu, L., Liu, Y., Zhang, X., Jia, S., Lü, Q. J., . . . Liu, L. (2010). A new troodontid theropod from the Late Cretaceous of central China, and the radiation of Asian troodontids. *Acta Palaeontologica Polonica, 55*(3), 381- 388. doi:10.4202/app.2009.0047

Lynch, M. (2012). Evolutionary layering and the limits to cellular perfection. *Proceedings of the National Academy of Sciences of the United States of America, 109*(46), 18851-18856. doi:10.1073/pnas.1216130109

MacCorquodale, K., & Meehl, P. E. (1948). On a distinction between hypothetical constructs and intervening variables. *Psychological Review, 55,* 95-107. doi:10.1037/h0056029

Manga, P., Kerr, R., Ramsay, M., & Kromberg, J. G. (2013). Biology and genetics of oculocutaneous albinism and vitiligo – common pigmentation disorders in southern Africa. *South African Medical Journal, 103*(12), 984-988. doi:10.7196/samj.7046

References

Manolio, T. A., Collins, F. S., Cox, N. J., Goldstein, D. B., Hindorff, L. A., Hunter, D. J., . . . Vissher, P. M. (2010). Finding the missing heritability of complex diseases. *Nature, 461*(7265). doi:10.1038/nature08494

Marbach-Ad, G. (2001). Attempting to break the code in student comprehension of genetic concepts. *Journal of Biological Education, 35*(4), 183-189. doi:10.1080/00219266.2001.9655775

Marini, M., Falqui, A., Moretti, M., Limongi, T., Allione, M., Genovese, A., . . . Di Fabrizio, E. (2015). The Structure of DNA made visible. *Science Advances, 1*(7), e1500734. doi:10.1126/sciadv.1500734

Martins, L. A.-C. (1999, June). Did Sutton and Boveri propose the so-called Sutton-Boveri chromosome hypothesis? *Genetics and Molecular Biology, 22*(2), 261-271. doi:10.1590/S1415-47571999000200022

Mayes, G. R. (n.d.). Theories of explanation. In *Internet Encyclopedia of Philosophy.* Retrieved from https://www.iep.utm.edu/

Mazel, F., Pennell, M. W., Cadotte, M. W., Diaz, S., Riva, G. V., Grenyer, R., . . . Pearse, W. D. (2018). Prioritizing phylogenetic diversity captures functional diversity unreliably. *Nature Communications, 9*(2888), 1-9. doi:10.1038/s41467-018-05126-3

McAdams, C. R., Foster, V. A., Dotson-Blake, K. P., & Brendel, J. M. (2009). Dysfunctional family structures and aggression in children: A case for school-based, systemic approaches with violent students. *Journal of School Counseling, 7*(9), 33. Retrieved from http://jsc.montana.edu/

McDermid, D. (n.d.). Pragmatism. In *Internet Encyclopedia of Philosophy.* Retrieved from https://www.iep.utm.edu/

Meehan, M. (2009). *The triumph of eugenics in prenatal testing: Part 1. How it happened.* Retrieved February 08, 2019, from Meehan Reports: https://www.meehanreports.com/

Mehler, B. (1997). Eliminating the inferior: American and Nazi sterilization programs. *Science for the People, 19*(6), 14-18, 32. Retrieved January 26, 2019, from http://ferris-pages.org/ISAR/archives/eliminating-inferior.htm

Melott, A. L., Lieberman, B. S., Laird, C. M., Martin, L. D., Medvedev, M. V., Thomas, B. C., . . . Jackman, C. H. (2004). Did a gamma-ray burst initiate the late Ordovician mass extinction? *International Journal of Astrobiology, 3*(1), 55-61. doi:10.1017/S1473550404001910

Mendel, G. (1996). *Experiments in plant hybridization (1865).* (W. Bateson, & R. Blumberg, Trans.) Electronic Scholarly Publishing. Retrieved from http://www.esp.org/

Metaphysical. (n.d.). In *Merriam-Webster's online dictionary.* Retrieved from https://www.merriam-webster.com/dictionary/metaphysical

Metaphysics. (n.d.). In *Merriam-Webster's online dictionary.* Retrieved from https://www.merriam-webster.com/dictionary/metaphysics

Metcalf, W. V. (1940). The reality of the unobservable. *Philosophy of Science, 7*(3), 337-341. doi:10.1086/286640

Meyer, S. C. (2013). *Darwin's doubt: The explosive origin of animal life and the case for intelligent design.* New York, NY: HarperOne.

Milholland, B., Dong, X., Zhang, L., Hao, X., Suh, Y., & Vijg, J. (2017, May). Differences between germline and somatic mutation rates in humans and mice. *Nature Communications, 8*(15183). doi:10.1038/ncomms15183

Minority Nurse Staff. (2013, March 30). Minority women and intimate partner violence. *Minority Nurse.* Retrieved from https://minoritynurse.com/

Monton, B., & Mohler, C. (2017). Constructive empricism. In E. N. Zalta (Ed.), *The Stanford Encyclopedia of Philosophy* (Summer 2017 ed.). Retrieved from https://plato.stanford.edu/archives/sum2017/entries/constructive-empiricism/

Morimoto, N., Nakatsukasa, M., Ponce de León, M. S., & Zollikofer, C. P. (2018). Femoral ontogeny in humans and great apes and its implications for their last common ancestor. *Scientific Reports, 8*(1), 1-11. doi:10.1038/s41598-018-20410-4

Mu, D. (2005). Trojan horse or legitimate science; Deconstructing the debate over intelligent design. *Harvard Science Review: Science, Religion, Politics, 19*(1). Retrieved from https://harvardsciencereview.com/

Myth Def. 1. (n.d.). In *Oxford English Dictionary (US) On Line.* Retrieved from https://en.oxforddictionaries.com/

Natarajan, D., & Caramaschi, D. (2010). Animal violence demystified. *Frontiers in Behavioral Neuroscience, 4*(9). doi:10.3389/fnbeh.2010.00009

National Academy of Sciences and Institute of Medicine. (2008). Is evolution a theory or a fact? In *Science, evolution, and creationism* (p. 11). Washington, DC: National Academies Press.

National Institutes of Health. (2013, March 18). *Common genetic factors found in 5 mental disorders.* National Institutes of Health. Retrieved from https://www.nih.gov/

National Research Council, Division on Earth and Life Studies, Commission on Life Sciences, Committee on Mapping and Sequencing the Human Genome . (1988). *Mapping and sequencing the human genome.* Washington, D.C.: The National Academies Press. doi:10.17226/1097

Negele, A., Kaufhold, J., Kallenbach, L., & Leuzinger-Bohleber, M. (2015). Childhood trauma and Its relation to chronic depression in adulthood. *Depression Research and Treatment, 2015*(650804), 1-11. doi:10.1155/2015/650804

Nehrenberg, D. L., Wang, S., Buus, R. J., Perkins, J., Pardo-Manuel de Villena, F., & Pomp, D. (2010). Genomic mapping of social behavior traits in a F2 cross derived from mice selectively bred for high aggression. *BMC Genetics, 113*(11). doi:10.1186/1471-2156-11-113

Nelson, R. J., & Chiavegatto, S. (2001). Molecular basis of aggression. *Trends in Neuroscience, 24*(12), 713-719. doi:10.1016/S0166-2236(00)01996-2

Newman, S. A. (2013). Evolution is not mainly a matter of genes. In S. Krimsky, & j. Gruber (Eds.), *Genetic Explanations: Sense and Nonsense.* Cambridge, MA: Harvard University Press.

Nickles, T. (2017). Historicist theories of scientific rationality. In E. N. Zalta (Ed.), *The Stanford Encyclopedia of Philosophy* (Summer 2017 ed.). Retrieved from https://plato.stanford.edu/archives/sum2017/entries/rationality-historicist/

Nilsson, E. E., & Skinner, M. K. (2015). Environmentally induced epigenetic transgenerational inheritance of reproductive disease. *Biology of Reproduction, 93*(6), 1-8. doi:10.1095/biolreprod.115.134817.

Nilsson, H. (1934, April 14). The problem of the origin of species since Darwin. Inauguration Address delivered at Lund University, Lund, Sweden. Retrieved from https://onlinelibrary.wiley.com/doi/pdf/10.1111/j.1601-5223.1935.tb03188.x

Noble, D. (2008). Genes and causation. *Philosophical Transactions of the Royal Society A: Mathematical, Physical, and Engineering Sciences, 366*(1878), 3001-3015. doi:10.1098/rsta.2008.0086

Nordquist, N., & Oreland, L. (2010). Serotonin, genetic variability, behaviour, and psychiatric disorders - a review. *Upsala Journal of Medical Sciences, 115*(1), 2 - 10. doi:10:3109/03009730903573246

O'Dwyer, J. P., Kembel, S. W., & Green, J. L. (2012). Phylogenetic diversity theory sheds light on the structure of microbial communities. *PLoS: Computational Biology, 8*(12), e1002832. doi:10.1371/journal.pcbi.1002832

Okasha, S. (2016). Population genetics. In N. Z. Edward (Ed.), *The Stanford Encyclopedia of Philosophy* (Winter 2016 ed.). Retrieved from https://plato.stanford.edu/archives/win2016/entries/population-genetics/

Ontogeny. (n.d.). In *Merriam-Webster's online dictionary.* Retrieved from https://www.merriam-webster.com/dictionary/ontogeny

Ontology. (n.d.). In *Merriam-Webster's online dictionary.* Retrieved from https://www.merriam-webster.com/dictionary/ontology

Oparin, A. I. (1957). *The origin of life on Earth* (3rd revised and enlarged ed.). (A. Synge, Trans.) New York, NY: Academic Press Inc. Retrieved from https://archive.org

Orgel, L. E. (2007). The origins of life: Molecules and natural selection, pg.189 (Chapman & Hall: London, 1973). In C. Luskin, *A Response to Dr. Dawkins' "Information Challenge" (Part 1): Specified Complexity Is the Measure of Biological Complexity In Evolution News & Science Today.* Retrieved from https://evolutionnews.org/2007/

Orthogenesis. (n.d.). In *Merriam-Webster's online dictionary.* Retrieved from https://www.merriam-webster.com/dictionary/orthogenesis

Osbourne, F. (1937). Development of a eugenic philosophy. *American Sociological Review, 2*(3), 389-397. doi:10.2307/2084871

References

Paley, W. (1809). *Natural theology; or, evidences of the existence and attributes of the Deity* (12th ed.). London, England: J. Faulder. Retrieved from http://darwin-online.org.uk/

Palmer, J. (2009, August 28). *Single molecule's stunning image.* Retrieved from BBC News: http://news.bbc.co.uk/2/hi/science/nature/8225491.stm

Palpable. (n.d.). In *Merriam-Webster's online dictionary.* Retrieved from https://www.merriam-webster.com/dictionary/palpable

Pandey, G. (2014, November 11). Why do Indian women go to sterilization camps? BBC News, Delhi. Retrieved from https://www.bbc.com/news/

Parker, M. (2007). The best possible child. *Journal of Medical Ethics, 33*(5), 279-283. doi:10.1136/jme.2006.018176

Paternotte, C. (2011). Rational choice theory. In I. C. Jarvie, & J. Zamora-Bonilla (Eds.), *The SAGE Handbook of The Philosophy of Social Sciences* (pp. 307-321). London, England: Sage Publications. doi:10.4135/9781473913868.n15

Paweletz, N. (2001). Walther Flemming: Pioneer of mitosis research. *Nature Reviews Molecular Cell Biology, 2*, 72-75. doi:10.1038/35048077

Paymar, M., & Barnes, G. (2017, March). *Countering confusion about the Duluth Model.* Domestic Abuse Intervention Programs. Retrieved from https://www.theduluthmodel.org/

Pearson, K. (1900). *The grammar of science* (2nd Revised and Enlarged ed.). London, England: Adam and Charles Black. Retrieved from https://archive.org

Peretó, J. (2005). Controversies on the origin of life. *International Microbiology, 8*(1), 23-31. Retrieved from http://revistes.iec.cat/index.php/IM

Peretó, J., Bada, J. L., & Lazcano, A. (2009). Charles Darwin and the origin of life. *Origins of life and evolution of the biosphere: The journal of the International Society for the Study of the Origin of Life, 39*(5), 395-406. doi:10.1007/s11084-009-9172-7

Petrosky, E., Blair, J. M., Betz, C. J., Fowler, K. A., Jack, S. P., & Lyons, B. H. (2017). Racial and ethnic difference in homicides of adult women and the role of intimate partner violence - United States, 2003-2014. *Morbidity and Mortality Weekly Report (MMWR), 66*(28), 741-746. doi:10.15585/mmwr.mm6628a1

Pew Research Center. (2015-1). *Public and scientists' views on science and society.* January 29. Retrieved from http://www.pewresearch.org/

Pew Research Center. (2015-7). Chapter 4: Evolution and perceptions of scientific consensus. In *Americans, politics and science issues.* July 1. Retrieved from www.pewresearch.org

Phenomenology. (n.d.). In *Merriam-Webster's online dictionary.* Retrieved from https://www.merriam-webster.com/dictionary/phenomenology

Phenotype. (n.d.). In *Merriam-Webster's online dictionary.* Retrieved from https://www.merriam-webster.com/dictionary/phenotype

Phillips, T. (2019). 5 common dyes for DNA staining and visualizing DNA. *The Balance.* Retrieved from https://www.thebalance.com

Philosophy. (n.d.). In *Merriam-Webster's online dictionary.* Retrieved from https://www.merriam-webster.com/dictionary/Philosophy

Phylogeny. (n.d.). Retrieved from Nature.com: https://www.nature.com

Plato. (1905). *The myths of Plato.* (J. A. Stewart, Trans.) London, England: MacMillan and Co. Limited. Retrieved from https://archive.org

Plomin, R., & Deary, I. J. (2015). Genetics and intelligence differences: Five special findings. *Molecular Psychiatry, 20*(1), 98-108. doi:10.1038/mp.2014.105

Pocheville, A. (2015). The ecological niche: History and recent controversy. In T. Heams, P. Huneman, G. Lecointre, & M. Silberstein (Eds.), *Handbook of Evolutionary Thinking in the Sciences* (pp. 547-586). Dordrecht, Netherlands: Springer. doi:10.1007/978-94-017-9014-7_26

Pomiankowski, A., & Iwasa, Y. (1998). Runaway ornament diversity caused by Fisherian sexual selection. *PNAS, 95*(9), 5106-5111. doi:10.1073/pnas.95.9.5106

Porte, T. M. (2018). Karl Pearson. In *Encyclopædia Britannica On Line.* Retrieved from https://www.britannica.com/

Pragmaticism. (n.d.). In *Merriam-Webster's online dictionary.* Retrieved from https://www.merriam-webster.com/dictionary/pragmaticism

Pragmatism. (n.d.). In *Merriam-Webster's online dictionary.* Retrieved from https://www.merriam-webster.com/dictionary/pragmatism

Pu, H., Kobayashi, Y., Lü, J., Xu, L., Wu, Y., Chang, H., . . . Jia, S. (2013). An unusual basal therizinosaur dinosaur with an ornithischian dental arrangement from Northeastern China. *PLoS One, 8*(5), e63423. doi:10.1371/journal.pone.0063423

Rationality. (n.d.). In *Merriam-Webster's online dictionary*. Retrieved from https://www.merriam-webster.com/dictionary/rationality

Rees, E., O'Donovan, M. C., & Owen, M. J. (2015). Genetics of schizophrenia. *Current Opinion in Behavioral Sciences, 2*, 8-14. doi:10.1016/j.cobeha.2014.07.001

Reeves, M. A., Gauger, A. K., & Axe, D. D. (2014). Enzyme families--shared evolutionary history or shared design? A study of the GABA-aminotransferase family. *BIO-Complexity, 2014*(4), 1-16. doi:10.5048/BIO-C.2014.4

Rehan, W., Antfolk, J., Johansson, A., Jern, P., & Santtila, P. (2017). Experiences of severe childhood maltreatment, depression, anxiety and alcohol abuse among adults in Finland. *PLoS One, 12*(5), e0177252. doi:10.1371/journal.pone.0177252

Reiss, J., & Sprenger, J. (2017). Scientific objectivity. In E. N. Zalta (Ed.), *The Stanford Encyclopedia of Philosophy* (Winter 2017 ed.). Retrieved from https://plato.stanford.edu/archives/win2017/entries/scientific-objectivity/

Resnik, D. B., & Vorhaus, D. B. (2006). Genetic modification and genetic determinism. *Philosophy, Ethics, and Humanities in Medicine, 1*(1), E9. doi:10.1186/1747-5341-1-9

Ridley, M. (2009). *Francis Crick: Discoverer of the Genetic Code (eminent lives)*. New York, NY: Harper Collins.

Ringman, J. M., Goate, A., Masters, C. L., Cairns, N. J., Danek, A., & Graff-Radford, N. (2014). Genetic heterogeneity in Alzheimer disease and implications for treatment strategies. *Current Neurology and Neuroscience Report, 14*(499). doi:10.1007/s11910-014-0499-8

Robinson, H. (2017). Dualism. In E. N. Zalta (Ed.), *The Stanford Encyclopedia of Philosophy* (Fall 2017 ed.). Retrieved from https://plato.stanford.edu/archives/fall2017/entries/dualism/

Robson, D. (2017). *The birth of half-human, half-animal chimeras*. (British Broadcasting Corporation) Retrieved from BBC earth: http://www.bbc.com/earth/world

Roige, A. (2014). Intelligence and IQ testing. Retrieved January 24, 2019, from http://eugenicsarchive.ca/discover/connections/535eecb77095aa0000023a

Roll-Hansen, N. (2014). Commentary: Wilhelm Johannsen and the problem of heredity at the turn of the 19th century. *International Journal of Epidemiology, 43*(4). doi:10.1093/ije/dyu066

Rosenfeld, A., Lieberman, J. A., & Jarskog, L. F. (2011). Oxytocin, dopamine, and the amygdala: A neurofunctional model of social cognitive deficits in schizophrenia. *Schizophrenia Bulletin, 37*(5), 1077-1087. doi:10.1093/schbul/sbq015

Rothstein, M. A., Harrell, H. L., & Marchant, G. E. (2017). Transgenerational epigenetics and environmental justice. *Environmental Epigenetics, 3*(3), 1-12. doi:10.1093/eep/dvx011

Russell, B. (2007). *A history of Western philosophy* (Reprint (2007) ed.). New York: Simon & Schuster.

Ryle, J. A. (1938). Medicine and eugenics. *The Eugenics Review, 30*(1), 9-19. Retrieved January 25, 2019, from https://www.ncbi.nlm.nih.gov/pmc/articles/PMC2985802/pdf/eugenrev00274-0018.pdf

Salgirli, S. G. (2011). Eugenics for the doctors: Medicine and social control in 1930s Turkey. *Journal of the History of Medicine and Allied Sciences, 66*(3), 281-312. doi:10.1093/jhmas/jrq040

Sanders, K. (2009). *Bodies in the bog and the archaeological imagination*. Chicago, IL: University of Chicago Press.

Sanford, J., Brewer, W., Smith, F., & Baumgardner, J. (2015). The waiting time problem in a model hominin population. *Theoretical Biology and Medical Modelling, 12*(18). doi:10.1186/s12976-015-0016-z

Santiago, E. F., & de Visser, J. G. (2003). Environmental stress and the effects of mutation. *Journal of Biology, 2*(2), 12. doi:10.1186/1475-4924-2-12

Satyanathan, D., & Pollack, A. (2001). Domestic violence and poverty. In E. Trzcinski, & D. Satyanathan (Eds.), *Moving families out of poverty (Michigan family impact seminars: Briefing report No. 2001-2)* (pp. 17-18). Retrieved from https://www.purdue.edu/hhs/hdfs/fii/wp-content/uploads/2015/07/s_mifis04report.pdf

References

Savitt, S. (2017). Being and becoming in modern physics. In E. N. Zalta (Ed.), *The Stanford Encyclopedia of Philosophy* (Fall 2017 ed.). Retrieved from https://plato.stanford.edu/archives/fall2017/entries/spacetime-bebecome/

Sawyer, S. A., Parsch, J., Zhang, Z., & Hartl, D. L. (2007). Prevalence of positive selection among nearly neutral amino acid replacements in Drosophila. *Proceedings of the National Academy of Sciences of the United States of America, 104*(16), 6504-6510. doi:10.1073/pnas.0701572104

Schäfer, I., Hansen, H., Schön, G., Höfels, S., Altiner, A., Dahlhaus, A., . . . Wiese, B. (2012). The influence of age, gender and socio-economic status on multimorbidity patterns in primary care. First results from the multicare cohort study. *BioMedical Central Health Services Research, 12*(89). doi:10.1186/1472-6963-12-89

Schaffer, J. (2016). Monism. In E. N. Zalta (Ed.), *The Stanford Encyclopedia of Philosophy* (Winter 2016 ed.). Retrieved from https://plato.stanford.edu/archives/win2016/entries/monism/

Scharf, C. A., Virgo, N., Cleaves II, H. J., Aono, M., Aubert-Kato, N., Aydinoglu, A., . . . Yabuta, H. (2015). A strategy for origins of life research. *Astrobiology, 15*(12), 1031-1042. doi:10.1089/ast.2015.1113

Schmidt, A. (1999, October 1). Watson advocates eugenics, screening. *The Tech, 119*(46), p. 16. Retrieved February 9, 2019, from https://thetech.com/

Schrum, J. P., Zhu, T. F., & Szostak, J. W. (2010). The origins of cellular life. *Cold Spring Harbor Perspectives in Biology, 2*(9), a002212. Retrieved September 26, 2018, from https://www.ncbi.nlm.nih.gov/pmc/articles/PMC2926753/pdf/cshperspect-ORI-a002212.pdf

Schwartz, R. C., & Blankenship, D. M. (2014). Racial disparities in psychotic disorder diagnosis: A review of empirical literature. *World Journal of Psychiatry, 4*(4), 133-140. doi:10.5498/wjp.v4.i4.133

Sebastian, K. L. (2010). The development of the concept atoms and molecules: Dalton and beyond. *Resonance, 15*(1), 8-15. doi:10.1007/s12045-011-0126-9

Serón-Ferré, M., Richter, H. G., Valenzuela, G. J., & Torres-Farfan, C. (2016). Circadian rhythms in the fetus and newborn: Significance of interactions with maternal physiology and the environment. In D. Walker (Ed.), *Prenatal and postnatal determinants of development. Neuromethods* (Vol. 109). New York, NY: Humana Press. doi:10.1007/978-1-4939-3014-2_7

Sharov, A. A. (2006). Genome increase as a clock for the origin and evolution of life. *Biology Direct, 1*(17). doi:10.1186/1745-6150-1-17

Sidorsky, D., & Talisse, R. (2018). Sidney Hook. In E. N. Zalta (Ed.), *The Stanford Encyclopedia of Philosophy* (Winter 2018 ed.). Retrieved from https://plato.stanford.edu/archives/win2015/entries/sidney-hook/

Silander, O. K., & Ackerman, M. (2009). The constancy of gene conservation across divergent bacterial order. *BMC Research Notes, 2*(2), 1-9. doi:10.1186/1756-0500-2-2

Sittig, L. J., & Redei, E. E. (2010). Paternal genetic contribution influences fetal vulnerability to maternal alcohol consumption in a rat model of fetal alcohol spectrum disorder. *PLoS One, 5*(4), e10058. doi:10.1371/journal.pone.0010058

Skodo, A. (2015). Eugenics and pragmatism: F. C. S. Schiller's Philosophical Politics. *Modern Intellectual History*, 1-27. doi:10:1017/S1479244315000177

Smeenk, C., & Ellis, G. (2017). Philosophy of cosmology. In E. N. Zalta (Ed.), *The Stanford Encyclopedia of Philosophy* (Winter 2017 ed.). Retrieved from https://plato.stanford.edu/archives/win2017/entries/cosmology/

Smith, D. W. (2018). Phenomenology. In E. N. Zalta (Ed.), *The Stanford Encyclopedia of Philosophy* (Summer 2018 ed.). Retrieved from https://plato.stanford.edu/archives/sum2018/entries/phenomenology/

Smith, G. (2008). Isaac Newton. In E. N. Zalta (Ed.), *The Stanford Encyclopedia of Philosophy* (Fall 2008 ed.). Retrieved from https://plato.stanford.edu/archives/fall2008/entries/newton/

Smith, L. C., & Murphy, B. D. (2004). Genetic and epigenetic aspects of cloning and potential effects on offspring of cloned mammals. *Cloning and Stem Cells, 6*(2), 126-132. doi:10.1089/1536230041372319

Smith, S. R., Petrik, N. G., Kimmel, G. A., & Kay, B. D. (2012). Thermal and nonthermal physiochemical processes in nanoscale films of amorphous solid water. *Accounts of Chemical Research, 45*(1), 33-42. doi:10.1021/ar200070w.

Sniegowski, P. D., & Lenski, R. E. (1995). Mutation and adaptation: The directed mutation controversy in evolutionary perspective. *Annual Review of Ecology and Systematics, 26*(1), 553-578. doi:10.1146/annurev.es.26.110195.003005

Snoke, D. W., Cox, J., & Petcher, D. (2014). Suboptimality and complexity in evolution. *Complexity, 21*(1), 322-327. doi:10.1002/cplx.21566

Snyder, L. J. (2017). William Whewell. In E. N. Zalta (Ed.), *The Stanford Encyclopedia of Philosophy* (Winter 2017 ed.). Retrieved from https://plato.stanford.edu/archives/win2017/entries/whewell/

Solana, J. (2013). Closing the circle of germline and stem cells: The primordial stem cell hypothesis. *EvoDevo, 4*(1), 2. doi:10.1186/2041-9139-4-2

Solt, I. (2011). Vestigial structures are important to the development of the human embryo [Abstract]. *Harefuah, 150*(7), 596-599, 616. Retrieved from https://www.ima.org.il/medicine/default.aspx

Spencer, H. (1852). A theory of population, deduced from the general law of human fertility. *Westminster Review, 57*, 468-501. Retrieved from http://onlinebooks.library.upenn.edu/webbin/serial?id=westminsterreview

Spencer, H. (1864). *The principles of biology* (Vol. 1). London, England: Williams and Norgate. Retrieved from https://archive.org/

SPLC. (1977). *Sterilization Abuse: Relf V. Weinberger (Case Number Civ. A. Nos. 73-1557, Consolidated with 74-243)*. Retrieved January 27, 2019, from Southern Poverty Law Center: https://www.splcenter.org/

Star, B., & Spencer, H. (2013). Effects of genetic drift and gene flow on the selective maintenance of genetic variation. *Genetics, 194*(1), 235-244. doi:10.1534/genetics.113.149781

Steup, M. (2018). Epistemology. In E. N. Zalta (Ed.), *The Stanford Encyclopedia of Philosophy* (Summer 2018 ed.). Retrieved from https://plato.stanford.edu/archives/sum2018/entries/epistemology/

Stoljar, D. (2017). Physicalism. In E. N. Zalta (Ed.), *The Stanford Encyclopedia of Philosophy* (Winter 2017 ed.). Retrieved from https://plato.stanford.edu/archives/win2017/entries/physicalism/

Suris, A., Lind, L., Emmett, G., Borman, P. D., Kashner, M., & Barratt, E. S. (2004). Measures of aggressive behavior: Overview of clinical and research instruments. *Aggression and Violent Behavior, 9*(2), 165-227. doi:10.1016/S1359-1789(03)00012-0

Swigon, D. (2009). The mathematics of DNA structure, mechanics, and dynamics. In C. J. Benham et al. (Ed.), *Mathematics of DNA Structure, Function, and Interaction, The IMA Volumes in Mathematics and its Applications 150* (pp. 293-320). Springer Science, Business Media. doi:10.1007/978-1-4419-0670-0_14

Systematics Association. (1964). *Phenetic and phylogenetic classification a symposium* (Vol. 6). (J. MacNeill, & V. H. Heywood, Eds.) London, UK: Systematics Association.

Tabery, J. (2014, April 29). Nature vs nurture. Retrieved January 25, 2019, from http://eugenicsarchive.ca/discover/connections/535eed0d7095aa0000000241

Tasca, C., Rapetti, M., Carta, M. G., & Fadda, B. (2012). Women and hysteria in the history of mental health. *Clinical Practice and Epidemiology in Mental Health, 8*, 110-119. doi:10.2174/1745017901208010110

Terwilliger, J. D., & Hiekkalinna, T. (2006). An utter refutation of the 'Fundamental Theorem of the HapMap'. *European Journal of Human Genetics, 14*, 426-437. doi:10.1038/sj.ejhg.5201583

The book of the people: POPUL VUH. (1954). (A. Recino, D. Goetz, & S. G. Morley, Trans.) Los Angeles: Plantin Press. Retrieved from https://www.holybooks.com

The Editors of Encyclopædia Britannica. (2007, December 6). Phaëthon. In *Encyclopædia Britannica On Line*. Retrieved from https://www.britannica.com/

The Editors of Encyclopædia Britannica. (2015, April 16). Tautology. In *Encyclopædia Britannica On Line*. Retrieved from https://www.britannica.com/

The Editors of Encyclopædia Britannica. (2018, February 08). Pan. In *Encyclopædia Britannica On Line*. Retrieved from https://www.britannica.com/

References

The Members of the Genetics Workgroup. (1997). *Genetics and mental disorders: Report of the National Institute of Mental Health's Genetics Workgroup.* National Institute of Mental Health. Retrieved from https://www.nimh.nih.gov/about/advisory-boards-and-groups/namhc/reports/genetics-and-mental-disorders-report-of-the-national-institute-of-mental-healths-genetics-workgroup.shtml

Theory. (n.d.). In *Merriam-Webster's online dictionary.* Retrieved from https://www.merriam-webster.com/dictionary/Theory

Thieme, F. P. (1952). The population as a unit of study. *American Anthropologist, 54*(4), 504-509. doi:10.1525/aa.1952.54.4.02a00050

Thorvaldsen, S., & Øhrstrøm, P. (2013). Darwin's perplexing paradox: Intelligent design in nature. *Perspectives in Biology and Medicine, 56*(1), 78-98. doi:10.1353/pbm.2013.0000

Toft, M. (2014). Advances in genetic diagnosis of neurological disorders. *Acta Neurologica Scandiavica, 129*(s198). doi:10.1111/ane.12232

Tomasello, M., & Gonzalez-Cabrera, I. (2017). The role of ontogeny in the evolution of human cooperation. *Human Nature, 28*(3), 274-288. doi:10.1007/s12110-017-9291-1

Truism. (n.d.). In *Merriam-Webster's online dictionary.* Retrieved from https://www.merriam-webster.com/dictionary/truism

Truman, J. L., & Morgan, R. E. (2014). *Nonfatal domestic violence, 2003 - 2012 (NCJ 244697).* U.S. Department of Justice, Office of Justice Programs, Bureau of Justice Statistics. Retrieved from https://www.bjs.gov/content/pub/pdf/ndv0312.pdf

Tylor, E. B. (1872). Quetelet on the science of man. *Popular Science Monthly Volume 1 reprinted from Nature (1872), 5*(7), 358-363. Retrieved from https://en.wikisource.org/wiki/Popular_Science_Monthly/Volume_1/May_1872/Quetelet_on_the_Science_of_Man

Ulett, M. A. (2014). Making the case for orthogenesis: The popularization of definitely directed evolution (1890–1926). *Studies in History and Philosophy of Biological and Biomedical Sciences, 45*, 124-132. doi:10.1016/j.shpsc.2013.11.009

UN. (2015). *The millennium development goals report, 2015.* New York, NY: United Nations. doi:10.18356/6cd11401-en

UNFPA. (2011). *Report of the international workshop on skewed sex ratios at birth: Addressing the issue and the way forward.* New York: UNFPA.

UNICEF. (2005). *Early Marriage, a harmful traditional practice.* New York: UNICEF. Retrieved from https://www.unicef.org/publications/index_26024.html

Validity. (n.d.). In *Merriam-Webster's online dictionary.* Retrieved from https://www.merriam-webster.com/dictionary/validity

Van Flandern, T. (2007). The challenge of the exploded planet hypothesis. *International Journal of Astrobiology, 6*(3), 185-197. doi:10.1017/S1473550407003758

van Ijzendoorn, M. H., & Bakermans-Kranenburg, M. J. (2015). Genetic differential susceptibility on trial: Meta-analytic support. *Development and Psychopathology, 27*(1), 151-162. doi:10.1017/S0954579414001369

Varol, E., Sotiras, A., & Davatzikos, C. (2017). HYDRA: Revealing heterogeneity of imaging and genetic patterns through a multiple max-margin discriminative analysis framework. *NeuroImage, 145*(Part B.), 346-364. doi:10.1016/j.neuroimage.2016.02.041

Vinci, T. C., & Robert, J. S. (2005). Aristotle and modern genetics. *Journal of the History of Ideas, 66*(2), 201-221. doi:10.1353/jhi.2005.0041

Wahlsten, D. (2014, April 26). *Natural and artificial selection.* Retrieved from Eugenics Archive: http://eugenicsarchive.ca/discover/connections/535eed017095aa0000000240

Wahowiak, L. (2015). Addressing stigma, disparities in minority mental health: Access to care among barriers. *The Nation's Health, 45*(1), 1-20. Retrieved from http://thenationshealth.aphapublications.org/

Wallis, J. H. (2014). Evidence of panspermia: From astronomy to meteorites (Doctoral dissertation). Cardiff, Wales. Retrieved from https://orca.cf.ac.uk/

Wallpe, C. S. (2010). *Engaging a systems approach to evaluate domestic violence intervention with abusive men: Reassessing the role of community (Doctoral Dissertation).* Portland: Portland State University. doi:10.15760/etd.439

Wassersug, J., & Wassersug, R. (1986, March). Fitness fallacies. *Natural History, 95*(3), p. 34. Retrieved February 06, 2019, from http://connection.ebscohost.com/

Wells, J. (2014). Membrane patterns carry ontogenetic information that is specified independently of DNA. *BIO-Complexity, 2014*(2), 1–28. doi:10.5048/BIO-C.2014.2

West, M. (2011, December 31). *Debunked: Agenda 21, ICLEI, sovereignty, UN, depopulation: Discussions in conspiracy theories.* Retrieved from Metabunk.org: https://www.metabunk.org/debunked-agenda-21-iclei-sovereignty-un-depopulation.t363/

WHO. (2014). *Global status report on violence prevention 2014.* Geneva: World Health Organization. Retrieved from http://www.who.int/violence_injury_prev ention/violence/status_report/2014/repo rt/report/en/

Wickramasinghe, N. C. (2018). The growing case for life as a cosmic phenomenon. *Paper presented at the 42nd Committee on Space Research Scientific Assembly (COSPAR).* Pasadena. Retrieved from http://cospar2018.org/wp-content/uploads/2018/07/COSPAR-2018-Abstract-Book_July21-2018-UPDATE.pdf

Winchester, A. M. (2018, October 22). Genetics. In *Encyclopædia Britannica On Line.* Retrieved from https://www.britannica.com/

Wolfram, S. (2002). *A new kind of science* (New Edition ed.). Wolfram Media, Incorporated. Retrieved from https://www.wolframscience.com

World Health Organization. (2002). *Environmental health in emergencies and disasters: A practical guide.* (B. Wisner, & J. Adams, Eds.) Geneva: World Health Organization. Retrieved from https://www.who.int

Worldview. (n.d.). In *Merriam-Webster's online dictionary.* Retrieved from https://www.merriam-webster.com/dictionary/worldview

Wrangham, R. W. (2018). Two types of aggression in human evolution. *Proceedings of the National Academy of Sciences of the United States of America, 115*(2), 245-253. doi:10.1073/pnas.1713611115

Wynn, M. R. (2016). Phenomenology of religion. In E. N. Zalta (Ed.), *The Stanford Encyclopedia of Philosophy* (Winter 2016 ed.). Retrieved from https://plato.stanford.edu/archives/win2 016/entries/phenomenology-religion/

Wynn, M. R. (2017). Between heaven and earth: sensory experience and the goods of the spiritual life. In D. McPherson (Ed.), *Spirituality and the Good Life.* Cambridge, UK: Cambridge University Press. doi:10.1017/9781316459461.007

Wyrobek, A. J., Mulvihill, J. J., Wassom, J. S., Malling, H. V., Shelby, M. D., Lewis, S. E., . . . Bishop, J. B. (2007). Assessing human germ-cell mutagenesis in the postgenome era: A celebration of the legacy of William Lawson (Bill) Russell. *Environmental and Molecular Mutagenesis, 48*(2), 71-95. doi:10.1002/em.20284

Xu, C., Hu, S., & Chen, X. (2016). Artificial cells: From basic science to applications. *Materials Today, 19*(9), 516–532. doi:10.1016/j.mattod.2016.02.020

Yang, J. (2014). John Norris. In E. N. Zalta (Ed.), *The Stanford Encyclopedia of Philosophy* (Spring 2014 ed.). Retrieved from https://plato.stanford.edu/archives/spr2 014/entries/john-norris/

Yong, E. (2013). Chinese project probes the genetics of genius. *Nature, 497*(7449), 297-299. doi:10.1038/497297a

Yunis, E. J., Zuniga, J., Romero, V., & Yunis, E. J. (2007). Chimerism and tetragametic chimerism in humans: Implications in autoimmunity, allorecognition and tolerance. *Immunologic Research, 38*(1-3), 213-236. doi:10.1007/s12026-007-0013-3

Yvert, G. (2014). 'Particle genetics': Treating every cell as unique. *Trends in Genetics, 30*(2), 49-56. doi:10.1016/j.tig.2013.11.002

Zajenkowski, M., & Zajenkowska, A. (2015). Intelligence and aggression: The role of cognitive control and test related stress. *Personality and Individual Differences, 81*, 23-26. doi:10.1016/j.paid.2014.12.062

Zelenkov, A. I., Anohina, V. V., Zhdanovskij, A. P., Kandrichin, N. A., Karako, P. S., Kisel, N. K., . . . Shavrova, O. G. (2011). *Philosophy and methodology of science (The textbook for post-graduate students and masters).* (A. I. Zelenkov, Ed.) Minsk, Belarus: The Belarusian State University. Retrieved May 15, 2018, from www.bsu.by/Cache/pdf/162823.pdf

Zhu, S., Ge, J., Liu, Z., Liu, L., Jing, D., Ran, M., . . . Luo, Z. (2017). Circadian rhythm influences the promoting role of pulsed electromagnetic fields on sciatic nerve regeneration in rats. *Frontiers in Neurology, 8*(101). doi:10.3389/fneur.2017.00101

References

Zou, Y. (2014). Charles Darwin's theory of Pangenesis. *The Embryo Project Encyclopedia (2014-07-20).* Retrieved from http://embryo.asu.edu/

Zukerman, W. (2011, September 28). Domestic violence gets evolutionary explanation. *New Scientist.* Retrieved from https://www.newscientist.com

TABLE OF ABBREVIATIONS

APR	Aggression in Proximity Relationships
ASHG	American Society of Human Genetics
BBC	British Broadcasting Corporation
CDC	Center for Disease Control and Prevention
CG	Chorionic gonadotropin
CRG	Council for Responsible Genetics
DNA	Deoxyribonucleic acid
DV	Domestic Violence
GWAS	Genome-wide association studies
HCG	Hyperglycosylated chorionic gonadotropin
ID	Intelligent Design
IPV	Intimate Partner Violence
IQ	Intelligence Quotient
NIMH	National Institute of Mental Health
NVDRS	National Violent Death Reporting System
PTSD	Post-traumatic stress disorder
RNA	Ribonucleic Acid
SNP	Single nucleotide polymorphism
SPLC	Southern Poverty Law Center
UN	United Nations
UNFPA	United Nations Population Fund
UNICEF	United Nations Children's Fund
WHO	World Health Organization

NAME LIST

ACCREDITATION LIST

1.	Table 2 1	US Census Bureau
2.	Figure 2 1	Anonymous/Unknown author (https://commons.wikimedia.org/wiki/File:Flammarion.jpg), "Flammarion", marked as public domain, more details on Wikimedia Commons: https://commons.wikimedia.org/wiki/Template:PD-old
3.	Figure 2 2	© Marie-Lan Nguyen / Wikimedia Commons (https://commons.wikimedia.org/wiki/File:Pan_goat_MAN_Napoli_Inv27709_n01.jpg), "Pan goat MAN Napoli Inv27709 n01", https://creativecommons.org/licenses/by/2.5/legalcode
4.	Figure 3 1	Rachel Kaplan (https://en.wikipedia.org/wiki/File:Reasonable_Person_Model_Diagram_2.png), "Reasonable Person Model Diagram 2", https://creativecommons.org/licenses/by-sa/3.0/legalcode
5.	Figure 5 1	Pieter Brueghel the Elder creator QS:P170,Q43270 (https://commons.wikimedia.org/wiki/File:Alchemist-small.png), "Alchemist-small", marked as public domain, more details on Wikimedia Commons: https://commons.wikimedia.org/wiki/Template:PD-old
6.	Figure 6 1	https://svgsilh.com/image/304353.html: CC0 1.0 Universal (CC0 1.0) Public Domain Dedication
7.	Figure 7 1	By Empirical_Cycle.png: TesseUndDaanderivative work: Beao (talk) - Empirical_Cycle.png, CC BY 3.0, https://commons.wikimedia.org/w/index.php?curid=7968500
8.	Figure 8 1	Krishnavedala (https://commons.wikimedia.org/wiki/File:Classical_definition_of_Kno.svg), "Classical definition of Kno", https://creativecommons.org/publicdomain/zero/1.0/legalcode
9.	Figure 9 1	ArchonMagnus (https://commons.wikimedia.org/wiki/File:The_Scientific_Method_as_an_Ongoing_Process.svg), https://creativecommons.org/licenses/by-sa/4.0/legalcode
10.	Figure 10 1	Spaynton (https://commons.wikimedia.org/wiki/File:Graphcause.png), https://creativecommons.org/licenses/by-sa/4.0/legalcode
11.	Figure 11 1	Sarah Greenwood (https://commons.wikimedia.org/wiki/File:Scientific_Method_Graphic.png), https://creativecommons.org/licenses/by/4.0/legalcode
12.	Figure 12 1	English: Artist is Olin Levi Warner (1844–1896). Photographed in 2007 by Carol Highsmith (1946–), who explicitly placed the photograph in the public domain. Español: El artista fue Olin Levi Warner (1844–1896). El autor de la foto del año 2007 fue Carol Highsmith, quien explícitamente ubicó esta imagen en el dominio público. (https://commons.wikimedia.org/wiki/File:Truth-Warner-Highsmith.jpeg), "Truth-Warner-Highsmith", marked as public domain, more details on Wikimedia Commons: https://commons.wikimedia.org/wiki/Template:PD-US
13.	Figure 13 1	WolfgangRieger (https://commons.wikimedia.org/wiki/File:Pompeii_-_Villa_del_Cicerone_-_Mosaic_-_MAN.jpg), "Pompeii - Villa del Cicerone - Mosaic - MAN", marked as public domain, more details on Wikimedia Commons: https://commons.wikimedia.org/wiki/Template:PD-old
14.	Figure 13 2	Dustin Dewynne (https://commons.wikimedia.org/wiki/File:Body-Mind-SOUL--Matter-Energy-SPIRIT.png), "Body-Mind-SOUL--Matter-Energy-SPIRIT", https://creativecommons.org/publicdomain/zero/1.0/legalcode
15.	Figure 13 3	UnknownUnknown author (https://commons.wikimedia.org/wiki/File:Leviathan_by_Thomas_Hobbes.jpg), "Leviathan by Thomas Hobbes", marked as public domain, more details on Wikimedia Commons: https://commons.wikimedia.org/wiki/Template:PD-old
16.	Figure 13 4	Photograph by Orren Jack Turner, Princeton, N.J. Modified with Photoshop by PM_Poon and later by Dantadd. (https://commons.wikimedia.org/wiki/File:Albert_Einstein_Head.jpg), "Albert Einstein Head", marked as public domain, more details on Wikimedia Commons: https://commons.wikimedia.org/wiki/Template:PD-US

17.   Figure 13 5   GYassineMrabetTalk This W3C-unspecified vector image was created with Inkscape. (https://commons.wikimedia.org/wiki/File:Modernphysicsfields.svg), „Modernphysicsfields", https://creativecommons.org/licenses/by-sa/3.0/legalcode

18.   Figure 13 6   Jean-François Millet creator QS:P170,Q148458 (https://commons.wikimedia.org/wiki/File:Jean-François_Millet_-_Gleaners_-_Google_Art_Project_2.jpg), „Jean-François Millet - Gleaners - Google Art Project 2", marked as public domain, more details on Wikimedia Commons: https://commons.wikimedia.org/wiki/Template:PD-old

19.   Figure 13 7   Micelle_scheme-en.svg: SuperManu derivative work: ZanderZ (talk) (https://commons.wikimedia.org/wiki/File:Micelle_scheme-nl.svg), „Micelle scheme-nl", https://creativecommons.org/licenses/by-sa/3.0/legalcode

20.   Figure 14 1   Ian Alexander (https://commons.wikimedia.org/wiki/File:Aristotelian_Soul.png), https://creativecommons.org/licenses/by-sa/4.0/legalcode

21.   Figure 14 2   Eric Gaba (Sting - fr:Sting) (https://commons.wikimedia.org/wiki/File:Phylogenetic_tree.svg), „Phylogenetic tree", marked as public domain, more details on Wikimedia Commons:

22.   Figure 15 1   Nicola Perscheid (https://commons.wikimedia.org/wiki/File:ErnstHaeckel.jpg), „ErnstHaeckel", marked as public domain, more details on Wikimedia Commons: https://commons.wikimedia.org/wiki/Template:PD-old

23.   Figure 15 2   Romanes, G. J.; uploaded to Wikipedia by en:User:Phlebas; authors of the description page: en:User:Phlebas, en:User:SeventyThree (https://commons.wikimedia.org/wiki/File:Haeckel_drawings.jpg), „Haeckel drawings", marked as public domain, more details on Wikimedia Commons: https://commons.wikimedia.org/wiki/Template:PD-old

24.   Figure 16 1   Chris Packard (https://commons.wikimedia.org/wiki/File:Characteristics_of_life.svg), https://creativecommons.org/licenses/by-sa/4.0/legalcode

25.   Figure 18 1   J. Cameron (https://commons.wikimedia.org/wiki/File:Charles_Darwin_01.jpg), „Charles Darwin 01", marked as public domain, more details on Wikimedia Commons: https://commons.wikimedia.org/wiki/Template:PD-old

26.   Figure 18 2   From: Arthur Shuster & Arthur E. Shipley: Britain's Heritage of Science. London, 1917. (https://commons.wikimedia.org/wiki/File:SS-newton.jpg), „SS-newton", marked as public domain, more details on Wikimedia Commons: https://commons.wikimedia.org/wiki/Template:PD-old

27.   Figure 18 3   Elembis (https://commons.wikimedia.org/wiki/File:Mutation_and_selection_diagram.svg), „Mutation and selection diagram", https://creativecommons.org/licenses/by-sa/3.0/legalcode

28.   Figure 18 4   OpenStax, Rice University (https://commons.wikimedia.org/wiki/File:Genetic_drift_in_a_population_Figure_19_02_02.png), https://creativecommons.org/licenses/by/4.0/legalcode

29.   Figure 18 5   Ian Alexander (https://commons.wikimedia.org/wiki/File:Darwin's_Pangenesis.svg), https://creativecommons.org/licenses/by-sa/4.0/legalcode

30.   Figure 18 6   Ccaldwell19 (https://commons.wikimedia.org/wiki/File:Natural_selection_and_coevolution.svg), https://creativecommons.org/licenses/by-sa/4.0/legalcode

31.   Figure 18 7   M. Garde (https://commons.wikimedia.org/wiki/File:Human_evolution_scheme.svg), „Human evolution scheme", https://creativecommons.org/licenses/by-sa/3.0/legalcode

32.   Figure 19 1   anonymous (https://commons.wikimedia.org/wiki/File:Herbert_Spencer.jpg), „Herbert Spencer ", marked as public domain, more details on Wikimedia Commons: https://commons.wikimedia.org/wiki/Template:PD-old

33.   Figure 19 2   Glackens, L. M. (1913) Eugenics makes the world go 'round / L.M. Glackens., 1913. N.Y.: Published by Keppler & Schwarzmann, Puck Building. [Photograph] Retrieved from the Library of Congress,

34.   Figure 19 3   Hugo Iltis (https://commons.wikimedia.org/wiki/File:Gregor_Mendel_oval.jpg), https://creativecommons.org/licenses/by/4.0/legalcode

35.   Figure 20 1   File:Chromosome-es.svg: KES47derivative work: KES47 (https://commons.wikimedia.org/wiki/File:Chromosome_en.svg), „Chromosome en", https://creativecommons.org/licenses/by/3.0/legalcode

36.	Figure 20 2	Unknown author (https://commons.wikimedia.org/wiki/File:Walther_Flemming.jpg), „Walther Flemming ", marked as public domain, more details on Wikimedia Commons: https://commons.wikimedia.org/wiki/Template:PD-old
37.	Chart 20 1	Friend of a friends (https://commons.wikimedia.org/wiki/File:Genes_and_base_pairs_on_chromosomes.svg), „Genes and base pairs on chromosomes ", https://creativecommons.org/licenses/by-sa/3.0/legalcode
38.	Figure 20 3	Difference_DNA_RNA-DE.svg: Sponk (talk) translation: Sponk (talk) (https://commons.wikimedia.org/wiki/File:Difference_DNA_RNA-EN.svg), „Difference DNA RNA-EN", https://creativecommons.org/licenses/by-sa/3.0/legalcode
39.	Figure 21 1	By en:User:Cburnett - Own work in Inkscape, CC BY-SA 3.0, https://commons.wikimedia.org/w/index.php?curid=1840082
40.	Chart 21 1	Mpluess (https://commons.wikimedia.org/wiki/File:Diathesisstressdualriskmodel.JPG), „Diathesisstressdualriskmodel", marked as public domain, more details on Wikimedia Commons: https://commons.wikimedia.org/wiki/Template:PD-self
41.	Chart 21 2	Differentialsusceptibilitymodel.JPG: Mpluess derivative work: Snubcube (talk) (https://commons.wikimedia.org/wiki/File:Differentialsusceptibilitymodel.svg), „Differentialsusceptibilitymodel", marked as public domain, more details on Wikimedia Commons: https://commons.wikimedia.org/wiki/Template:PD-self
42.	Figure 22 1	National Institutes of Health (https://commons.wikimedia.org/wiki/File:Epigenetic_mechanisms.jpg), „Epigenetic mechanisms ", marked as public domain, more details on Wikimedia Commons: https://commons.wikimedia.org/wiki/Template:PD-US
43.	Figure 23 1	domdomegg (https://commons.wikimedia.org/wiki/File:Three_cell_growth_types.svg), Cropped to show only Mitosis and Meiosis by BritFix, https://creativecommons.org/licenses/by-sa/4.0/legalcode
44.	Figure 24 1	Wellcome Library, London (https://commons.wikimedia.org/wiki/File:A_frightened_and_an_angry_face,_left_and_right_respectively._Wellcome_V0009326.jpg), https://creativecommons.org/licenses/by/4.0/legalcode
45.	Figure 24 2	Wellcome Library, London (https://commons.wikimedia.org/wiki/File:Sixteen_faces_expressing_the_human_passions._Wellcome_L0068375_(cropped).jpg), https://creativecommons.org/licenses/by/4.0/legalcode
46.	Figure 25-1	(Scharf et al., 2015)
47.	Figure 25 2	Silver Spoon Sokpop (https://commons.wikimedia.org/wiki/File:Panspermie.svg), „Panspermie", https://creativecommons.org/licenses/by-sa/3.0/legalcode
48.	Figure 25 3	André Thévet creator QS:P170,Q523054 (https://commons.wikimedia.org/wiki/File:PhiloThevet.jpg), „PhiloThevet", marked as public domain, more details on Wikimedia Commons: https://commons.wikimedia.org/wiki/Template:PD-old
49.	Figure 25 4	anonymous (https://commons.wikimedia.org/wiki/File:Liceti,_De_monstris,_1668_Wellcome_L0027463.jpg), https://creativecommons.org/licenses/by/4.0/legalcode
50.	Figure 26 1	Lemuel Francis Abbott creator QS:P170,Q725410 (https://commons.wikimedia.org/wiki/File:William_Herschel01.jpg), „William Herschel01", marked as public domain, more details on Wikimedia Commons: https://commons.wikimedia.org/wiki/Template:PD-old
51.	Figure 26 2	Hannes Grobe/Hannes Grobe (talk) (https://commons.wikimedia.org/wiki/File:Watch_with_no_background.png), „Watch with no background", https://creativecommons.org/licenses/by/3.0/legalcode
52.	Figure 27 1	Unknown (https://commons.wikimedia.org/wiki/File:Sir_Francis_Galton,_circa_1905.jpg), „Sir Francis Galton, circa 1905", marked as public domain, more details on Wikimedia Commons: https://commons.wikimedia.org/wiki/Template:PD-old
53.	Figure 27 2	Phot-colorization (https://commons.wikimedia.org/wiki/File:Adolf_Hitler_colorized.jpg), https://creativecommons.org/licenses/by-sa/4.0/legalcode

Accreditation List

54.	Figure 27 3	James_D_Watson_Genome_Image.jpg: Cold Spring Harbor Laboratory derivative work: Jan Arkesteijn (talk) (https://commons.wikimedia.org/wiki/File:James_D_Watson.jpg), „James D Watson ", marked as public domain, more details on Wikimedia Commons: https://commons.wikimedia.org/wiki/Template:PD-US
55.	Figure 27 4	Francis_Crick.png: Photo: Marc Lieberman derivative work: Materialscientist (talk) (https://commons.wikimedia.org/wiki/File:Francis_Crick_crop.jpg), „Francis Crick crop", https://creativecommons.org/licenses/by/2.5/legalcode
56.	Figure 27 5	Unknown (https://commons.wikimedia.org/wiki/File:Charles_Benedict_Davenport.jpg), „Charles Benedict Davenport ", marked as public domain, more details on Wikimedia Commons: https://commons.wikimedia.org/wiki/Template:PD-US
57.	Figure 27 6	Underwood & Underwood (https://commons.wikimedia.org/wiki/File:MargaretSanger-Underwood.LOC.jpg), „MargaretSanger-Underwood.LOC", marked as public domain, more details on Wikimedia Commons: https://commons.wikimedia.org/wiki/Template:PD-US
58.	Chart 27 1	Data from (Bhattacharya, 2012; Hohmann, Lefèvre, & Garenne, 2014)
59.	Chart 27 2	Data from (Bhattacharya, 2012; Hohmann, Lefèvre, & Garenne, 2014)

INDEX

C

Index

F

G

Index

H

I

O

Index

U

V